FUNDAMENTALS OF
ELECTRICAL ENGINEERING

By Arthur Morley, O.B.E., D.Sc., Hon. M.I.Mech.E.
and Edward Hughes, D.Sc.(Eng.), Ph.D., M.I.E.E.

First-Year Course
ELEMENTARY ENGINEERING SCIENCE

Second-Year Course

MECHANICAL	ELECTRICAL
ENGINEERING	ENGINEERING
SCIENCE	SCIENCE

First and Second-Year Courses
PRINCIPLES OF ELECTRICITY
IN M.K.S. UNITS

Third-Year Course
APPLIED MECHANICS
By Arthur Morley, O.B.E., D.Sc., Hon. M.I.Mech.E.

APPLIED ELECTRICITY
By Edward Hughes, D.Sc.(Eng.), Ph.D., M.I.E.E.

FUNDAMENTALS OF ELECTRICAL
ENGINEERING IN M.K.S. UNITS
By Edward Hughes, D.Sc.(Eng.), Ph.D., M.I.E.E.

FUNDAMENTALS OF
ELECTRICAL
ENGINEERING

Based on the Rationalized
M.K.S. System of Units

BY

EDWARD HUGHES

D.Sc. (Eng.), Ph.D., M.I.E.E.

Formerly Vice-Principal and Head of the Engineering Department,
Brighton Technical College

WITH DIAGRAMS

LONGMANS GREEN AND CO
LONDON • NEW YORK • TORONTO

LONGMANS, GREEN AND CO LTD
6 & 7 CLIFFORD STREET LONDON W I
BOSTON HOUSE STRAND STREET CAPE TOWN
531 LITTLE COLLINS STREET MELBOURNE

LONGMANS, GREEN AND CO INC
55 FIFTH AVENUE NEW YORK 3

LONGMANS, GREEN AND CO
20 CRANFIELD ROAD TORONTO 16

ORIENT LONGMANS LTD
CALCUTTA BOMBAY MADRAS
DELHI VIJAYAWADA DACCA

First Published 1954
Second Impression 1955

Made and printed in Great Britain by
William Clowes and Sons, Limited, London and Beccles

PREFACE

This volume is a sequel to *Principles of Electricity in M.K.S. Units* by Morley and Hughes, and covers the electrical engineering syllabuses of the Third Year Course for the Ordinary National Certificate in Electrical Engineering, the first year course for an Engineering degree and the Intermediate examinations in "Electrical Engineering Practice" of the City and Guilds of London Institute.

The rationalized M.K.S. system of units has been used throughout this book, but for the convenience of those who may have to refer to data expressed in the C.G.S. electromagnetic or electrostatic system, a conversion table is given on page 450. The symbols and nomenclature are in accordance with the recommendations of the British Standards Institution and the Institution of Electrical Engineers; and for the convenience of students, the symbols and abbreviations used in this book have been tabulated on pages xi–xiv. The "per-unit" notation has been used wherever possible so that the student may have ample opportunity of becoming familiar with this term.

The section dealing with the Symbolic Notation has been left to the last chapter. This was done deliberately. The student should not be introduced to the symbolic method until he has had a thorough grounding in the use of vector diagrams for the solution of problems on a.c. circuits; and as far as National Certificate courses are concerned, it is unwise to introduce the Symbolic Notation before the A1 stage.

Included in the text are 63 worked examples and 424 problems. The answers given to the problems are of slide-rule accuracy—in general, they are given to three significant figures. The greatest care has been taken to eliminate errors in both the text and the answers; but if any mistakes are found, I shall be very grateful to have them brought to my notice.

Most of the questions included in this book have been taken from examination papers; and for permission to use these questions I am indebted to the University of London, the Institution of Electrical Engineers, the City and Guilds of London Institute, the East Midland Educational Union, the Northern Counties Technical Examinations Council, the Union of Educational Institutions and the Union of Lancashire and Cheshire Institutes. The questions of the last four examining organizations have been taken from their S3 papers, except where otherwise stated; and those of the University of London are from the "Applied Electricity," Part I, B.Sc.(Eng.) papers.

I wish to express my thanks to Dr. F. T. Chapman, C.B.E., M.I.E.E., and Mr. E. F. Piper, A.M.I.E.E., for reading through the manuscript and making a number of valuable suggestions.

EDWARD HUGHES

HOVE,
  March, 1954

CONTENTS

CHAPTER   PAGE

SYMBOLS AND ABBREVIATIONS   xi

I. THE ELECTRIC CIRCUIT   .   .   .   1
Units — standards — temperature rise — super-position theorem — Kirchhoff's laws — Thévenin's theorem — delta-star and star-delta transformations — two-wire and three-wire systems.

II. ELECTROMAGNETISM   .   .   .   36
Magnetic units — Kirchhoff's laws for magnetic circuit — hysteresis — magnetic field of long solenoid — minimum volume of permanent magnet — — magnetic pull — magnetic field of straight current-carrying conductor — Laplace's theorem — force between current-carrying conductors — self-inductance — inductance of parallel wires and of concentric cylinders — growth of current in inductive circuit — energy in inductive circuit — mutual inductance — coefficient of coupling.

III. ELECTROSTATICS   92
Electrostatic units — capacitance of parallel-plate capacitor — force on isolated charge in electric field — electric field due to isolated charge — force between charges — Coulomb's law — electric field due to charged cylindrical conductor — capacitance of parallel wires and of concentric cylinders — charging and discharging currents of capacitor — energy in charged capacitor — force of attraction between charged plates — dielectric strength.

IV. D.C. GENERATORS AND MOTORS   .   .   126
Equalizing connections — resistance of armature winding — armature reaction — demagnetizing and cross ampere-turns — compensating winding — commutation, commutating poles — parallel operation of shunt and compound generators — grading of starting resistance for shunt motor — losses in d.c. machines — condition for maximum efficiency — determination of efficiency.

CHAPTER   PAGE
V. SINGLE-PHASE CIRCUITS . . . 172
Average and r.m.s. values — addition and subtraction of vectors — circuits with R, L and C in series and in parallel — series and parallel resonance — Q-factor — locus diagrams — power factor — active and reactive currents.

VI. THREE-PHASE CIRCUITS 217
Star and delta connections — relationships between line and phase voltages in star-connected systems and between line and phase currents in delta-connected systems with balanced load — power with balanced load — measurement of power and power factor — two-wattmeter method.

VII. TRANSFORMERS 244
Principle of action — e.m.f. equation — useful and leakage fluxes — leakage reactance — equivalent circuits — voltage regulation — losses and efficiency — condition for maximum efficiency — open-circuit and short-circuit tests — three-phase transformer — cooling of transformers — auto-transformer — current transformer.

VIII. ALTERNATORS 288
Construction of salient-pole and cylindrical-rotor types — stator windings — e.m.f. equation — distribution factor.

IX. PRODUCTION OF A ROTATING MAGNETIC
FLUX 302
Resultant magnetic flux due to three-phase currents — synchronous speed — reversal of direction of rotation of magnetic flux.

X. ALTERNATORS (continued) . . . 309
Armature reaction in three-phase alternator — synchronous impedance — voltage regulation — synchronizing and parallel operation — effects of varying driving torque and excitation.

XI. SYNCHRONOUS MOTORS 325
Principle of action — effects of varying load and excitation — advantages and disadvantages of synchronous motors.

XII. INDUCTION MOTORS 332
Principle of action — squirrel-cage and slip-ring rotors — relationship between slip and rotor I^2R loss — torque/slip characteristics — condition for maximum torque — speed control of motor with slip-ring rotor — starting of motor having cage rotor.

CHAPTER   PAGE

XIII. THERMIONICS 350

Vacuum diode — Richardson's formula — gas-filled rectifier — mercury-arc rectifier — metal rectifiers — vacuum triode — static characteristics — equivalent circuit — voltage amplification — coupling of two triodes — gas-filled triode or thyratron — cathode-ray oscillograph.

XIV. ELECTRIC LAMPS AND ILLUMINATION . 397

The spectrum — relative luminosity efficiency — incandescent filament lamps — arc lamps — high-pressure mercury-vapour lamp — sodium-vapour lamp — fluorescent mercury-vapour lamp — units of light and illumination — measurement of candle-power, luminous flux and illumination.

XV. SYMBOLIC NOTATION 426

The j operator — symbolic expression for impedance — admittance, conductance and susceptance—admittance of a circuit having resistance and reactance (a) in series, (b) in parallel — power and reactive volt-amperes — conjugate of complex number.

APPENDIX 446

Supplementary questions on d.c. machines.

COMPARISON OF RATIONALIZED M.K.S. AND UNRATIONALIZED C.G.S. UNITS 450

MATHEMATICAL CONSTANTS . . . 450

PHYSICAL CONSTANTS AND CONVERSION FACTORS 451

LOG AND TRIGONOMETRICAL TABLES . 452

ANSWERS TO EXAMPLES 457

INDEX 465

SYMBOLS AND ABBREVIATIONS

Based upon British Standard Specification No. 560 (1934), Amendment No. 1 (1945) and Draft 9511 (1953), and "List of Symbols and Abbreviations" published by The Institution of Electrical Engineers.

NOTES ON THE USE OF ABBREVIATIONS

1. Abbreviations should be used only when the meaning is clear.

2. An abbreviation is the same for the singular and the plural: for example, 10 lb, 5 V.

3. Full point should be omitted after abbreviation of a single word or when two abbreviations of single words are separated by a solidus (/), unless its omission is likely to cause ambiguity: for example, 5 mA, 10 Mc/s, 3 in. (for inch).

4. Full points should be used in a multi-word abbreviation: for example, e.m.f., h.p., ft.lb.

5. The solidus (/) should be used for "per" except in such well-established abbreviations as r.p.m. and m.p.h.: for example, c/s.

6. The use of capital letters is discouraged, but capitals should be used where it is customary: for example, M.K.S., C.G.S., B.T.U.; p.d., m.m.f., r.m.s.

7. The abbreviated forms a.c. and d.c. should be used only as adjectives: for example, d.c. motor, a.c. circuit.

8. A hyphen is inserted between the numerical value and the unit when the combination is used adjectivally: for example, a 230-volt (or 230-V) motor, a 3-phase 50-c/s supply, a 2-ohm (or 2-Ω) resistor.

PRIMARY UNITS

Term	Unit	Abbreviation	Term	Unit	Abbreviation
Length	inch foot millimetre centimetre metre	in. ft mm cm m	Volume	cubic inch ,, centimetre ,, metre	in.^{3} cm^3 m^3
			Mass	pound gram kilogram	lb g kg
Area	square inch ,, foot ,, millimetre ,, centimetre ,, metre	in.^{2} ft^2 mm^2 cm^2 m^2	Time	second minute hour	sec* min* h

* s and m may be used when combined with other abbreviations as in c/s, r.p.m.

ELECTRICAL QUANTITIES (M.K.S. SYSTEM)

Term	Symbol	Unit	Abbreviation of unit after numerical values
Angular velocity .	ω	radian per second	radian/sec
Capacitance . .	C	farad	F
		microfarad	μF
Charge or Quantity of electricity . .	Q	coulomb	C
Conductance . .	G	mho	
Conductivity . .	σ	mho per centimetre	mho/cm
Current			
Steady or r.m.s. value	I	ampere	A
		milliampere	mA
		microampere	μA
Instantaneous value	i		
Maximum value .	I_m		
Current density .	J	ampere per metre^2	A/m^2
Difference of potential			
Steady or r.m.s. value	V	volt	V
		millivolt	mV
		kilovolt	kV
Instantaneous value	v		
Maximum value .	V_m		
Electric force (Electric field strength) .	E	volt per metre	V/m
Electric flux . .	Ψ	coulomb	C
Electric flux density .	D	coulomb per square metre	C/m^2
Electromotive force			
Steady or r.m.s. value	E	volt	V
Instantaneous value	e		
Maximum value .	E_m		
Energy . . .	W	joule	J
		watt-hour	Wh
		kilowatt-hour	kWh
		electron-volt	eV
Force . . .	F	newton	N
Frequency . .	f	cycle per second	c/s
		kilocycle per second	kc/s
		megacycle per cycle	Mc/s
Impedance . .	Z	ohm	Ω
Inductance, self .	L	henry (plural, henrys)	H
Inductance, mutual .	M	henry (plural, henrys)	H
Magnetizing force (Magnetic field strength)	H	ampere-turn per metre	AT/m
Magnetic flux . .	Φ	weber	Wb
Magnetic flux density .	B	weber per square metre	Wb/m^2
Magnetomotive force .	F	ampere-turn	AT
Permeability of free space . . .	μ_0		
Permeability, relative	μ_r		
Permeability, absolute	μ		

Term	Symbol	Unit	Abbreviation of unit after numerical values
Permittivity of free space	ϵ_0		
Permittivity, relative (Dielectric constant)	ϵ_r		
Permittivity, absolute	ϵ		
Power	P	watt	W
		kilowatt	kW
		megawatt	MW
Reactance	X	ohm	Ω
Reactive volt-ampere	—	volt-ampere (reactive)	VAr
Reluctance	S	ampere-turn per weber	AT/Wb
Resistance	R	ohm	Ω
		microhm	$\mu\Omega$
		megohm	MΩ
Resistivity	ρ	ohm-metre	Ω-m
		microhm-metre	$\mu\Omega$-m
		ohm-centimetre	Ω-cm
Susceptance	B	mho	—
Volt-ampere	—	volt-ampere	VA
		kilovolt-ampere	kVA
Wavelength	λ	metre	m
		micron	μ
		ångström	Å

LIGHT

Term	Symbol	Unit	Abbreviation
Luminous flux	F	lumen	lm
Luminous intensity	I	candela	cd
Luminance (objective brightness)	L	candela per square centimetre	cd/cm^2
		candela per square metre	cd/m^2
Illumination	E	lumen per square foot [foot-candle (deprecated)]	lm/ft^2
		lumen per square metre (or lux)	lx

ELECTRICAL MACHINES AND THERMIONIC VALVES

Term	Symbol
Number of armature conductors	Z
,, commutator segments or bars	C
,, pairs of poles	p
,, parallel circuits	c
,, phases	m
,, turns	N
Amplification factor	μ
Mutual conductance	g_m
Anode slope resistance	r_a

ABBREVIATIONS FOR MULTIPLES AND SUB-MULTIPLES

M	.	.	mega or meg	10^6
k	.	.	kilo	10^3
c	.	.	centi	10^{-2}
m	.	.	milli	10^{-3}
μ	.	.	micro	10^{-6}
$\mu\mu$ or p	.	.	micromicro or pico	10^{-12}

GREEK LETTERS USED AS SYMBOLS IN THIS BOOK

Letter		Capital	Small
Alpha	.	—	α (angle, temperature coefficient of resistance)
Delta	.	Δ (increment, mesh connection)	δ (small increment)
Epsilon	.	—	ϵ (permittivity)
Eta	.	—	η (efficiency)
Theta	.	—	θ (angle, temperature)
Lambda	.	—	λ (wavelength)
Mu	.	—	μ (micro, permeability, amplification factor)
Pi	.	—	π (circumference/diameter)
Rho	.	—	ρ (resistivity)
Sigma	.	Σ (sum of)	σ (conductivity)
Phi	.	Φ (magnetic flux)	ϕ (angle, phase difference)
Psi	.	Ψ (electric flux)	—
Omega	.	Ω (ohm)	ω (solid angle, angular velocity, angular frequency)

MISCELLANEOUS

Term	Symbol	Term	Symbol
Approximately equal to	$\simeq$	Base of natural logarithms	e
Proportional to . .	$\propto$		
Infinity . . .	∞	Common logarithm of x	$\log x$
Sum of . . .	Σ	Natural logarithm of x	$\ln x$
Increment or finite difference operator .	Δ, δ	Complex operator $\sqrt{-1}$ . . .	j
Greater than . .	$>$	Temperature . .	θ
Less than . . .	$<$	Time constant . .	T
Much greater than .	$\gg$	Efficiency . .	η
Much less than . .	$\ll$	Per unit . . .	p.u.

CHAPTER I

THE ELECTRIC CIRCUIT

1. Fundamental and Mechanical Units. In the M.K.S. system, the units of length, mass and time are the *metre*, the *kilogram* and the *second* respectively. The mechanical units derived from these fundamental units may be summarized thus:

(a) The *unit of force* is the *newton*, namely the force which gives a mass of 1 kilogram an acceleration of 1 metre/second^2. Hence the force, F newtons, required to give a mass of m kilograms an acceleration of f metres/second^2 is:

$$F \text{ (newtons)} = m \text{ (kg)} \times f \text{ (m/sec}^2).$$

For a gravitational acceleration of 9·81 m/sec^2,

a force of 1 kg = 9·81 newtons
and a force of 1 lb = 4·45 newtons.

The relative magnitudes of the newton, the kilogram (force) and the pound (force) are represented by the lengths of the lines in Fig. 1.

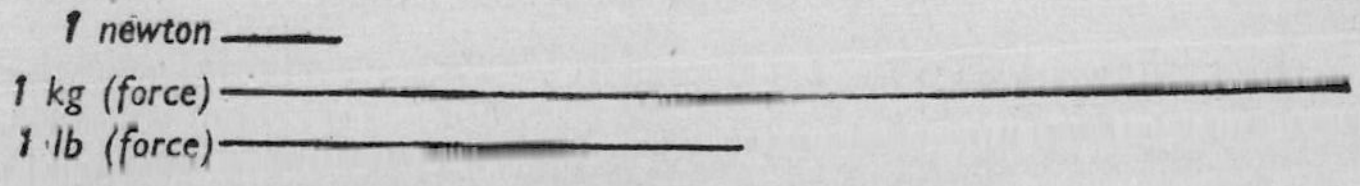

Fig. 1.—The relative magnitudes of the newton, the kilogram (force) and the pound (force).

(b) The *unit of work* or *energy* is the *joule*, namely the work done when a force of 1 newton acts through a distance of 1 metre in the direction of the force. Hence if a force of F newtons acts through a distance of d metres in its own direction,

$$\text{work done} = Fd \text{ joules.}$$

1

If a body of mass m kilograms has a velocity of v metres/second,

$$\text{kinetic energy} = \tfrac{1}{2}mv^2 \text{ joules.}$$

(c) The *unit of power* is the *watt*, namely 1 joule/second.

$$1 \text{ kilowatt} = 1000 \text{ watts}$$

and $\qquad 1 \text{ megawatt} = 1,000,000 \text{ watts.}$

Also, $\qquad 1 \text{ kilowatt-hour} = 1000 \text{ watt-hours}$
$$= 3,600,000 \text{ joules.}$$

If $\quad T =$ torque, in *newton-metres*, due to a force acting about an axis of rotation,

and $\quad \omega =$ angular velocity in radians/second,

$$\text{power} = \omega T \text{ watts}$$

$$= \frac{2\pi N T}{60} \text{ watts} \qquad \ldots \ldots \ldots \quad (1)$$

where $N =$ speed in revolutions/minute.

Example 1. *An electric motor is developing* 20 *h.p. at a speed of* 600 *r.p.m. Calculate the torque* (a) *in newton-metres,* (b) *in kilogram-metres and* (c) *in pound-feet.*

(a) $\qquad$ Since 1 h.p. $= 746$ W,

$$\therefore \text{power} = 20 \times 746 = 14,920 \text{ W.}$$

From (1), $\qquad 14,920 = \dfrac{2\pi T \times 600}{60}$

$$\therefore T = 237 \cdot 6 \text{ newton-metres.}$$

(b) Since a force of 1 kilogram $= 9 \cdot 81$ newtons,

$$\therefore \text{torque} = \frac{237 \cdot 6}{9 \cdot 81} = 24 \cdot 2 \text{ kg.m.}$$

(c) Since a force of 1 pound $= 4 \cdot 45$ newtons and 1 foot $= 0 \cdot 3048$ metre,

$$\therefore \text{torque} = \frac{237 \cdot 6}{4 \cdot 45 \times 0 \cdot 3048} = 175 \text{ lb.ft.}$$

2. Electrical Units. In 1950, the International Electrotechnical Commission adopted the *ampere*, namely the unit of electric current, as the basic electrical unit.

We may therefore summarize the definitions of the principal electrical units thus:

(a) The *ampere* is that *current which, when maintained in each of two infinitely long parallel conductors, situated in a vacuum and separated 1 metre between centres, produces between these conductors a force of* 2×10^{-7} *newton per metre length.* The conductors are attracted towards each other if the currents are in the same direction, whereas they repel each other if the currents are in opposite directions.

The value of the current in terms of this definition can be determined by means of a very elaborate and carefully constructed balance in which the force between the fixed and moving coils carrying the current is balanced by the force of gravity acting on a known mass.

(b) The *unit of electrical quantity* is the *coulomb*, namely the *quantity of electricity passing a given point in a circuit when a current of 1 ampere is maintained for 1 second.* Hence,

$$Q \text{ (coulombs)} = I \text{ (amperes)} \times t \text{ (seconds)}.$$

Also, 1 ampere-hour = 3600 coulombs.

When a current is passed through an electrolyte, chemical decomposition takes place, and the mass of a substance liberated by 1 coulomb is termed the *electro-chemical equivalent* of that substance.

If z = electrochemical equivalent of a substance in grams per coulomb,

and I = current in amperes for time t seconds,
mass of substance liberated = zIt grams.

(c) The *unit of resistance* is the *ohm*, namely *the resistance in which a steady current of 1 ampere generates heat at the rate of 1 watt.* If a current of I amperes flows through a resistance of R ohms for t seconds,

$$\text{power} = I^2 R \text{ watts}$$

and heat energy generated = $I^2 Rt$ joules.

(d) The *unit of potential difference* is the *volt*, namely *the difference of potential across a resistance of 1 ohm carrying a current of 1 ampere.* If V represents the p.d. in volts across a resistance R ohms carrying a current I amperes, then, by Ohm's law,

$$V = IR \quad \text{or} \quad I = V/R$$

and
$$\text{power} = I^2R \text{ watts}$$
$$= IV \text{ watts}$$
$$= \frac{V^2}{R} \text{ watts.}$$

(e) The *electromotive force* is that which tends to produce an electric current in a circuit, and the *unit of e.m.f.* is the *volt*. The principal sources of e.m.f. are:

  (i) the electrodes of dissimilar materials immersed in an electrolyte, as in primary and secondary cells;

 (ii) the relative movement of a conductor and a magnetic flux, as in electric generators and transformers;

(iii) the difference of temperature between junctions of dissimilar metals, as in thermo-junctions.

Consider, for example, a cell having an internal resistance of R_i ohms connected across a resistance R

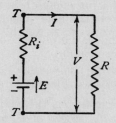

FIG. 2.—E.M.F. of a cell.

ohms, as in Fig. 2, and suppose I amperes to be the current, then:

$$\text{p.d. across } R = IR \text{ volts}$$
and
$$\text{p.d. across } R_i = IR_i \text{ volts.}$$

$$\left.\begin{array}{l}\text{Total power dissipated} \\ \text{in } R \text{ and } R_i\end{array}\right\} = I^2(R + R_i) \text{ watts.}$$

The e.m.f. of the cell is responsible for maintaining the electric current in the circuit; and the value of the e.m.f., E volts, must be such that the electrical power generated in the cell is equal to that dissipated as heat in the resistance of the circuit,

i.e.
$$IE = I^2(R + R_i)$$
$$\therefore \quad E = I(R + R_i)$$

It follows that the difference of potential, V volts, across terminals TT (Fig. 2) is given by:

$$V = IR = E - IR_i.$$

3. Electrical Reference Standards. It was mentioned in Art. 2(a) that the absolute value of the ampere is determined by means of a current balance. The fixed and moving coils are made to known dimensions, and from these dimensions and the relative position of the coils, the value of the current to exert a certain force can be calculated. Also, the absolute value of the ohm can be determined by means of a copper disc rotated in a uniform magnetic field. Both of these methods require such elaborate and expensive equipment that they are only carried out at infrequent intervals at national laboratories. During intervals between the absolute determinations, use is made of standards of resistance and of e.m.f. in the form of manganin*-wire resistors and Weston cells respectively.

The Weston cadmium standard cell is shown in section in Fig. 3. The positive electrode is mercury and the negative electrode is an amalgam of mercury and cadmium. The electrolyte is a saturated solution of cadmium sulphate in water slightly acidulated with sulphuric acid. The mercurous sulphate acts as a depolarizer. When this cell is manufactured to a specification prescribed by the International Electrotechnical Commission, its e.m.f. is exactly 1·0186 volts at 20°C. Consequently the volt can be taken as 1/1·0186

---

* Manganin is an alloy of copper, manganese and nickel, with sometimes a trace of iron; its temperature coefficient of resistance may be as low as 0·000003 per °C. (See *Dictionary of Applied Physics*, Vol. II, p. 710.)

of the e.m.f. of a cadmium cell at 20°C. The e.m.f. of the cell falls by about 40 microvolts per °C rise of temperature. Since the internal resistance is about 1000 ohms, this cell is intended only as a standard of e.m.f. and not as a source of electrical energy.

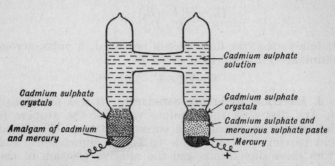

FIG. 3.—Weston cadmium standard cell.

4. Resistance. If resistors of resistance R_1, R_2, R_3, etc., are connected in series, the total resistance R is given by:

$$R = R_1 + R_2 + R_3 + \ldots$$

If the resistors are connected in parallel, the total resistance is given by R, where:

$$\frac{1}{R} = \frac{1}{R_1} + \frac{1}{R_2} + \frac{1}{R_3} + \ldots$$

Hence for two resistances R_1 and R_2 in parallel,

$$\text{equivalent resistance} = R = \frac{R_1 R_2}{R_1 + R_2}.$$

The reciprocal of the resistance is termed the *conductance*, the unit of conductance being 1 *mho*.

If l = length of an electrical circuit
and a = cross-sectional area of the circuit,

$$\text{resistance of circuit} = \frac{\rho l}{a} \text{ ohms}$$

where ρ = resistivity of the material.

If l is in metres and a in square metres, then ρ is expressed in ohm-metres. If l and a are in inches and square inches respectively, ρ is in ohm-inches. Thus the resistivity of annealed copper at 20°C is $1{\cdot}725 \times 10^{-8}$ ohm-metre or $0{\cdot}679 \times 10^{-6}$ ohm-inch. The International Electrotechnical Commission, in 1913, specified the resistance of standard annealed copper wire, 1 metre long and 1 mm² in cross-section, as 1/58 ohm at 20°C.

If a conductor, l metres long and a square metres in cross-section, is carrying a current I amperes,

$$\text{current density} = I/a \text{ amperes/metre}^2$$

and voltage drop in conductor $= \dfrac{I\rho l}{a}$ volts,

$\therefore$ voltage drop per metre $= \dfrac{I\rho}{a}$ volts.

The voltage drop per unit length of a conductor is referred to as the *potential gradient* in that conductor;

$$\therefore \frac{\text{current density in amperes/metre}^2}{\text{potential gradient in volts/metre}} = \frac{1}{\rho}$$
$$= \sigma \quad . \quad . \quad (2)$$

where σ = conductivity in mhos/metre
= reciprocal of the resistivity in ohm-metres.

The similarity of expression (2) to expressions for permeability and permittivity is referred to in Art. 45.

5. Temperature Coefficient of Resistance. The resistance of all pure metals increases with increase of temperature, whereas the resistance of carbon, electrolytes and insulating materials decreases with increase of temperature. Certain alloys, such as eureka (60 per cent copper, 40 per cent nickel) and manganin (Art. 3) show practically no change of resistance for a considerable variation of temperature. For a moderate range of temperature, such as 100°C, the change of resistance is usually proportional to the change of temperature; and the ratio of the increase of resistance per °C rise of temperature to the resistance at 0°C is termed the *temperature coefficient of resistance* and is represented by the symbol α.

The variation of resistance of copper for the range over which copper conductors are usually operated is represented by the graph in Fig. 4. If this graph is extended backwards, the point of intersection with the horizontal axis is found to be −234·5°C. Hence, for a standard

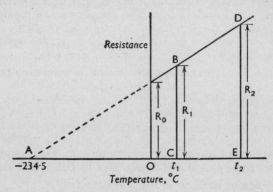

FIG. 4.—Variation of resistance of copper with temperature.

annealed copper conductor having a resistance of 1 ohm at 0°C, the variation of resistance over a range of 234·5°C is 1 ohm,

$$\therefore \qquad \alpha = 1/234 \cdot 5 = 0 \cdot 004264.$$

In general, if a material having a resistance R_0 at 0°C has a resistance R_1 at t_1°C and R_2 at t_2°C,

$$R_1 = R_0(1 + \alpha t_1)$$

and

$$R_2 = R_0(1 + \alpha t_2)$$

$$\therefore \qquad \frac{R_1}{R_2} = \frac{1 + \alpha t_1}{1 + \alpha t_2}.$$

Since $\alpha = 1/234 \cdot 5$ for standard annealed copper, then for this material,

$$\frac{R_1}{R_2} = \frac{234 \cdot 5 + t_1}{234 \cdot 5 + t_2}$$

and

$$t_2 = \frac{R_2}{R_1}(234 \cdot 5 + t_1) - 234 \cdot 5 \qquad . \quad . \quad . \quad (3)$$

Hence if the resistance of a coil, such as a field winding of an electrical machine, is measured at the beginning and at the end of a test, the temperature rise can be calculated from expression (3).

6. Temperature Rise in Electrical Apparatus and Machines. The maximum power which can be dissipated as heat in an electrical circuit is limited by the maximum permissible temperature, and the latter depends upon the nature of the insulating material employed. Materials such as paper and cotton become brittle if their temperature is allowed to exceed about 100°C; whereas materials such as mica and glass can withstand a much higher temperature without any injurious effect on their insulating and mechanical properties.

When an electrical machine is *loaded* (i.e. when supplying electrical power in the case of a generator or mechanical power in the case of a motor), the temperature rise of that machine is largely due to the I^2R loss in the windings; and the greater the load, the greater is the loss and therefore the higher the temperature rise. The *full load* or *rated output* of the machine is the maximum output obtainable under specified conditions, e.g. for a specified temperature rise after the machine has supplied that load continuously for several hours.

Let us now determine the temperature rise of a coil, assuming the I^2R loss to remain constant at P watts.

Let H = energy, in joules, to raise the temperature of the coil 1°C,

$\quad k$ = power, in watts, dissipated by convection and radiation from the surface of the coil per °C rise of temperature,

$\quad \theta$ = temperature rise after t seconds, as shown in Fig. 5

and $\quad d\theta$ = temperature rise in dt second.

During this interval of dt second,

$$\text{heat energy generated} = P \cdot dt \text{ joules}$$
$$\text{heat energy absorbed by coil} = H \cdot d\theta \text{ joules}$$
and heat energy dissipated from surface $= k\theta \cdot dt$ joules.

But total heat energy generated is equal to the sum of the

1*

heat energy absorbed by the coil and that dissipated from
the surface,

i.e. $$P \, . \, dt = H \, . \, d\theta + k\theta \, . \, dt \quad . \quad . \quad . \quad (4)$$

When the temperature rise of the coil attains its final
steady value θ_f, all the power generated as heat in the
coil is being dissipated from the surface,

$\therefore$ $$P = k\theta_f \quad . \quad . \quad . \quad . \quad (5)$$

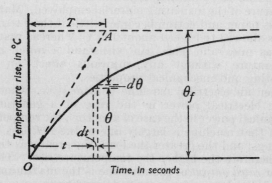

Fig. 5.—Curve of temperature rise.

Had there been no loss of heat from the coil, the
temperature rise would follow the dotted line OA and
would reach θ_f in T seconds, where

$$PT = H\theta_f$$

$\therefore$ $$T = \frac{H\theta_f}{P} = \frac{H}{k} \quad . \quad . \quad . \quad . \quad (6)$$

This interval, T seconds, is termed the *heating time
constant* of the coil; and from (6) it is evident that the
value of T is directly proportional to the energy absorbed
per °C rise of temperature and inversely proportional to
the power dissipated per °C rise of temperature; i.e.
the greater the mass and the specific heat of the coil and
the poorer the cooling of the surface of the coil, the larger
is the value of T.

From (4), $(P - k\theta)dt = H \, . \, d\theta.$

Substituting for P and H from (5) and (6) respectively, we have:

$$(k\theta_f - k\theta)dt = kT \cdot d\theta$$

$$\therefore \qquad \frac{d\theta}{\theta_f - \theta} = \frac{dt}{T}$$

Integrating both sides, we have:

$$-\ln (\theta_f - \theta)^* = t/T + A$$

where $A =$ the constant of integration.

When $t = 0$, $\theta = 0$,

$$\therefore \qquad A = -\ln \theta_f.$$

Hence, $\qquad t/T = \ln \theta_f - \ln (\theta_f - \theta)$

$$= \ln \frac{\theta_f}{\theta_f - \theta}$$

$$\therefore \qquad \theta = \theta_f(1 - e^{-t/T}) \quad \cdot \quad \cdot \quad \cdot \quad (7)$$

For $t = T$, $\qquad \theta = 0 \cdot 632 \, \theta_f,$

i.e. the time taken for the temperature rise to reach 63·2 per cent of the final value is equal to the heating time constant of the coil.

The exponential relationship (7) is represented by the graph in Fig. 5 and is similar in shape to those representing the growth of current in an inductive circuit (Art. 39) and of p.d. across a capacitor connected in series with a resistor (Art. 58).

It can similarly be shown that when a coil in which no heat is being generated cools from an initial temperature θ_i above the surrounding atmosphere, the temperature after t seconds is given by:

$$\theta = \theta_i e^{-t/T}.$$

It should be mentioned that the value of T during cooling may be different from that during heating; for instance, the value of k in expression (6) is smaller for a machine when it is stationary than when it is running. Consequently, if a machine is stopped after a heating

---

* British Standards Institution recommends the use of ln and log in preference to $\log_e$ and $\log_{10}$ respectively.

test, the cooling time constant is greater than the heating time constant.

The temperature may be measured by (1) a thermometer, (2) the increase of resistance of the coil and (3) thermo-junctions embedded in the coil. The third method enables the distribution of temperature throughout the coil to be determined but is only possible when the thermo-junctions have been inserted in the coil when the latter is being wound. Since the heat generated at the centre of the coil has to flow outwards, the temperature at the centre may be considerably higher than that at the surface.

7. Network Theorems. Electric circuits frequently consist of a mixture of series and parallel elements, which may or may not contain sources of e.m.f.

A network is said to be *passive* if it contains no source of e.m.f., and the equivalent resistance between any two terminals of a passive network is the ratio of the p.d. across the two terminals to the current flowing into (or out of) the network. We shall now consider the principal theorems that have been developed for solving problems on electrical networks.

8. Superposition Theorem. *In any network containing more than one source of e.m.f., the resultant current in any branch is the algebraic sum of the currents that would*

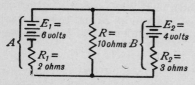

be produced by each e.m.f., acting alone, all the other sources of e.m.f. being replaced meanwhile by their respective internal resistances.

FIG. 6.—Circuit diagram for Example 2.

Let us consider the application of this theorem to the solution of the following problem.

Example 2. *Battery A in Fig. 6 has an e.m.f. of 6 V and an internal resistance of 2Ω. The corresponding values for battery B are 4V and 3Ω respectively. The two* *batteries are connected in parallel across a resistance R of* 10Ω. *Calculate the current in each branch of the network.*

Fig. 7 (a) represents the network with battery A only

$$\left.\begin{array}{l}\text{Equivalent resistance of } R\\ \text{and } R_2 \text{ in parallel}\end{array}\right\} = \frac{10 \times 3}{10 + 3} = 2\cdot31\Omega.$$

$\therefore$ $$I_1 = \frac{6}{2 + 2\cdot31} = 1\cdot392 \text{ A.}$$

Hence, $$I_2 = 1\cdot392 \times \frac{3}{10 + 3} = 0\cdot321 \text{ A}$$

and $$I_3 = 1\cdot392 - 0\cdot321 = 1\cdot071 \text{ A.}$$

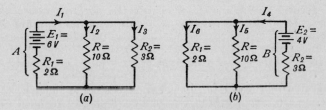

FIG. 7.—Diagrams for solution of Example 2.

Fig. 7 (b) represents the network with battery B only.

$$\left.\begin{array}{l}\text{Equivalent resistance of } R\\ \text{and } R_1 \text{ in parallel}\end{array}\right\} = \frac{2 \times 10}{2 + 10} = 1\cdot667 \text{ }\Omega.$$

$\therefore$ $$I_4 = \frac{4}{3 + 1\cdot667} = 0\cdot856 \text{ A.}$$

Hence, $$I_5 = 0\cdot856 \times \frac{2}{2 + 10} = 0\cdot143 \text{ A}$$

and $$I_6 = 0\cdot856 - 0\cdot143 = 0\cdot713 \text{ A.}$$

Superimposing the results for Fig. 7 (b) on those for Fig. 7 (a), we have:

resultant current through A $= I_1 - I_6$
$= 1\cdot392 - 0\cdot713 = 0\cdot679 \text{ } A$

and resultant current through $B = I_4 - I_3$
$= 0\cdot856 - 1\cdot071$
$= -0\cdot215 \text{ A,}$

i.e. battery B is being charged at 0·215 A.

Resultant current through $R = I_2 + I_5$
$$= 0 \cdot 321 + 0 \cdot 143 = 0 \cdot 464 \text{ A.}$$

9. Kirchhoff's Laws.   First Law: *The total current flowing towards a junction is equal to the total current flowing away from that junction,* i.e. *the algebraic sum of the currents flowing towards a junction is zero.* Thus at junction C in Fig. 8,

$$I_1 + I_2 = I_3 \quad \text{or} \quad I_1 + I_2 - I_3 = 0$$

In general, $\Sigma I = 0$

where Σ represents the algebraic sum.

Second Law: *In a closed circuit, the algebraic sum of the products of the current and the resistance of each part of the*

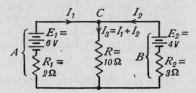

Fig. 8.—Circuit to illustrate Kirchhoff's Laws.

circuit is equal to the resultant e.m.f. in the circuit. Thus for the closed circuit formed by E_1, E_2, R_1 and R_2 in Fig. 8,

$$E_1 - E_2 = I_1 R_1 - I_2 R_2$$

and for the mesh formed by E_2, R_2 and R,

$$E_2 = I_2 R_2 + I_3 R$$

In general, $\Sigma E = \Sigma I R.$

Example 3. *Using Kirchhoff's Laws, calculate the current in each branch of the circuit shown in Fig. 8, the e.m.f.'s and resistances of which are the same as those of Fig. 6.*

Applying Kirchhoff's Laws to the circuit formed by A and R, we have:

$$6 = 2I_1 + 10(I_1 + I_2)$$
$$= 12I_1 + 10I_2 \quad . \quad . \quad . \quad . \quad (8)$$

Similarly, for the closed circuit formed by A and B,
$$6-4=2=2I_1-3I_2 \qquad . \quad . \quad (9)$$
Multiplying (9) by 6 and subtracting from (8), we have:
$$-6=28I_2$$
$$\therefore \qquad\qquad I_2=-0\cdot2143 \text{ A.}$$
Substituting for I_2 in (9), we have:
$$I_1=1-1\cdot5\times0\cdot2143=0\cdot6786 \text{ A}$$
and $\qquad\qquad I_3=0\cdot6786-0\cdot2143=0\cdot4643 \text{ A.}$

10. Thévenin's Theorem. *The current through a resistance R connected across any two points A and B of an active network* (i.e. a network containing one or more sources of e.m.f.) *is obtained by dividing the p.d. between A and B, with R disconnected, by $(R+r)$, where r is the resistance of the network measured between points A and B with R disconnected and the sources of e.m.f. replaced by their internal resistances.*

An alternative way of stating Thévenin's Theorem is as follows: *An active network having two terminals A and B behaves, as far as any load connected across those terminals is concerned, as if the network contained a single source of e.m.f. E with an internal resistance r, where E is equal to the p.d. between A and B with the load disconnected and r is the resistance of the network measured between A and B with the load disconnected and the sources of e.m.f. replaced by their internal resistances.*

Suppose A and B in Fig. 9 (a) to be the two terminals of a network consisting of resistances R_2 and R_3 and a battery having an e.m.f. E_1 and an internal resistance R_1. It is required to determine the current through a load R connected across AB. With R disconnected as in Fig. 9 (b),

$$\text{current through } R_3=\frac{E_1}{R_1+R_3}$$

and $\qquad$ p.d. across $R_3=\dfrac{E_1R_3}{R_1+R_3}.$

Since there is no current through R_2,

$$\text{p.d. across } AB=V=\frac{E_1R_3}{R_1+R_3}.$$

Fig. 9 (c) shows the network with R disconnected and the battery replaced by its internal resistance R_1.

$$\left.\begin{matrix}\text{Resistance of network}\\ \text{between } A \text{ and } B\end{matrix}\right\} = r = R_2 + \frac{R_1 R_3}{R_1 + R_3}.$$

Thévenin's Theorem merely states that the active network enclosed by the dotted line in Fig. 9 (a) can be replaced by the very simple circuit enclosed by the dotted

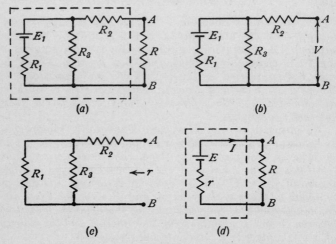

(a)

(b)

(c)

(d)

Fig. 9.—Circuits to illustrate Thévenin's Theorem.

line in Fig. 9 (d) and consisting of a source having an e.m.f. E equal to the open-circuit potential difference V between A and B, and an internal resistance r, where V and r have the values determined above.   Hence,

$$\text{current through } R = I = \frac{E}{r + R}.$$

Thévenin's Theorem—sometimes referred to as Helmholtz's Theorem—is an application of the Superposition Theorem.   Thus, if a source having an e.m.f. E equal to the open-circuit p.d. between A and B in Fig. 9 (b) were inserted in the circuit between R and terminal A

in Fig. 9 (a), the positive terminal of the source being
connected to A, no current would flow through R.
Hence, this source could be regarded as circulating
through R a current superimposed upon but opposite in
direction to the current through R due to E_1 *alone*.
Since the resultant current is zero, it follows that a
source of e.m.f. E connected in series with R and the
equivalent resistance r of the network, as in Fig. 9
(d), would circulate a current I having the same value

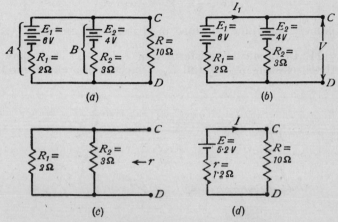

FIG. 10.—Circuit diagrams for Example 4.

as that through R in Fig. 9 (a); but in order that the
direction of the current through R may be from A
towards B, the polarity of the source must be as shown
in Fig. 9 (d).

Example 4. *C and D in Fig. 10 (a) (which is similar to
Fig. 6) represent the two terminals of an active network.
Calculate the current through resistance R.*

With R disconnected as in Fig. 10 (b),

$$I_1 = \frac{6-4}{2+3} = 0 \cdot 4 \text{ A}$$

and   p.d. across $CD = E_1 - I_1 R_1$
i.e. $V = 6 - (0 \cdot 4 \times 2) = 5 \cdot 2$ volts.

When the e.m.f.'s are removed as in Fig. 10 (c),

$$\left.\begin{array}{c}\text{total resistance}\\ \text{between } C \text{ and } D\end{array}\right\} = \frac{2 \times 3}{2+3}$$

i.e. $r = 1 \cdot 2 \ \Omega.$

Hence the network AB in Fig. 10 (a) can be replaced by a single source having an e.m.f. of $5 \cdot 2$ V and an internal resistance of $1 \cdot 2 \ \Omega$, as in Fig. 10(d); consequently,

$$I = \frac{5 \cdot 2}{1 \cdot 2 + 10} = 0 \cdot 4643 \text{ A,}$$

namely the value obtained in Examples 2 and 3.

11. Delta-star Transformation.   Fig. 11 (a) shows three resistors R_1, R_2 and R_3 connected in a closed mesh

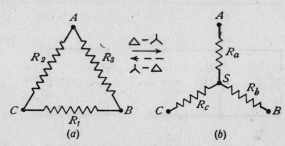

FIG. 11.—Delta-star transformation.

or delta to three terminals A, B and C, *their numerical subscripts* 1, 2 *and* 3 *being opposite to the terminals A, B and C respectively*.   It is possible to replace these delta-connected resistors by three resistors R_a, R_b and R_c connected respectively between the same terminals A, B and C and a common point S, as in Fig. 11 (b). Such an arrangement is said to be star-connected.   It will be noted that the letter subscripts are now those of the terminals to which the respective resistors are connected.   If the star-connected network is to be equivalent to the delta-connected network, the resistance between any two terminals in Fig. 11 (b) must be the same as that between the same two terminals in Fig. 11 (a). Thus if we consider terminals A and B in Fig. 11 (a), we have R_3 in parallel with a circuit consisting of R_1 and R_2 in series; hence

$$R_{AB} = \frac{R_3(R_1 + R_2)}{R_1 + R_2 + R_3} \quad \cdots \quad (10)$$

For Fig. 11 (b), we have:

$$R_{AB} = R_a + R_b \quad \cdots \quad (11)$$

In order that the networks of Fig. 11 (a) and (b) may be equivalent to each other, the values of R_{AB} represented by equations (10) and (11) must be equal,

$$\therefore \qquad R_a + R_b = \frac{R_1 R_3 + R_2 R_3}{R_1 + R_2 + R_3} \quad \cdots \quad (12)$$

Similarly, $\qquad R_b + R_c = \dfrac{R_1 R_2 + R_1 R_3}{R_1 + R_2 + R_3} \quad \cdots \quad (13)$

and $\qquad R_a + R_c = \dfrac{R_1 R_2 + R_2 R_3}{R_1 + R_2 + R_3} \quad \cdots \quad (14)$

Subtracting (13) from (12), we have:

$$R_a - R_c = \frac{R_2 R_3 - R_1 R_2}{R_1 + R_2 + R_3} \quad \cdots \quad (15)$$

Adding (14) and (15) and dividing by 2, we have:

$$R_a = \frac{R_2 R_3}{R_1 + R_2 + R_3} \quad \cdots \quad (16)$$

Similarly, $\qquad R_b = \dfrac{R_1 R_3}{R_1 + R_2 + R_3} \quad \cdots \quad (17)$

and $\qquad R_c = \dfrac{R_1 R_2}{R_1 + R_2 + R_.} \quad \cdots \quad (18)$

Note that the numerical subscripts in the numerators on the right-hand side are those of the resistors connected to the terminals corresponding to the letter subscripts on the left-hand side. Hence, the above equations may be expressed thus: *the equivalent star resistance connected to a given terminal is equal to the product of the two delta resistances connected to the same terminal divided by the sum of the delta resistances.*

12. Star-delta Transformation. Let us next consider how to replace the star-connected network of Fig. 11 (b) by the equivalent delta-connected network of Fig. 11 (a). Dividing equation (16) by equation (17), we have:

$$\frac{R_a}{R_b} = \frac{R_2}{R_1} \quad \therefore R_2 = R_1 R_a / R_b.$$

Similarly, dividing (16) by (18), we have:

$$\frac{R_a}{R_c} = \frac{R_3}{R_1} \quad \therefore R_3 = R_1 R_a / R_c.$$

Substituting for R_2 and R_3 in (16), we have:

$$R_1 = R_b + R_c + R_b R_c / R_a \qquad . \quad . \quad (19)$$

Similarly $\qquad R_2 = R_a + R_c + R_a R_c / R_b \qquad . \quad . \quad (20)$

and $\qquad R_3 = R_a + R_b + R_a R_b / R_c \qquad . \quad . \quad (21)$

The symmetry of the subscripts will again be obvious. Hence the above equations may be expressed thus: *the equivalent delta resistance between two terminals is the sum of the two star resistances connected to those terminals plus the product of the same two star resistances divided by the third star resistance.*

Example 5. *The resistances of the various arms of an unbalanced Wheatstone bridge are given in Fig.* 12. *The battery has an e.m.f. of 2 volts and a negligible internal resistance.* *Determine the value and direction of the current in the galvanometer circuit BD, using* (a) *Kirchhoff's Laws,* (b) *Thévenin's Theorem,* (c) *Mesh-star transformation.*

(a) *By Kirchhoff's Laws.* Let I_1, I_2 and I_3 be the currents in arms AB, AD and BD respectively, as shown in Fig. 12. Then by Kirchhoff's First Law,

current in $BC = I_1 - I_3$

and $\qquad$ current in $DC = I_2 + I_3$.

Applying Kirchhoff's Second Law to the mesh formed by ABC and the battery, we have:

$$\begin{aligned} 2 &= 10I_1 + 30(I_1 - I_3) \\ &= 40I_1 - 30I_3 \quad . \quad . \quad . \quad . \quad . \quad . \quad (22) \end{aligned}$$

Similarly for mesh $ABDA$,

$$0 = 10I_1 + 40I_3 - 20I_2 \quad \ldots \quad (23)$$

and for mesh $BDCB$,

$$0 = 40I_3 + 15(I_2 + I_3) - 30(I_1 - I_3)$$
$$= -30I_1 + 15I_2 + 85I_3 \ . \quad \ldots \quad (24)$$

Multiplying (23) by 3 and (24) by 4, and adding the two expressions thus obtained, we have:

$$0 = -90I_1 + 460I_3$$

$$\therefore \qquad I_1 = 5 \cdot 111 I_3.$$

Substituting for I_1 in (22), we have:

$$I_3 = 0 \cdot 0115 \text{ A} = 11 \cdot 5 \text{ mA}.$$

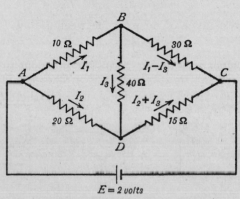

FIG. 12.—Circuit for Example 5.

Since the value of I_3 is positive, the direction of I_3 is that assumed in Fig. 12, namely from B to D.

(b) *By Thévenin's Theorem.* Since we require to find the current in the 40-Ω resistor between B and D, the first step is to remove this resistor, as in Fig. 13 (a). Then:

$$\text{p.d. between } A \text{ and } B = 2 \times \frac{10}{10 + 30} = 0 \cdot 5 \text{ V}$$

and p.d. between A and $D = 2 \times \dfrac{20}{20 + 15} = 1 \cdot 143 \text{ V}$

$$\therefore \qquad \text{p.d. between } B \text{ and } D = 0 \cdot 643 \text{ V},$$

B being positive relative to D. Consequently, current in the 40-Ω resistor, when connected between B and D, will flow from B to D.

The next step is to replace the battery by a resistance equal to its internal resistance. Since the latter is negligible in this problem, junctions A and C can be short-circuited, as in Fig. 13 (b).

Equivalent resistance of BA and BC

$$=\frac{10 \times 30}{10+30}=7 \cdot 5 \ \Omega$$

and equivalent resistance of AD and CD

$$=\frac{20 \times 15}{20+15}=8 \cdot 57 \ \Omega,$$

$\therefore$ total resistance of network between B and D

$$=16 \cdot 07 \ \Omega.$$

Hence the network of Fig. 13 (a) is equivalent to a source

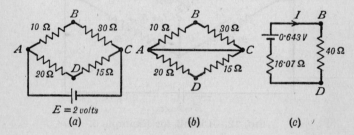

FIG. 13.—Diagrams for solution of Example 5 by Thévenin's Theorem.

having an e.m.f. of $0 \cdot 643$ V and an internal resistance of $16 \cdot 07 \ \Omega$, as in Fig. 13 (c).

$$\therefore \quad \text{current through } BD=\frac{0 \cdot 643}{16 \cdot 07+40}=0 \cdot 0115 \text{ A}$$
$$=11 \cdot 5 \text{ mA from } B \text{ to } D.$$

(c) *By mesh-star transformation.* Let us replace the mesh BCD of Fig. 12 by the equivalent star-connected resistors BN, CN and DN of Fig. 14. Using equations (16), (17) and (18), we have:

$$R_{BN} = \frac{30 \times 40}{30 + 40 + 15} = 14 \cdot 12 \ \Omega$$

$$R_{CN} = \frac{30 \times 15}{30 + 40 + 15} = 5 \cdot 29 \ \Omega$$

and
$$R_{DN} = \frac{40 \times 15}{30 + 40 + 15} = 7 \cdot 06 \ \Omega.$$

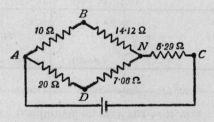

FIG. 14.—Diagram for solution of Example 5 by mesh-star transformation.

Equivalent resistance of parallel circuits ABN and ADN $\Bigg\} = \dfrac{24 \cdot 12 \times 27 \cdot 06}{51 \cdot 18} = 12 \cdot 77 \ \Omega$

and total resistance of bridge $= 12 \cdot 77 + 5 \cdot 29 = 18 \cdot 06 \ \Omega$.

∴ current from battery $= 2/18 \cdot 06 = 0 \cdot 1108$ A.

Current through arm $AB = 0 \cdot 1108 \times \dfrac{27 \cdot 06}{51 \cdot 18} = 0 \cdot 0586$ A

and current through arm $AD = 0 \cdot 1108 - 0 \cdot 0586 = 0 \cdot 0522$ A.

Hence, p.d. across arm $AB = 0 \cdot 0586 \times 10 = 0 \cdot 586$ V

and p.d. across arm $AD = 0 \cdot 0522 \times 20 = 1 \cdot 044$ V

∴ p.d. between B and $D = 0 \cdot 458$ V,

B being at a higher potential than D.

Hence, current through the 40-Ω resistor connected between B and D $\Bigg\} = \dfrac{0 \cdot 458}{40} = 0 \cdot 0115$ A

$= 11 \cdot 5$ mA from B to D.

13. D.C. Systems of Distribution. Two-Wire Systems.
The general arrangement of a two-wire system of distribution has been dealt with in *Principles of Electricity*, Art. 32, and in this volume attention will be confined to (a) a distributor fed at both ends and (b) a distributor with uniformly distributed load.

Example 6. *A distributor, 450 yards long, is loaded as shown in Fig. 15. The p.d. at AB is 250 V and that at*

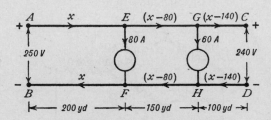

FIG. 15.—Diagram for Example 6.

CD is 240 *V. The resistance of the distributor is* 0·02 Ω *per* 100 *yards of single conductor. Calculate the p.d. at each load point.*

Let x amperes be the current in AE and FB.
From Kirchhoff's First Law,

current in EG and $HF = x - 80$ amperes
and   current in GC and $DH = x - 140$ amperes.
Resistance of AE and $FB = 0·02 \times 4 = 0·08$ Ω,
resistance of EG and $HF = 0·02 \times 3 = 0·06$ Ω
and   resistance of GC and $DH = 0·02 \times 2 = 0·04$ Ω.
∴ voltage drop in AE and $FB = 0·08x$ volts,
voltage drop in EG and $HF = 0·06(x - 80)$ volts
and voltage drop in GC and $DH = 0·04(x - 140)$ volts.

But voltage drop in AC and $DB = 250 - 240 = 10$ volts.

∴ $0·08x + 0·06(x - 80) + 0·04(x - 140) = 10$
so that $x = 113·3$ A.

Hence, p.d. across load $EF = 250 - (113 \cdot 3 \times 0 \cdot 08)$
$$= 240 \cdot 93 \text{ V}$$

and   p.d. across load $GH = 240 \cdot 93 - (33 \cdot 3 \times 0 \cdot 06)$
$$= 238 \cdot 93 \text{ V}.$$

Alternatively, p.d. across $GH = 240 - (26 \cdot 7 \times 0 \cdot 04)$
$$= 238 \cdot 93 \text{ V}.$$

14. Voltage Drop due to a Uniformly Distributed Load. Suppose a distributor to be fed at one end and to be loaded at regular short intervals so that the load

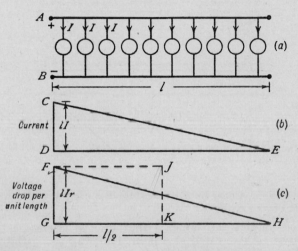

Fig. 16.—Uniformly loaded distributor.

per unit length of distributor is I amperes, as shown in Fig. 16 (a). If the length of the distributor is l units, the total current at AB is lI amperes; and, if there is a large number of load points, the variation of current along the distributor can be represented by line CE in Fig. 16 (b), where DC represents lI amperes.

Let r be the resistance per unit length of distributor (including outward and return conductors). Consequently, the variation of the voltage drop per unit length is represented by line FH in Fig. 16 (c), where

FG is *llr* volts. The total voltage drop along the distributor is therefore represented by the area of triangle *GFH*, namely $\frac{1}{2}Irl^2$ volts.

If a single load taking the same total current *ll* amperes were concentrated midway along the distributor, the voltage drop would be represented by the area of rectangle *GFJK* and is equal to $\frac{1}{2}Irl^2$ volts. Hence the *total* voltage drop due to a uniformly distri-

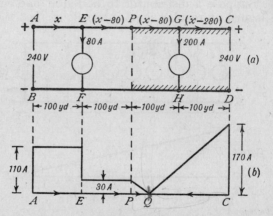

Fig. 17.—Diagrams for Example 7.

buted load is the same as that due to the same total current concentrated at a point half-way along the part of the cable that is uniformly loaded.

Example 7. *A distributor, 400 yd long, is fed at each end at 240 V. There is a concentrated load of 80 A at a distance of 100 yd from one end and a load of 1 A per yard is uniformly distributed over the 200-yd length adjacent to the other end. The resistance per 100 loop yards of the distributor is 0·04 Ω. Calculate the minimum voltage between the conductors.*

The uniformly distributed load can be replaced by a concentrated load of 200 A at a distance of 100 yd from *CD* in Fig. 17 (a).

Let x amperes be the current in AE and FB; then:

current in EG and $HF = x - 80$ amperes

and current in GC and $DH = x - 280$ amperes.

Resistance of AE and $FB = 0 \cdot 04\ \Omega$,

resistance of EG and $HF = 0 \cdot 08\ \Omega$

and resistance of GC and $DH = 0 \cdot 04\ \Omega$.

Since p.d. across $AB =$ p.d. across CD,

$$0 \cdot 04x + 0 \cdot 08(x - 80) + 0 \cdot 04(x - 280) = 0$$

$$\therefore \qquad\qquad\qquad x = 110\ \text{A}$$

and current at $C = 280 - 110 = 170$ A.

Hence, the distribution of current along the line is represented by the ordinates of Fig 17 (b) and Q is the point of zero current, i.e. in the positive conductor AQ, current flows from left to right, whereas in QC, it flows from right to left. Consequently, Q is the point at which the p.d. between the conductors is a minimum.

Since current entering distributor at $C = 170$ A,

$$\therefore \qquad\qquad \text{distance } CQ = 170\ \text{yd.}$$

Also the voltage drop along length CQ of the distributor is the same as that due to a concentrated load of 170 A at a distance of 85 yd from C, i.e.

voltage drop from C to $Q = 170 \times 0 \cdot 04 \times 0 \cdot 85 = 5 \cdot 78$ V

and minimum voltage across load

$$= 240 - 5 \cdot 78 = 234 \cdot 22\ \text{V}.$$

This value should be checked by calculating the voltage drop from end A; thus:

drop from A to $Q = (110 \times 0 \cdot 04) + 30(0 \cdot 04 + 0 \cdot 04 \times 0 \cdot 15)$
$$= 5 \cdot 78\ \text{V},$$

which is the same as the value for the drop from C to Q.

15. Three-wire D.C. System of Distribution. The Regulations relating to low-voltage distribution systems stipulate that the voltage of a two-wire supply delivered to a consumer must not exceed 250 V (except in special cases) and that one side of the system must be earthed.

This means that the maximum voltage to earth must not exceed 250 V.   This voltage is also the highest for which incandescent lamps, heaters, etc., can conveniently be manufactured.   But if the voltage could be doubled, the current required for a given power would be halved, and this would enable the cross-sectional area of the distributor conductor to be reduced.   Fig. 18 shows how this voltage doubling can be effected without the maximum potential above or below earth exceeding 250 V.   Two

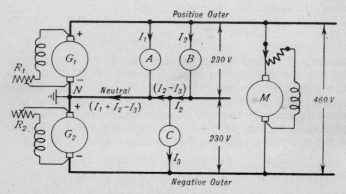

Fig. 18.—Three-wire system of distribution.

generators, G_1 and G_2, are connected in series and the mid-point N is earthed.   The conductor connected to N is referred to as the *neutral* and the conductors connected to the positive side of G_1 and the negative side of G_2 are termed the *outers*.

If G_1 and G_2 have a terminal voltage of, say, 230 V each, then all 230-V equipments, such as lamps, heaters, small motors, etc., are connected between the neutral and either outer, as shown by A, B and C, and large motors, such as M, are connected directly across the outers.   By balancing the 230-V loads as equally as possible between the two sides, the resultant current in the neutral can be reduced to a very small value; hence it is usual to make the cross-sectional area of the neutral half that of one outer.

The voltages across the two sides of the three-wire system can be controlled independently of each other by means of R_1 and R_2 in Fig. 18. Alternatively, the main generator may be connected across the outers and G_1 and G_2 could then form a *rotary balancer*, namely two shunt machines mechanically coupled to each other. If the heavier load were on, say, the positive side, then G_1 would act as a generator supplying nearly half of the out-of-balance current. The remainder of this current would flow through G_2, which would then be running as a motor driving G_1 as a generator. The performance of the balancer can be improved by cross-connecting the field windings. This improvement is due to the fact that the decrease of the terminal voltage on the heavier-loaded side and the corresponding increase of voltage on the other side result in a decreased excitation of the motor and an increased excitation of the generator. Consequently, the higher speed and the larger flux enable the generator to maintain its terminal voltage at a higher value than that with the field windings shunt-connected.

16. Comparison of Volume of Copper in the Two-wire and Three-wire Systems. This comparison is made on the basis of (a) same length of distributor, (b) same power to load, (c) same loss in distributors, (d) balanced load for the three-wire system, so that no power is lost in the neutral and (e) area of the neutral is half of that of each outer.

If A is the cross-sectional area of each conductor of the two-wire system, then the total sectional area of copper is $2A$. Since the current in each outer of the three-wire system is half that in the two-wire system, then for the same I^2R loss the resistance of each outer is four times that of each conductor of the two-wire system. Hence the sectional area of each outer is $\frac{1}{4}A$ and that of the neutral is $\frac{1}{8}A$; so that the total sectional area of copper in the three-wire system is $(\frac{1}{4}+\frac{1}{4}+\frac{1}{8})A$, namely $0{\cdot}625A$.

$$\therefore \frac{\text{volume of copper for the three-wire system}}{\text{volume of copper for the two-wire system}} = \frac{0{\cdot}625A}{2A}$$
$$=0{\cdot}3125$$

It also follows that the voltage drop in each outer of the three-wire system is twice that in each conductor of the two-wire system; but since the voltage of the former is twice that of the latter and there is no voltage drop in the neutral when the load is balanced, the percentage voltage drop is the same in the two systems.

EXAMPLES I

1. A force of 80 newtons is applied to a mass of 200 kg. Calculate the acceleration in m/sec².

2. Calculate the force in newtons required to give a mass of 500 lb an acceleration of 4 ft/sec², assuming the frictional resistance to be negligible.

3. A train weighing 300 tons is hauled at a constant speed of 50 m.p.h. along a horizontal track. The track resistance is 10 lb/ton. Calculate (a) the tractive effort in newtons, (b) the energy in joules and in kWh expended in 10 minutes, (c) the power in kW and (d) the kinetic energy of the train in kWh (neglecting rotational inertia).

4. The power required to drive a certain dynamo at 350 r.p.m. is 600 kW. Calculate the driving torque in (a) newton-metres and (b) lb.ft.

5. A 230-V d.c. motor is developing 20 h.p. at a speed of 900 r.p.m. Calculate the torque in (a) lb.ft, (b) newton-metres.

6. If the efficiency of the motor referred to in Q. 5 is 88 per cent, calculate (a) the current and (b) the cost of the energy absorbed if the load is maintained constant for 6 hours. Assume the cost of electrical energy to be 1·3d/kWh.

7. An electric kettle is required to heat 0·6 kg of water from 10°C to the boiling point in 5 minutes, the supply voltage being 230 V. The efficiency of the kettle is 78 per cent. Calculate (a) the resistance of the heating element and (b) the cost of the energy consumed at 2d/kWh. Assume 1 kg-calorie = 4200 joules.

8. A steady current of 5 A is passed through a copper voltameter for 20 minutes. Calculate the mass of copper deposited on the cathode, assuming the electrochemical equivalent of copper to be 0·33 mg/C.

9. A plate having a total surface area of 200 cm² is to be nickel-plated to a thickness of 0·15 mm. If the current available is 6 A, calculate the time required. Assume the electrochemical equivalent of nickel to be 0·304 mg/C and the density to be 8·8 g/cm³.

10. Two coils having resistances of 5 Ω and 8 Ω respectively are connected across a battery having an e.m.f. of 6 V and an internal resistance of 1·5 Ω. Calculate (a) the terminal voltage and (b) the energy in joules dissipated in the 5-Ω coil if the current remains constant for 4 minutes.

11. A coil of 12-Ω resistance is in parallel with a coil of 20-Ω resistance. This combination is connected in series with a third coil of 8-Ω resistance. If the whole circuit is connected across a battery having an e.m.f. of 30 V and an internal resistance of 2 Ω, calculate (a) the terminal voltage of the battery and (b) the power in the 12-Ω coil.

12. A coil consists of 2000 turns of copper wire having a cross-sectional area of 0·8 mm². The mean length per turn is 80 cm and the resistivity of copper is 2 $\mu\Omega$-cm at normal working temperature. Calculate the resistance of the coil and the power dissipated when the coil is connected across a 110-V d.c. supply.

13. The field winding of a d.c. motor is connected directly across a 440-V supply. When the winding is at the room temperature of 17°C, the current is 2·3 A. After the machine has been running for some hours, the current has fallen to 1·9 A, the voltage remaining unaltered. Calculate the average temperature throughout the winding, assuming the temperature coefficient of copper to be 1/234·5 at 0°C.

14. Explain what is meant by (a) resistivity, (b) temperature coefficient of resistance, (c) insulation resistance.

It is required to construct a resistance of 100 Ω having a temperature coefficient of 0·001. Wires of two materials of suitable cross-sectional area are available. For material A the resistance is 97 Ω/100 yd, and for material B the resistance is 40 Ω/100 yd. The temperature coefficient of resistance for material A is 0·003, and for material B is 0·0005. Determine suitable lengths of wire of materials A and B. All data are referred to the same temperature.

(App. El., L.U.)

15. Owing to a short circuit, a copper conductor having a cross-sectional area of 0·25 cm² carries a current of 20,000 A for 30 milli-seconds. Neglecting heat loss, calculate the temperature rise of the conductor. Assume specific heat of copper = 0·092, specific gravity = 8·9 and resistivity = 1·8 microhm-cm. Also, assume 1 kilogram-calorie = 4200 joules.

16. A coil has a heating time constant of 40 minutes. Under working conditions, it is found that the temperature rise increases from zero to 30°C in 50 minutes. Calculate the final temperature rise, assuming the power to remain constant.

17. After the coil in Q. 16 has attained its final steady temperature, the power is switched off. Calculate the time for the temperature to fall to 15°C above the room temperature. Assume the cooling time constant to be the same as the heating time constant.

18. When a relay coil is supplied at its rated voltage, it is found that the temperature rise is 20°C during the first 25 minutes. If the final temperature rise is 43°C, calculate (a) the heating time constant of the coil and (b) the temperature rise during the first 60 minutes.

Calculate also the time taken for the temperature to fall from 35°C to 20°C above that of the room, when the coil has been disconnected from the supply. Assume the cooling time constant to be the same as the heating time constant.

19. A tank filled with 100 kg of water has a 10-kW immersion heater. The water equivalent of the tank is 5 kg, and the surface area of the tank is 1·7 m². Assuming the loss from the surface of the tank to be 15 W/m² per °C, calculate (a) the heating time constant and (b) the time taken for the temperature to rise from 0 to 30°C above that of the surrounding air.

20. A network is arranged as shown in Fig. A. Calculate the value of the current in the 8-Ω resistor by (a) the Superposition Theorem and (b) Kirchhoff's Laws.

21. A bridge network $ABCD$ is arranged as follows: resistances between terminals A–B, B–C, C–D, D–A and B–D are 10, 20, 15, 5 and 40 ohms respectively. A 20-V battery of negligible internal

resistance is connected between terminals A and C.   Determine the current in each resistor.   (E.M.E.U.)

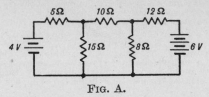

FIG. A.

22. Two batteries, A and B, are connected in parallel.   The e.m.f. and internal resistance of A are 110 V and 6 Ω respectively; and the corresponding values for B are 130 V and 4Ω respectively.   A resistance of 20 Ω is connected across the battery terminals.   Calculate (a) the terminal voltage and (b) the value and direction of the current in each battery.

23. State Kirchhoff's Laws as applied to an electric circuit. Calculate the voltage across AB in the network shown in Fig. B and indicate the polarity of the voltage.   (U.E.I.)

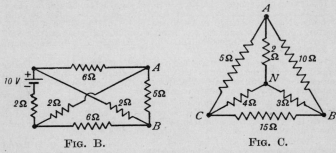

FIG. B.   FIG. C.

24. A network is arranged as in Fig. C.   Calculate the equivalent resistance between (a) A and B, and (b) A and N.

25. A network is arranged as in Fig. D, and a battery having an e.m.f. of 2 V and negligible internal resistance is connected across AC.   Determine the value and direction of the current in branch BE.

26. Calculate the value of the current through the 40-Ω resistor in Fig. E.

27. Using Thévenin's Theorem, calculate the current through the 10-Ω resistor in Fig. F.

28. Three resistors having resistances 50 Ω, 100 Ω and 150 Ω are star-connected to terminals A, B and C respectively.   Calculate the resistances of equivalent delta-connected resistors.

29. Three resistors having resistances 20 Ω, 80 Ω and 30 Ω are delta-connected between terminals AB, BC and CA respectively. Calculate the resistances of equivalent star-connected resistors.

30. A two-wire feeder, fed at one end, supplies a load A of 70 A at a distance of 200 yd and another load B of 50 A at a distance of 300 yd

from the feeding end. The cross-sectional area of each conductor is 0·12 in² and the resistivity of copper at working temperature is 0·7 microhm-inch. If the voltage across load A is 230 V, calculate (a) the voltages at the feeding point and across load B, (b) the total power wasted in the cable.   (App. El., L.U.)

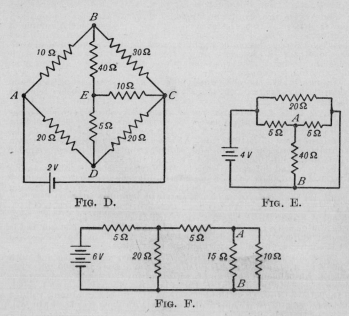

FIG. D.   FIG. E.

FIG. F.

31. A distributor is fed from both ends. At feeding point A the voltage is maintained at 236 V, and at B at 235 V. The total length of the feeder is 200 yd and loads are tapped off as follows:

20 A at 50 yards from A,
40 A ,, 75   ,,   ,,   A,
25 A ,, 100   ,,   ,,   A,
30 A ,, 150   ,,   ,,   A.

The resistance per 1000 yd of one conductor is 0·4 Ω. Calculate the current in the various sections of the feeder, the minimum voltage and the point at which it occurs.   (App. El., L.U.)

32. A number of loaded sockets are fed by a "ring main" system $ABCDE$, as follows:

Socket outlet	Load
B	15 A radiator
C	10 A wash boiler
D	5 A kettle
E	15 A water heater.

2

Each conductor of the ring main is 7/0·036 copper cable and the length of the cable (go and return) between points is as follows: $AB = 24$ yd, $BC = 12$ yd, $CD = 24$ yd, $DE = 18$ yd, $EA = 12$ yd. The resistivity of copper may be taken at 2/3 microhm per inch cube. Calculate the current in each part of the circuit and the voltage at each socket outlet if the voltage at A is 200 V. (E.M.E.U.)

33. A two-wire d.c. transmission line, 0·25 km long, supplies a power of 125 kW to a distribution network. Calculate the volume of conductor copper required for the line when the p.d. maintained between the distributors is (a) 250 V and (b) 400 V, the current density in the copper in each case being 3 A/mm². Calculate also in each case the power loss in the line, taking the resistivity of copper as $1·7 \times 10^{-8}$ metre-ohm.

Discuss briefly the choice of voltage on a transmission line, using your derived results in illustration and mentioning any other relevant factors. (App. El., L.U.)

34. A 250-V d.c. motor is fed at its rated voltage from a feeding-point 500 yd away by a two-wire distributor cable. The full-load current of the motor is 100 A and the resistance of each core of the distributor is 0·05 Ω/1000 yd. At a point 200 yd from the motor, a subsidiary load is tapped off the same distributor and fed by a similar cable to a point 100 yd away. If, when this load is switched on, the motor potential difference drops to 248 V (the motor current remaining at 100 A), calculate (a) the potential difference across the subsidiary load and the current it takes, (b) the potential difference at the feeding point, (c) the total power loss in the cables to both loads.

(U.L.C.I.)

35. A distributor, 200 yd long, is fed at one end at 235 V. The distributor has a resistance of 0·03 Ω/100 yd of single conductor and is loaded uniformly at a rate of 0·4 A/yd. Calculate the voltage (a) at the far end, (b) midway along the distributor.

36. A 0·1 sq in distributor $ABCDE$, 1000 yd long, is fed with 250 V at A, D and E; $AD = DE = 500$ yd, $AB = CD = 200$ yd. The distributor is loaded at B and C with loads of 100 A and 50 A respectively, and between D and E there is a distributed load of 1 A/yd. Calculate the voltage at the loads B and C and the minimum voltage between D and E. The resistance per 1000 loop yards of the distributor is 0·5 ohm. (E.M.E.U.)

37. A portion AB of a two-core distributor is l yd long and supplies a uniformly distributed load of i amperes per yard. Calculate the voltage drop from A to B if each conductor has a resistance of r Ω/yd.

A two-core distributor AB, 200 yd long, is fed at one end A and supplies a uniformly distributed load of 0·5 A per yd. The maximum permissible voltage drop in the distributor is 5 V. Calculate the necessary section of the distributor. If a concentrated load of 20 A is added at C, where C is 50 yd from A, how will the necessary section of the distributor be modified? (Resistivity of copper = 0·7 microhm-inch.) (Assoc. Mem., I.E.E.)

38. A distributor, 300 yd long, is fed at each end at 235 V. There is a concentrated load of 60 A at a point 100 yd from one end and a uniformly distributed load of 0·8 A/yd over the 100-yd length adjacent to the other end. The resistance/100 yd of single conductor is 0·03 Ω. Calculate the minimum voltage between the conductors.

39. In a three-wire distribution system, 250 V is maintained at the distribution point between each outer and the neutral. Load resistances of 3 Ω and 4 Ω respectively are connected between positive and neutral and negative and neutral. The resistance of each of the

three conductors between the load and the distribution point is 0·05 Ω.
Find the voltages at the load.   (C. & G., El. Eng. Pract., Int.)

40. A three-wire system AB is 300 yd long and loaded as follows:

Distance from A (yards)	Load between positive outer and neutral (amperes)	Load between negative outer and neutral (amperes)
100	40	—
150	—	70
200	60	—
250	—	40
300	30	—

The resistance of each outer is 0·2 Ω per 1000 yd and the mid-wire
is half the section of each outer. A p.d. of 200 V is maintained between
each outer and the mid-wire at the supply end. Find the directions
and magnitudes of the current in each section of the mid-wire and
calculate the p.d. across the load of 70 A on the negative side.

(U.L.C.I)

41. A three-wire system is supplied at 240 V between each outer
and middle wire, and loaded as follows:

Distance from supply end (yards)	Load between positive and middle wires (amperes)	Load between negative and middle wires (amperes)
50	20	—
100	—	40
150	30	80
200	40	—

Draw the current distribution diagram, showing the directions and
magnitudes of the currents in each section, and find the p.d. across
the 40-A load on the negative side. Resistance of each outer is
0·05 Ω/100yd, and the neutral is half the section of each outer.

(N.C.T.E.C.)

42. What are the advantages of three-wire d.c. distribution as
compared with the two-wire system?

A two-wire d.c. distributor delivers a load of 20 kW at 250 V to a
load with a transmission efficiency of 90 per cent. Calculate the
resistance of each conductor. If these conductors were used as the
outers of a three-wire system, find the magnitude of the balanced load
which could be transmitted with the same efficiency, assuming the
potential difference between each outer and the mid-wire at the load
to be maintained at 250 V.   (U.L.C.I.)

43. A three-wire d.c. distribution cable is 1500 yd long and a p.d.
of 440 V is maintained between the outers at the input end, the
potential of the mid-wire at this point being midway between the two
outers. At points 200, 500 and 1000 yd respectively from the input
end, load currents of 100 A, 150 A and 200 A are tapped from the
positive end of the system; at points 300, 800 and 1500 yd respectively
from the input end, load currents of 120 A, 300 A and 50 A are taken
from the negative side.

Make a diagram showing the magnitude and direction of the current
in each section of the outers and of the mid-wire.

If the resistance of the outers is each 0·03 Ω/1000 yd and of the mid-
wire is 0·06 Ω/1000 yd, calculate the p.d. between each outer and the
mid-wire at the far end of the cable.   (U.L.C.I.)

CHAPTER II

ELECTROMAGNETISM

17. Introductory. The magnetic circuit has been dealt with in Chapters V–VII of *Principles of Electricity*; but the following summary of the principal terms and their relationships may be useful at this stage.

(a) The *unit of flux density* is the density of a magnetic field such that a force of 1 newton is exerted per metre length of a conductor carrying 1 ampere at right angles to the magnetic field.

If B = flux density in webers/square metre,
l = length of conductor in metres

and I = current in amperes,
force on conductor = BlI newtons . (25)

If a = area of magnetic field in square metres,
total magnetic flux = $\Phi = Ba$ webers.

(b) The *unit of magnetic flux*, namely the *weber*, may alternatively be defined as that magnetic flux which, when cut by a conductor in 1 second, generates an e.m.f. of 1 volt. Hence if a conductor cuts or is cut by $d\Phi$ weber in dt second,

e.m.f. generated in conductor = $d\Phi/dt$ volts . (26)

If the magnetic flux through a coil of N turns increases by $d\Phi$ weber in dt second,

e.m.f. induced in coil = $-N \cdot d\Phi/dt$ volts . (27)

The minus sign signifies that the e.m.f. tends to circulate a current in such a direction as to try to prevent the increase of flux (Lenz's Law).

(c) In the rationalized M.K.S. system of units, the *unit of magnetomotive force* is the *ampere-turn*. Consequently if a current of I amperes is flowing through a coil of N turns,

magnetomotive force $=NI$ ampere-turns . (28)

(d) Magnetic flux $=\dfrac{\text{magnetomotive force}}{\text{reluctance}}$. (29)

i.e. $$\Phi=\frac{NI}{S}$$

where $\Phi=$ total magnetic flux in webers
and $S=$ reluctance in ampere-turns/weber.

(e) The *magnetizing force* or *magnetic field strength* at any point of a magnetic circuit is the ampere-turns/ metre required at that point to maintain the magnetic flux.

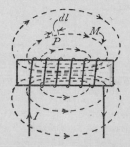

Lines of magnetic flux are continuous, i.e. they form closed loops; but the density of the flux may be different at different points of the magnetic field, as shown in Fig. 19. If H represents the magnetizing force in ampere-turns/metre at a point P, then the ampere-turns required for a length dl metre in that region is $H.dl$. The value of H varies from point to point along the flux line M, and the total

FIG. 19. — Magnetic field of a solenoid.

number of ampere-turns is the summation of the quantity $H.dl$ for elements along the *whole* of flux line M; i.e.,

m.m.f. =line integral of the magnetizing force along the whole of a flux line

$$=\oint H . dl \text{ ampere-turns . . . . . (30)}$$

The small circle on the integral sign merely signifies that the integration is taken round the whole of the closed path.

18. Kirchhoff's Laws for the Magnetic Circuit. Kirchhoff's Laws for the electric circuit are given in Art. 9. These Laws can also be applied to the magnetic circuit thus:

First Law. *The total magnetic flux towards a junction is equal to the total magnetic flux away from that junction.* This law follows from the fact that each line of flux forms a complete closed path; for instance, if an iron core is arranged as shown in Fig. 20 and if a coil C wound on limb L carries a current, the magnetic flux through C divides at P, a part passing along limb M and the remainder along limb N, to join again at Q. There is no break or discontinuity in any of the lines of flux at P and Q; consequently the number of lines of flux from L

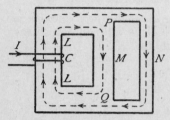

Fig. 20.—Magnetic circuit to illustrate Kirchhoff's Laws.

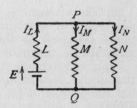

Fig. 21.—Electric circuit equivalent to Fig. 20.

towards P is exactly the same as the sum of the lines from P towards M and N, i.e.

$$\Phi_L = \Phi_M + \Phi_N$$

or

$$\Phi_L - \Phi_M - \Phi_N = 0.$$

In general,

$$\Sigma\Phi = 0.$$

Second Law. *In any closed magnetic circuit, the algebraic sum of the product of the magnetizing force and the length of each part of the circuit is equal to the resultant magnetomotive force.* For instance, if H_L is the magnetizing force in ampere-turns/metre required for limb L and l_L is the length of the circuit from Q via L to P, and if H_M and l_M are the corresponding values for limb M and H_N and l_N are those for the limb extending from P via N to Q, then:

$$\text{total m.m.f. of coil } C = H_L l_L + H_M l_M$$
$$= H_L l_L + H_N l_N$$

and

$$0 = H_M l_M - H_N l_N.$$

In general,

$$\Sigma \text{ m.m.f.} = \Sigma\, Hl.$$

It may be useful to compare the magnetic circuit of Fig. 20 with the corresponding electric circuit shown in Fig. 21.

19. Permeability of Free Space. Suppose A in Fig. 22 to represent the cross-section of a long straight conductor, situated in a vacuum and carrying a current of 1 ampere towards the paper; and suppose the return path of this current to be some considerable distance away from A so that the effect of the return current on the magnetic field in the vicinity of A may be neglected. The flux lines surrounding A will therefore be in the form of concentric circles and the dotted circle in Fig. 22 represents the path of a flux line at a radius of 1 metre. Since conductor A and its return conductor form one turn, the

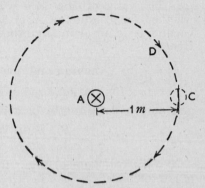

FIG. 22.—Magnetic field at 1-metre radius due to current in a long straight conductor.

m.m.f. acting on path D is 1 ampere-turn; and since the length of this flux line is 2π metres, the magnetizing force, H, at a radius of 1 metre is $1/2\pi$ ampere-turn/metre.

If B is the flux density in webers/metre^2 in the region of line D, it follows from expression (25) that the force per metre length on a conductor C (parallel to A) carrying 1 ampere at right angles to the flux is given by:

Force per metre length $= B$ (Wb/m^2) $\times 1$ (m) $\times 1$ (A)
$$= B \text{ newtons.}$$

But from the definition of the ampere given in Art. 2, this force is 2×10^{-7} newton,

$\therefore$ flux density at 1-m radius from conductor carrying 1 A $\Big\} = B = 2 \times 10^{-7}$ Wb/m^2.

Hence,

$$\frac{\text{flux density at } C}{\text{magnetizing force at } C} = \frac{B}{H} = \frac{2 \times 10^{-7} \text{ Wb/m}^2}{1/2\pi \text{ ampere-turn/m}}$$
$$= 4\pi \times 10^{-7} \text{ M.K.S. units.}$$

The ratio B/H for the above condition is termed the *permeability of free space* and is represented by the symbol μ_0. The value of this ratio is almost exactly the same whether the conductor A of Fig. 22 is situated in a vacuum or in air or in any other non-magnetic material. Hence,

$\mu_0 = \dfrac{B}{H}$ for a vacuum and non-magnetic materials

$= 4\pi \times 10^{-7}$ rationalized M.K.S. units   . (31)

and ampere-turns/metre for non-magnetic materials

$$= \frac{B}{\mu_0} = \frac{B \text{ (in Wb/m}^2)}{12 \cdot 57 \times 10^{-7}} \quad \cdots \quad (32)$$

20. Relative Permeability. If the non-magnetic core of a toroid, such as that shown in Fig. 23, is replaced by an iron core, the flux produced by a given number of

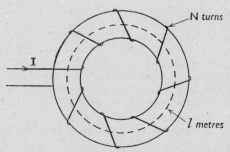

FIG. 23.—A toroid.

ampere-turns is greatly increased; and the ratio of the flux density produced in a material to the flux density in a vacuum (or in a non-magnetic core) by the same magnetizing force is termed the relative permeability of that material and is denoted by the symbol μ_r. For air,

$\mu_r = 1$; but for iron, the value varies over a very wide range and may be as high as 100,000 for certain nickel-iron alloys (Art. 25). It is therefore convenient to represent the relationship between the flux density and the magnetizing force graphically, as in Fig. 24; and the curves in Fig. 25 and 26 represent the corresponding

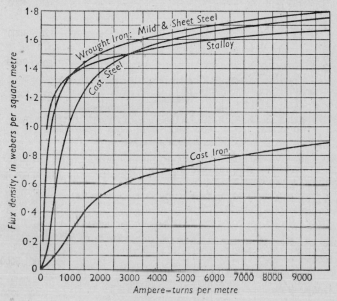

FIG. 24.—Variation of flux density with ampere-turns/metre for cast steel, etc.

values of the relative permeability plotted against the magnetizing force and the flux density respectively.

From (31), $B = \mu_0 H$ for a non-magnetic material; hence, for a material having relative permeability μ_r,

$$B = \mu_r \mu_0 H$$

∴ $B/H = \mu_r \mu_0 = \mu$ = absolute permeability . (33)

21. Reluctance. Let us consider an iron ring having a cross-sectional area of a square metres and a mean

2*

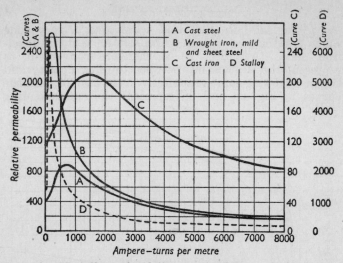

FIG. 25.—Variation of relative permeability with ampere-turns/metre for cast steel, etc.

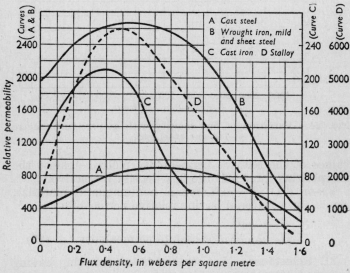

FIG. 26.—Variation of relative permeability with flux density for cast steel, etc.

circumference of l metres (Fig. 23), uniformly wound with N turns carrying a current I amperes; then:

$$\text{total flux} = \Phi = \text{flux density} \times \text{area} = Ba \quad . \quad (34)$$

and m.m.f. = magnetizing force × length = Hl . (35)

Dividing (34) by (35), we have:

$$\frac{\Phi}{\text{m.m.f.}} = \frac{Ba}{Hl} = \mu \times \frac{a}{l}$$

$$\therefore \qquad \Phi = \frac{\text{m.m.f.}}{l/(\mu a)} \quad . \quad . \quad . \quad (36)$$

From a comparison of expressions (29) and (36), it follows that:

$$\text{reluctance} = \frac{l}{\mu a} \quad . \quad . \quad . \quad . \quad . \quad . \quad . \quad (37)$$

$$= \frac{l}{\mu_0 a} \quad \text{for non-magnetic materials.}$$

Expression (37) is similar in form to $\rho l/a$ for the resistance of a conductor except that the absolute permeability, μ, for the magnetic material corresponds to the reciprocal of the resistivity, namely the conductivity of the electrical material.

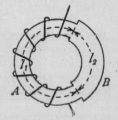

FIG 27.—Composite magnetic circuit.

22. Composite Magnetic Circuit. Suppose a magnetic circuit to consist of two specimens of iron, A and B, arranged as in Fig. 27. If l_1 and l_2 be the mean lengths in metres of the magnetic circuits of A and B respectively, a_1 and a_2 their cross-sectional areas in square metres, and μ_1 and μ_2 their absolute permeabilities,

then $\qquad$ reluctance of $A = \dfrac{l_1}{\mu_1 a_1}$

and $\qquad$ reluctance of $B = \dfrac{l_2}{\mu_2 a_2}$

If a coil is wound on core A as in Fig. 27 and if the

magnetic flux is assumed to be confined to the iron core, then

$$\text{total reluctance of magnetic circuit} = \frac{l_1}{\mu_1 a_1} + \frac{l_2}{\mu_2 a_2}$$

$$\text{and total flux} = \Phi = \frac{\text{m.m.f. of coil}}{\text{total reluctance}} = \frac{NI}{\dfrac{l_1}{\mu_1 a_1} + \dfrac{l_2}{\mu_2 a_2}} \qquad (38)$$

Fig. 28 shows an iron ring with a small radial gap. Practically all the flux goes straight across from the one face to the other, so that the area of the gap may be assumed to be the same as that of the iron. Hence, if

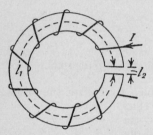

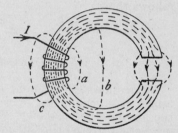

FIG. 28.—Iron ring with an airgap.

FIG. 29.—Magnetic leakage and fringing.

a is the cross-sectional area and if l_1 and l_2 are the lengths of the iron core and gap respectively,

$$\text{total reluctance} = \frac{l_1}{\mu_1 a} + \frac{l_2}{\mu_0 a}$$

23. Magnetic Leakage and Fringing. If the magnetizing coil is concentrated as in Fig. 29, then some of the flux takes paths such as a, b and c. This is referred to as leakage flux, since it does not pass across the gap in the ring. If this gap is long, some of the flux passing across it will bulge outwards as shown roughly in Fig. 29, thereby causing the effective area of the gap to be increased and the flux density in the gap to be correspondingly reduced. In this case, however, it is impossible to make a sharp distinction between leakage flux and fringing flux. A clearer distinction between these two fluxes can be drawn in the case of electrical machines. For instance, Fig. 30 shows two poles of a six-pole machine. The armature slots have, for simplicity, been omitted. Some of the dotted lines do not enter the armature core and thus do not assist in generating an e.m.f. in the armature winding; consequently, they represent leakage flux. On the other hand, some of the flux passes between the pole tips and the armature core, as shown in Fig. 30; hence such lines of force are referred

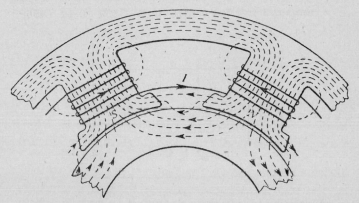

FIG. 30.—Magnetic leakage and fringing in a machine.

to as fringing flux. Since this fringing flux is cut by the armature conductors, it forms part of the useful flux.

From Fig. 29 and 30 it is seen that the effect of leakage flux is to increase the total flux through the exciting winding,

and leakage coefficient

$$= \frac{\text{total flux through exciting winding}}{\text{useful flux}} \quad . \quad (39)$$

The value of the leakage coefficient for electrical machines is usually about 1·15 to 1·25.

Example 8. *A magnetic circuit is made of mild steel arranged as in Fig. 31. The centre limb is wound with*

500 *turns and has a cross-sectional area of* 8 *cm². Each of the outer limbs has a cross-sectional area of* 5 *cm². The airgap has a length of* 1 *mm. Calculate the current required to set up a flux of* 1·3 *milliwebers in the centre limb, assuming no magnetic leakage and fringing. The mean lengths of the various magnetic paths are shown on the diagram.*

Flux density in centre limb $= \dfrac{0\cdot0013}{0\cdot0008} = 1\cdot625$ Wb/m².

From Fig. 24, ampere-turns/metre for mild steel $= 3800$,

$\therefore$ ampere-turns for centre limb $= 3800 \times 0\cdot12 = 456$.

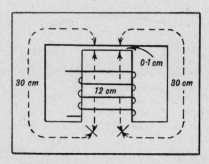

FIG. 31.—Magnetic circuit for Example 8.

Since half the flux returns through one outer limb and half through the other, the two outer limbs are magnetically equivalent to a single limb having a cross-sectional area of 10 cm² and a length of 30 cm,

$\therefore$ flux density in outer limbs $= \dfrac{0\cdot0013}{0\cdot001} = 1\cdot3$ Wb/m².

From Fig. 24, ampere-turns/metre for mild steel $= 850$

$\therefore$ ampere-turns for outer limbs $= 850 \times 0\cdot3 = 255$.

Flux density in airgap $= 1\cdot625$ Wb/m²

$\therefore$ ampere-turns/metre for gap $= \dfrac{1\cdot625}{4\pi \times 10^{-7}} = 1\cdot292 \times 10^6$

and ampere-turns for gap $= 1\cdot292 \times 10^6 \times 0\cdot001 = 1292$.

Hence,   total ampere-turns $= 456 + 255 + 1292$
$$= 2003$$

and   magnetizing current $= \dfrac{2003}{500} = 4$ A.

Example 9. *A magnetic circuit is made up of steel laminations shaped as in Fig. 32. The width of the iron is 4 cm and the core is built up to a depth of 5 cm, of which 8 per cent is taken up by insulation between the laminations. The gap is 2 mm long and the effective area of the gap is 25 cm². The coil is wound with 800 turns. If the leakage coefficient is 1·2, calculate the magnetizing current required to produce a flux of 0·0025 weber across the airgap.*

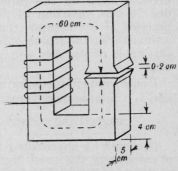

Fig. 32.—Magnetic circuit for Example 9.

Flux density in airgap $= \dfrac{0 \cdot 0025}{0 \cdot 0025} = 1$ Wb/m²,

$\therefore$ ampere-turns/metre for gap $= \dfrac{1}{4\pi \times 10^{-7}} = 796{,}000$

and   ampere-turns for gap $= 796{,}000 \times 0 \cdot 002$
$$= 1592.$$

Total flux through coil $=$ flux in gap $\times$ leakage coeff.
$$= 0 \cdot 0025 \times 1 \cdot 2 = 0 \cdot 003 \text{ Wb}$$

Since only 92 per cent of the cross-section of the core consists of iron,

$\therefore$ area of iron in core
$$= 4 \times 5 \times 0 \cdot 92 = 18 \cdot 4 \text{ cm}^2 = 0 \cdot 00184 \text{ m}^2$$

and   flux density in core
$$= \dfrac{0 \cdot 003}{0 \cdot 00184} = 1 \cdot 63 \text{ Wb/m}^2.$$

From Fig. 24, corresponding ampere-turns/metre for laminations $= 4000$.

It will be evident from Fig. 29 that when there is magnetic leakage, the flux density is not uniform over the whole length of the iron core. It is impossible, however, to allow for the variation of ampere-turns/metre due to this variation of flux density; and the usual practice is to assume that the ampere-turns/metre estimated for the region of maximum density applies to the whole of the iron core, thereby erring on the safe side.

Hence, ampere-turns for iron core $= 4000 \times 0 \cdot 6 = 2400$
and total ampere-turns $= 1592 + 2400 = 3992$

$$\therefore \quad \text{magnetizing current} = \frac{3992}{800} \simeq 5 \text{ amperes.}$$

It should be appreciated that owing to the difficulty of calculating the exact flux densities at various points of the magnetic circuit and to the uncertainty regarding the exact magnetic property of the iron, the results obtained in magnetic calculations are only approximately correct.

When we are dealing with composite magnetic circuits, it is usually helpful to tabulate the results thus:

Part	Area (m²)	Length (m)	Flux (Wb)	Flux density (Wb/m²)	Ampere-turns/metre	Ampere-turns
Iron .	0·00184	0·6	0·003	1·63	4,000	2400
Airgap	0·0025	0·002	0·0025	1·0	796,000	1592

Total ampere-turns $= 3992$

24. Experimental Determination of the Magnetization Curve. (a) *By means of a Ballistic Galvanometer.* The most satisfactory method is to use a closed ring of uniform cross-section, uniformly wound with a coil P, as in Fig. 33, thereby eliminating magnetic leakage. Coil P is connected to a battery through a reversing switch RS, an ammeter A and a variable resistance R_1. Another coil S, which need not be distributed around the whole of the ring, is connected through a high resistance to a ballistic galvanometer BG. Switch S_2 and variable resistance R_2 are not required for this test, but will be used when this circuit is employed for determining the hysteresis loop (Art. 26).

A ballistic galvanometer has a moving-coil suspended between the poles of a permanent magnet, but the coil is wound on a non-metallic former such as wood, so that there is very little damping when the coil has a high resistance in series. It is usual to provide a key or switch K, which, when closed, short-circuits the

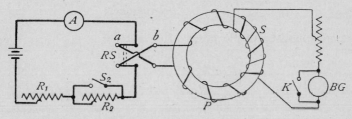

Fig. 33.—Determination of a magnetization curve.

galvanometer, thereby enabling the e.m.f. induced in the moving-coil by its oscillation to circulate enough current to stop that oscillation.

When the current through P is reversed by means of RS, the reversal of the flux induces an e.m.f. in S and sends a current through BG. But this current is of very short duration since it ceases immediately the flux has reached its full value in the reversed direction. The galvanometer deflection is proportional to the *quantity* of electricity discharged through it, and the moving-coil then oscillates backwards and forwards with decreasing amplitude.

If $\theta =$ first deflection or "throw" of the galvanometer and $k =$ ballistic constant of the galvanometer

$\qquad =$ quantity of electricity in coulombs per unit deflection,

$\therefore \qquad$ quantity of electricity through galvanometer $\Big\} = k\theta$ coulombs $\qquad$ (40)

If $\Phi=$ flux produced in ring by I amperes through P
and $t=$ time (in seconds) of reversal of flux,
then   change of flux $=2\Phi$
and rate of change of flux $=2\Phi/t$ webers/second.

If $N_s=$ number of turns on coil S,

average e.m.f. induced in $S=\dfrac{2\Phi}{t}\times N_s$ volts.

If $R=$ total resistance of the secondary circuit,
then average current through BG

$$=\frac{2\Phi\times N_s}{t\times R}\text{ amperes}$$

and quantity of electricity through BG

$$=\text{average current}\times\text{time}$$
$$=\frac{2\Phi N_s}{t\times R}\times t$$
$$=\frac{2\Phi N_s}{R}\text{ coulombs}\qquad . \quad . \quad . \quad (41)$$

Equating (40) and (41), we have:

$$k\theta=\frac{2\Phi N_s}{R}$$

$\therefore$ $\Phi=\dfrac{k\theta R}{2N_s}$ webers.

If $a=$ cross-sectional area of core in square metres,

flux density in core $=B=\Phi/a$

$$=\frac{k\theta R}{2aN_s}\text{webers/m}^2\qquad . \quad (42)$$

If $N_p=$ number of turns on coil P
and $l=$ mean circumference of ring in metres,
then   magnetizing force $=H=IN_p/l$.

This test is repeated with different values of the
current; and from the data we can plot the flux density
against either the ampere-turns/cm or the magnetizing
force in ampere-turns/metre.

(b) *By means of a Fluxmeter.* A fluxmeter is a special type of ballistic galvanometer. The moving system is either pivoted or suspended by a silk fibre, and the current is led into and out of the coil by fine wires or ligaments so arranged as to exert negligible control over the position of the moving coil. The pointer movement is rendered dead-beat by electromagnetic damping.

The fluxmeter is connected directly across the secondary coil S in Fig. 33. When the current through coil P is reversed, the deflection on the fluxmeter is proportional to the change of flux and to the number of turns on S, i.e. to the change of flux-linkages with coil S. Thus, if the flux is reversed from Φ to $-\Phi$ and if N_s is the number of turns on S,

$$\begin{array}{l}\text{change of flux-linkages}\\ \text{with coil } S\end{array}\Bigg\} = \begin{cases}\text{change of flux} \times\\ \text{ no. of turns on } S\end{cases}$$
$$= 2\Phi N_s \quad . \quad . \quad . \quad (43)$$

If $\theta =$ corresponding deflection on fluxmeter
and $c =$ fluxmeter constant
$\qquad$ = no. of weber-turns per unit of scale deflection,

then $\qquad$ change of flux-linkages with $S = c\theta$. (44)

Equating (43) and (44), we have:

$$2\Phi N_s = c\theta$$
$$\therefore \qquad \Phi = \frac{c\theta}{2N_s}\text{webers.}$$

The values of the flux density, etc., can then be calculated exactly as described for the preceding method.

25. Hysteresis. If we take a closed iron ring which has been completely demagnetized * and measure the flux density with increasing values of the magnetizing force, the relationship between the two quantities is represented by curve OAC in Fig. 34. If the magnetizing force is then reduced, it is found that the flux density follows curve CD, and that when the magnetiz-

---

* The simplest method of demagnetizing is to reverse the magnetizing current a large number of times while, at the same time, reducing the current to zero.

ing force has been reduced to zero, the flux density remaining in the iron is *OD* and is referred to as the *remanent flux density*.

If the magnetizing force is increased in the reverse direction, the flux density decreases, until at some value *OE*, the flux has been reduced to zero. The magnetizing force *OE* required to wipe out the residual magnetism is

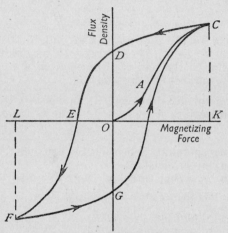

FIG. 34.—Hysteresis loop.

termed the *coercive force*. Further increase of the magnetizing force causes the flux density to grow in the reverse direction as represented by curve *EF*. If the reversed magnetizing force *OL* be adjusted to the same value as the maximum magnetizing force *OK* in the initial direction, the final flux density *LF* is the same as *KC*.

If the magnetizing force is varied backwards from *OL* to *OK*, the flux density follows a curve *FGC* similar to curve *CDEF*, and the closed figure *CDEFGC* is termed the *hysteresis loop*.

If hysteresis loops for a given iron ring are determined for different maximum values of the magnetizing force, they are found to lie within one another, as shown in Fig. 35. The apexes A, C, D and E of the respective loops lie on the B-H curve determined with increasing values of the magnetizing force. It will be seen that the value of the remanent flux density depends upon the value of the peak magnetization; thus, for loop A, the remanent flux density is OX, whereas for loop E, corresponding to a maximum magnetization that is approaching saturation, the remanent flux density is OY. The value of the remanent flux density obtained when the maximum magnetization reaches the saturation value of the material is termed the *remanence* of that material. Thus for the material having the hysteresis loops of Fig. 35, the remanence is approximately OY.

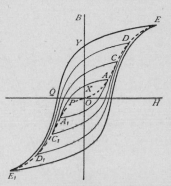

FIG. 35.—A family of hysteresis loops.

The value of the coercive force in Fig. 35 varies from OP for loop AA_1 to OQ for loop EE_1; and the value of the coercive force when the maximum magnetization reaches the saturation value of the material is termed the *coercivity* of that material. Thus, for Fig. 35, the coercivity is approximately OQ. The value of the coercivity varies enormously for different materials, being about 40,000 AT/m for Alnico (an alloy of iron, aluminium, nickel, cobalt and copper, used largely for permanent magnets) and about 3 AT/m for Mumetal (an alloy of nickel, iron, copper and molybdenum).

26. Determination of the Hysteresis Loop. The circuit arrangement is shown in Fig. 33.* With reversing switch RS on side a and S_2 closed, the current is

* In actual practice, it is more convenient to insert R_2 in the connection between a pair of diagonally opposite contacts of RS; but the arrangement shown in Fig. 33 makes it easier to follow the procedure.

adjusted by means of R_1 to the value corresponding to the maximum magnetizing force OA (Fig. 36) for which the loop is to be determined. RS is then reversed several times to ensure that the iron ring is in a cyclic state so that when magnetizing force OA is reversed, the flux density AC changes to exactly the same value in the reverse direction. During these operations, K should be closed, thereby short-circuiting the galvanometer. Then with K open, the "throw" or first deflection θ_m of

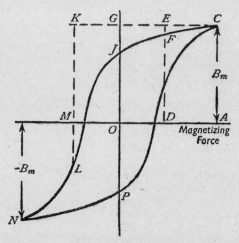

FIG. 36.—Plotting of a hysteresis loop.

BG is noted when RS is reversed. In Art. 24 it was shown that the corresponding flux density B_m is given by:

$$B_m = \frac{kR}{2aN_s} \times \theta_m$$

where R represents the total resistance of the secondary circuit. Hence points C and N of Fig. 36 can be plotted.

From the above expression, it follows that

$$\textit{change} \text{ of flux density} = \frac{kR}{aN_s} \times \left(\begin{matrix}\text{galvanometer} \\ \text{deflection}\end{matrix}\right)$$

and it is with the aid of this formula that we derive the remaining points required for plotting the loop.

To derive portion CFJ of loop. With RS on a, S_2 is opened and R_2 adjusted to give a current corresponding to a magnetizing force OD (Fig. 36). S_2 is then closed to bring the magnetizing force back to OA; RS is reversed several times to restore the iron to the cyclic condition. Galvanometer deflection θ_1 is then noted when S_2 is opened.

$$\text{Corresponding change of flux density} = \frac{kR}{aN_s} \times \theta_1.$$

This change of flux density is represented by EF in Fig. 36, so that the actual flux density corresponding to magnetizing force $OD = B_m - EF = DF$.

This test is repeated with different values of OD down to zero, the latter value being obtained by breaking the circuit of R_2 so that when S_2 is opened, the current is reduced to zero and the corresponding change of flux density is represented by GJ.

To derive portion JLN of loop. Thus to obtain point L, S_2 is opened and R_2 adjusted to give a current corresponding to magnetizing force OM. S_2 is closed and RS reversed several times to bring the iron back to the cyclic state. Then S_2 is opened and RS simultaneously moved over from a to b, and the deflection θ_2 of the galvanometer is noted. (Actually, S_2 should be opened the slightest fraction of a second before RS is reversed so as to ensure that the magnetizing force on the negative side does not exceed OM.) Then:

$$\textit{change of flux density} = KL = \frac{kR}{aN_s} \times \theta_2.$$

When the change of flux density exceeds B_m, as shown for KL in Fig. 36, then:

$$\left. \begin{array}{l} \textit{actual} \text{ flux density corresponding to} \\ \quad \text{magnetizing force } OM \end{array} \right\} = KL - B_m$$
$$= ML.$$

This test is repeated for sufficient number of negative values of the magnetizing force to enable curve JLN to be

drawn.   The return portion NPC of the loop is exactly
the reverse of CJN.

27. Hysteresis Loss.   In *Principles of Electricity*
(p. 122), it was pointed out that residual magnetism in
iron is probably due to revolving electrons (i.e. negative
charges of electricity) having had their axes aligned by
the initial magnetization.   Energy has to be expended
in forcing them to change the directions of their axes.
This energy appears as heat and is referred to as *hysteresis*

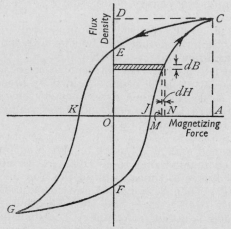

Fig. 37.—Hysteresis loss.

loss.   As a very crude analogy, we might regard the
atoms with their planetary electrons like a squad of
soldiers, tightly packed, being ordered to right-about-
turn a number of times in quick succession; the heat
generated might be quite considerable!

It will now be shown that the loss involved in taking
a specimen of iron through a complete cycle of magnetization is proportional to the area of the hysteresis loop.
Suppose Fig. 37 to represent the hysteresis loop obtained
on an iron ring of mean circumference l metres and
having a cross-sectional area of a square metres.   Let N
be the number of turns on the magnetizing coil.

Let dB=increase of flux density when the magnetizing force is increased by a very small amount MN in dt second, and i=current in amperes corresponding to OM,

i.e. $$OM = \frac{Ni}{l} \qquad . \quad . \quad . \quad . \quad . \quad . \quad (45)$$

Instantaneous e.m.f. induced in winding

$$= -\frac{a \times dB \times N}{dt} \text{ volts}$$

and component of applied voltage to neutralize this e.m.f.

$$= \frac{aN \times dB}{dt} \text{ volts}$$

∴ instantaneous power supplied to magnetic field

$$= i \times \frac{aN \times dB}{dt} \text{ watts}$$

and energy supplied to magnetic field in time dt second

$$= iaN \times dB \text{ joules.}$$

From (45), $$i = \frac{l \times OM}{N}$$

∴ energy supplied to magnetic field in time dt

$$= \frac{l \times OM}{N} \times aN \times dB \text{ joules}$$

$$= OM \times dB \times la \text{ joules}$$

=area of shaded strip, joules/m³

∴ energy supplied to magnetic field when H is increased from zero to OA

=area $FJCDF$ joules/m³

Similarly, energy returned from magnetic field when H is reduced from OA to zero

=area $CDEC$ joules/m³

∴ net energy absorbed by magnetic field

=area $FJCEF$ joules/m³

Hence, hysteresis loss for a complete cycle

=area of loop $GFCEG$ joules/m³ (46)

From the areas of a number of loops similar to those shown in Fig. 35, the hysteresis loss per cycle was found by Steinmetz to be proportional to $B_{max}^{1.6}$ for a certain quality of iron, where B_{max} represents the maximum value of the flux density. It is important to realize that this index of 1·6 is purely empirical and appears to have no theoretical basis. In fact, indices as high as 3·5 have been obtained, and in general we may say that

$$\text{hysteresis loss per cubic metre per cycle} \propto B_{max}^{x}$$

where $x=1·5$ to 2·5, depending upon the quality of the iron and the range of flux density over which the measurement has been made.

From the above proof, it is evident that the hysteresis loss is proportional to the volume and to the number of cycles through which the magnetization is taken. Hence,

if $f=$frequency of alternating magnetization in c/s and $v=$volume of iron in cubic metres,

$$\text{hysteresis loss}=kvfB_{max}^{x} \text{ watts} \qquad . \quad (47)$$

where k is a constant for a given specimen and a given range of flux density.

Example 10. *The area of the hysteresis loop obtained with a certain specimen of iron was 9·3 cm². The co-ordinates were such that 1 cm =1000 AT/m and 1 cm =0·2 Wb/m². Calculate* (a) *the hysteresis loss per cubic metre per cycle and* (b) *the hysteresis loss per cubic metre at a frequency of 50 c/s.* (c) *If the maximum flux density was 1·5 Wb/m², calculate the hysteresis loss per cubic metre for a maximum density of 1·2 Wb/m² and a frequency of 30 c/s, assuming the loss to be proportional to $B_{max}^{1.8}$.*

(a) Area of hysteresis loop
   in BH units $\Big\}=9·3 \times 1000 \times 0·2 = 1860$

∴ hysteresis loss per cubic
   metre per cycle $\Big\}=1860$ joules.

(b) Hysteresis   loss   per
   cubic metre at 50 c/s $\Big\}=1860 \times 50 = 93,000$ W.

(c) From expression (47),

$$93,000 = k \times 1 \times 50 \times (1 \cdot 5)^{1 \cdot 8}$$

$$\log (1 \cdot 5)^{1 \cdot 8} = 1 \cdot 8 \times 0 \cdot 176 = 0 \cdot 3168 = \log 2 \cdot 074$$

$$\therefore \qquad k = \frac{93,000}{50 \times 2 \cdot 074} = 896$$

For $B_{max} = 1 \cdot 2$ Wb/m^2 and $f = 30$ c/s,

$$\left. \begin{array}{l} \text{hysteresis loss per} \\ \text{cubic metre} \end{array} \right\} = 896 \times 30 \times (1 \cdot 2)^{1 \cdot 8} = 37,350 \text{ W.}$$

$$\left. \begin{array}{l} \text{Or, hysteresis loss} \\ \text{at } 1 \cdot 2 \text{ Wb/m}^2 \text{ and} \\ 30 \text{ c/s} \end{array} \right\} = 93,000 \times \frac{30}{50} \times \left(\frac{1 \cdot 2}{1 \cdot 5} \right)^{1 \cdot 8} = 37,350 \text{W.}$$

28. Magnetic Field of a Long Solenoid. Fig. 38 (a) shows a uniformly wound solenoid, the axial length, l,

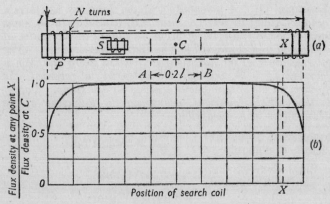

FIG. 38.—The magnetic field of a long solenoid.

of which is very large compared with the diameter. The magnetic flux density at various points inside the solenoid can be determined by means of a small search-coil S connected to a ballistic galvanometer. The deflections of the galvanometer are noted for the reversal of a given current through the solenoid winding P with the search-coil in different positions along the axis of the solenoid. The curve * in Fig. 38 (b) represents the result obtained with a solenoid having a length equal to 10 times the diameter. It is found that between two planes, A and B, situated $0.1l$ on each side of the centre C of such a solenoid, the variation of the flux density inside the solenoid is only about 0.1 per cent. This length of the solenoid may therefore be regarded as a part of a uniformly-wound ring (Art. 24); hence the magnetizing force inside the central portion of a long solenoid is $I \times$no. of turns per metre length,

i.e. $$H = \frac{NI}{l} \text{ ampere-turns/metre} \quad . \quad . \quad (48)$$

where I = the magnetizing current in amperes
       N = total number of turns on the solenoid
and l = length of solenoid in metres.

Example 11. *A solenoid, 120 cm long, is uniformly wound with 800 turns. A short coil, wound with 50 turns having a mean diameter of 3 cm, is placed at the centre of the solenoid and connected to a ballistic galvanometer. The total resistance of the search-coil circuit is 2000 Ω. When a current of 5 A through the solenoid is reversed, the deflection on the galvanometer scale is 85 divisions. Calculate the ballistic constant, assuming the damping of the galvanometer to be negligible.*

$$\left.\begin{array}{r}\text{Magnetizing force at}\\ \text{centre of solenoid}\end{array}\right\} = \frac{5 \times 800}{1 \cdot 2} = 3333 \text{ AT/m}$$

$$\left.\begin{array}{r}\therefore \text{ flux density at}\\ \text{centre of solenoid}\end{array}\right\} = 4\pi \times 10^{-7} \times 3333$$

$$= 0 \cdot 004185 \text{ Wb/m}^2.$$

$$\text{Area of search-coil} = \frac{\pi}{4} \times (0 \cdot 03)^2 = 0 \cdot 0007065 \text{ m}^2.$$

$$\left.\begin{array}{r}\text{Flux through search-}\\ \text{coil}\end{array}\right\} = 0 \cdot 004185 \times 0 \cdot 0007065$$

$$= 2 \cdot 96 \times 10^{-6} \text{ Wb.}$$

* This curve can also be calculated from first principles, but the proof is too lengthy for incorporation in this volume. It is given in Golding's *Electrical Measurements* p. 33.

If the current is reversed in t seconds,
average e.m.f. induced in search-coil

$$=\frac{2 \times 2 \cdot 96 \times 10^{-6} \times 50}{t}=\frac{296}{t} \times 10^{-6} \text{ volt}$$

and average current through galvanometer

$$=\frac{296 \times 10^{-6}}{t \times 2000}=\frac{0 \cdot 148}{t} \times 10^{-6} \text{ ampere}$$

∴ quantity of electricity through galvanometer
$$=0 \cdot 148 \times 10^{-6} \text{ coulomb}$$

and ballistic constant of galvanometer

$$=\frac{0 \cdot 148 \times 10^{-6}}{85}$$

$$=1 \cdot 74 \times 10^{-9} \text{ coulomb per division.}$$

This is one of the standard methods used for determining the ballistic constant of a galvanometer.

29. Condition for Minimum Volume of a Permanent Magnet.   Let M in Fig. 39 be the steel core to be magnetized by passing current through winding W, and let PP

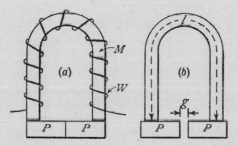

Fig. 39.—Permanent-magnet steel core with
soft-iron pole-shoes.

be soft-iron pole-shoes of negligible reluctance.   Suppose curve CDE in Fig. 40 to represent the demagnetizing portion of the hysteresis loop for a maximum magnetizing force OA obtained with the closed magnetic circuit of Fig. 39 (a).   It was pointed out in Article 27 that the remanent flux density OD may be regarded as being maintained by the rotation of electrons at extremely high speed around their respective nuclei, the axes of rotation of most of these current rings having been orientated by the external excitation so that they are pointing in the same direction. To neutralize the residual magnetism, it is necessary to apply, by means of winding W, demagnetizing ampere-turns equal to (coercive force $OE \times$ the length l of the magnet). We may therefore regard $(OE \times l)$ as the ampere-turns produced

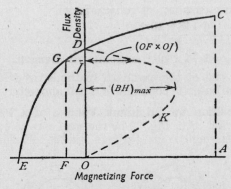

Fig. 40.—Demagnetizing portion of hysteresis loop.

by the electronic current-rings responsible for maintaining the remanent flux density OD; hence, the product $(OE \times l)$ may be termed the *inherent ampere-turns* of the magnet.

With the pole-shoes PP in contact, as in Fig 39 (a), let us reduce the magnetizing force from OA to zero and then increase it to OF in the *reverse* direction, so that the flux density is reduced to FG (or OJ). The net number of ampere-turns available to produce this flux density in the magnet is $(OE \times l - OF \times l)$, namely $(EF \times l)$. Next, let us gradually pull the pole-shoes apart and at the same time reduce the demagnetizing current in W so as to keep the flux density constant at OJ. Suppose the procedure to be continued until the current in W has been reduced to zero and suppose g in Fig. 39 (b) to be the corresponding gap length. Since this gap has been introduced without any change of flux density in the steel, it follows that the number of ampere-turns required to send the flux through the magnet steel has remained unaltered at $(EF \times l)$ and that the number of ampere-turns now available to send the flux across the gap is therefore $(OF \times l)$, namely that neutralized by the negative ampere-turns of the magnetizing coil before the gap was introduced.

Let B_g = flux density in gap corresponding to flux density OJ in magnet,
A = effective area of gap
and a = cross-sectional area of magnet core.

Then, neglecting any magnetic leakage flux,

$$\text{total flux} = OJ \times a = B_g A \quad . \quad . \quad (49)$$

Also, no. of ampere-turns required to send flux across gap $\Big\} = \dfrac{B_g}{\mu_0} \times g.$

But it was shown above that the number of ampere-turns required to send the flux across the gap $= OF \times l.$

$$\therefore \qquad OF \times l = \frac{B_g}{\mu_0} \times g \quad . \quad . \quad . \quad (50)$$

From (49) and (50), it follows that

$$\text{volume of magnet} = la = \frac{B_g g}{\mu_0 \times OF} \times \frac{B_g A}{OJ}$$
$$= B_g^2 g A / (OF \times OJ)\mu_0 \quad . \quad (51)$$

For any particular application of a magnet, a certain size of gap and a certain gap density are required, the most suitable values being determined partly by permissible dimensions and partly by working out alternative designs and comparing their cost and performance.

From expression (51), it is evident that for a given flux density in and given dimensions of the gap, the volume of the magnet is a minimum when the product $(OF \times OJ)$ is a maximum. The variation of this product for different flux densities in the *magnet core* is represented by curve K in Fig. 40, from which it follows that the volume of magnet is a minimum when it is operated at flux density OL. The value of the product $(BH)_{max}$ for a steel specimen is the best criterion of its suitability for use as a permanent magnet. The following table gives the magnetic data for some of the principal magnet materials:

Material	Remanence in Wb/m²	Coercivity in AT/m	Value of B for $(BH)_{max}$	Value of H for $(BH)_{max}$	$(BH)_{max}$
1% carbon steel	0·9	4,000	0·6	2,600	1,560
6% tungsten steel	1·05	5,200	0·7	3,750	2,620
35% cobalt steel	0·9	20,000	0·6	13,000	7,800
Alnico (Fe–Al–Ni–Co–Cu)	0·8	40,000	0·56	24,000	13,500
Alcomax III	1·25	54,000	0·95	40,000	38,000
Ticonal G (Fe–Al–Ni–Co–Cu)	1·35	47,000	1·1	42,000	46,000

Example 12. *Estimate the minimum dimensions of (a) a tungsten-steel magnet and (b) an Alnico magnet to maintain a flux density of 0·5 Wb/m² across an airgap, 4 mm long, having an effective cross-sectional area of 6 cm². Assume the data for tungsten steel and Alnico to be those given in the above table.*

(a) Total flux in airgap $= 0·5 \times 0·0006 = 0·0003$ Wb. For tungsten steel, value of B for $(BH)_{max}$ is $0·7$ Wb/m²,

$\therefore$ cross-sectional area of tung-$\left.\begin{array}{l}\\ \end{array}\right\} = \dfrac{0·0003}{0·7} = 0·000429\text{m}^2$
sten magnet required

$= 4·29$ cm².

Ampere-turns/m for airgap $= \dfrac{0·5}{4\pi \times 10^{-7}} = 398,000$

$\therefore$ ampere-turns to maintain$\left.\begin{array}{l}\\ \end{array}\right\} = 398,000 \times 0·004 = 1592.$
the flux across gap

For tungsten steel, value of H for $(BH)_{max}$ is 3750 AT/m,

$\therefore$ length of magnet required $= \dfrac{1592}{3750} = 0·425$ m $= 42·5$ cm.

$$\left.\begin{array}{r}\text{Hence, minimum volume}\\ \text{of tungsten}\\ \text{magnet}\end{array}\right\}=4{\cdot}29\times42{\cdot}5=182{\cdot}5\ \text{cm}^3$$

$$\text{(b)}\left.\begin{array}{r}\text{Cross-sectional area}\\ \text{of Alnico magnet}\end{array}\right\}=\frac{0{\cdot}0003}{0{\cdot}56}=0{\cdot}000536\ \text{m}^2$$

$$=5{\cdot}36\ \text{cm}^2.$$

$$\text{Length of Alnico magnet}=\frac{1592}{24{,}000}=0{\cdot}0664\ \text{m}=6{\cdot}64\ \text{cm}$$

$$\therefore\quad\left.\begin{array}{r}\text{minimum volume of}\\ \text{Alnico magnet}\end{array}\right\}=5{\cdot}36\times6{\cdot}64=35{\cdot}6\ \text{cm}^3.$$

$$\text{Hence}\ \frac{\text{minimum volume of tungsten magnet}}{\text{minimum volume of Alnico magnet}}$$

$$=\frac{182{\cdot}5}{35{\cdot}6}=5{\cdot}13$$

i.e. the volume of an Alnico magnet is only about a fifth of that of a tungsten magnet for the same duty.

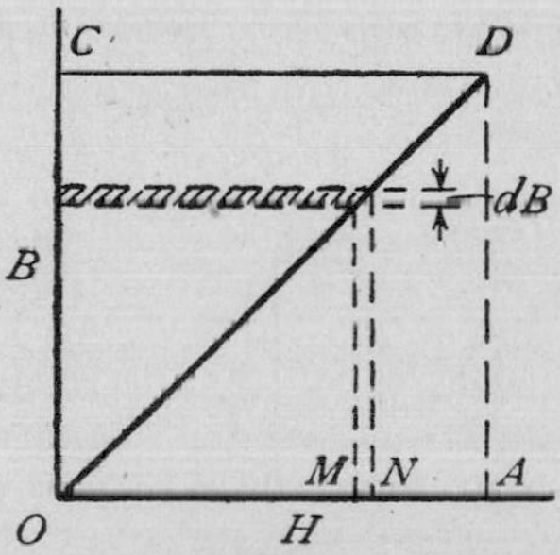

FIG. 41.—*B–H* relationship for a non-magnetic medium.

30. Magnetic Energy in a Non-magnetic Medium. For a non-magnetic medium, the relative permeability is unity, so that the magnetizing force and the flux density are proportional to each other and the relationship between them is represented by a straight line *OD* in Fig. 41.

It was shown in Art. 27 that when the flux density is increased by dB due to a very small increase *MN* of the magnetizing force,

$$\left.\begin{array}{r}\text{energy supplied to}\\ \text{magnetic circuit}\end{array}\right\}=\text{area of shaded strip, joules/m}^3$$

Hence, for a maximum flux density *OC* in Fig. 41,

$$\left.\begin{array}{l}\text{total energy stored} \\ \text{in magnetic field}\end{array}\right\} = \text{area of triangle } OCD \text{ in joules/m}^3$$

$$= \tfrac{1}{2}OA \times OC = \tfrac{1}{2} \cdot \frac{OC}{\mu_0} \cdot OC$$

$$= \frac{OC^2}{2\mu_0} \text{ joules/m}^3$$

Consequently, for a flux density of B webers/square metre,

$$\left.\begin{array}{l}\text{energy stored in a} \\ \text{non-magnetic} \\ \text{medium}\end{array}\right\} = \tfrac{1}{2}HB = \frac{B^2}{2\mu_0} \text{ joules/m}^3 . \quad (52)$$

31. Magnetic Pull between Two Iron Surfaces. Consider a fixed iron core D wound with coil C and a movable iron core E, as shown in Fig. 42. Suppose D and E to have the same cross-sectional area of A square metres. Also, suppose the opposite surfaces of D and E to be g metres apart and that a current I amperes through coil C produces a flux density of B webers/square metre in the airgap. From expression (52),

$$\left.\begin{array}{l}\text{energy stored per cubic} \\ \text{metre of airgap}\end{array}\right\} = B^2/2\mu_0 \text{ joules.}$$

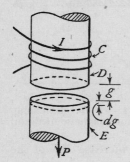

Let P be the force of attraction in newtons between the two surfaces of D and E. Suppose iron core E to be moved a short distance dg metre away from D and that the current through coil C be increased at the same time so as to keep the flux density unaltered. No e.m.f. will therefore have been induced in coil C, so that no energy will have been supplied either from the electrical circuit to the magnetic circuit or vice-versa. Hence all the energy stored in the *additional* volume of airgap must have been derived from the work done when force P newtons acted through a distance dg metre, namely $P \times dg$ joules,

FIG. 42. — Magnetic pull between two iron surfaces.

i.e.
$$P \times dg = \frac{B^2}{2\mu_0} \times A \times dg$$

$$P = \frac{B^2 A}{2\mu_0} \text{ newtons} \quad . \quad . \quad . \quad (53)$$

32. Magnetic Field around a Straight Current-Carrying Conductor. Let C in Fig. 43 represent the cross-section of a conductor carrying a current of I amperes towards the paper. The return conductor is assumed to be some distance away so that its magnetic field may be neglected.

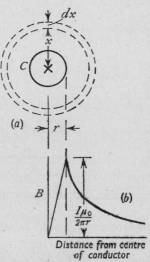

The magnetic flux set up by the current forms concentric circles around the conductor. Let us therefore consider the flux in the cylinder of radius x metres and thickness dx metre, shown dotted in Fig. 43. Since the outward and return conductors form one turn, it follows that the magnetizing force acting on this path is $I/(2\pi x)$ ampere-turns/metre; and

Fig. 43. — Magnetic field around a conductor situated in a non-magnetic medium.

since the relative permeability of air and other non-magnetic mediums is unity,

flux density at radius $x = \dfrac{I\mu_0}{2\pi x}$ . . . . . (54)

Hence the flux density around a conductor is inversely proportional to the distance from the centre of the conductor, as represented by the hyperbola in Fig. 43 (b). The density is a maximum at the surface of the conductor and is equal to $I\mu_0/2\pi r$ webers/square metre, where r is the radius of the conductor in metres.

33. Magnetic Field due to a Very Short Length of Conductor carrying a Current. Let us consider a very short length, dx metre, of a conductor carrying a current of I amperes, as in Fig. 44. It was suggested by Laplace that the magnetizing force, dH, at a point A in air, l

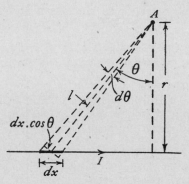

FIG. 44.—Magnetic field due to a current element.

metres away, could be represented by the expression (in M.K.S. units):

$$dH = \frac{I \cdot dx \cdot \cos \theta}{4\pi l^2} \text{ ampere-turns/metre} \quad . \quad (55)$$

a relationship that is usually known as Laplace's Theorem (sometimes referred to as Ampère's Theorem).

If r is the perpendicular distance between A and the conductor, then:

$$\cos \theta = \frac{r}{l} \quad \text{and} \quad d\theta = \frac{dx \cdot \cos \theta}{l}$$

$$\therefore \qquad \frac{dx \cdot \cos \theta}{l^2} = \frac{d\theta}{l} = \frac{\cos \theta \cdot d\theta}{r}$$

and

$$dH = \frac{I}{4\pi r} \cdot \cos \theta \cdot d\theta \quad . \quad . \quad (56)$$

Hence the resultant magnetizing force at A due to a very long conductor carrying I amperes

$$= \int_{\theta=-\pi/2}^{\theta=\pi/2} \frac{I}{4\pi r} . \cos\theta . d\theta = \frac{I}{4\pi r}\Big[\sin\theta\Big]_{-\pi/2}^{\pi/2}$$

$$= \frac{I}{2\pi r} \text{ ampere-turns/metre.}$$

This value is the same as that derived by a different method in Art. 32 and confirms Laplace's Theorem.

Example 13. *A conductor is bent into a square, 10 cm ×10 cm, in air, as shown in Fig. 45. Calculate the*

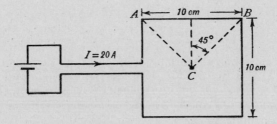

FIG. 45.—Circuit for Example 13.

flux density at the centre of the square due to a current of 20 A.

From expression (56),

$$\left.\begin{array}{c}\text{magnetizing force at } C \text{ due}\\ \text{to one side } AB \text{ of square}\end{array}\right\} = \int_{\theta=-\pi/4}^{\theta=\pi/4} \frac{I . \cos\theta . d\theta}{4\pi r}$$

$$= \frac{I}{2\pi r} \sin 45°.$$

Since $r = 5$ cm $= 0.05$ metre, and $I = 20$ A,

total magnetizing force at $C = \dfrac{4 \times 20 \times 0.707}{2\pi \times 0.05} = 180$ AT/m,

and flux density at $C = 4\pi \times 10^{-7} \times 180$
$$= 226 \times 10^{-6} \text{ Wb/m}^2$$
$$= 226 \ \mu\text{Wb/m}^2.$$

Example 14. *A wire is bent into a circle of radius 5 cm in air, as in Fig. 46, and carries a current of 20 A. Calculate the flux density at the centre of the circle.*

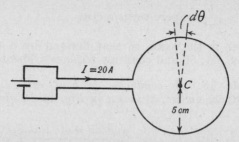

FIG. 46.—Circuit for Example 14.

An element subtending an angle $d\theta$ at the centre is at right angles to the line between the element and C, so that $\theta = 0°$ and $\cos\theta = 1$.   Hence, from expression (56),

$$\text{magnetizing force at } C = \int_0^{2\pi} \frac{I}{4\pi r} \cdot d\theta$$

$$= \frac{I}{2r} \text{ ampere-turns/metre}   (57)$$

$$= \frac{20}{2 \times 0 \cdot 05} = 200 \text{ AT/m}$$

and flux density at C $\quad = 4\pi \times 10^{-7} \times 200$
$$= 251 \times 10^{-6} \text{ Wb/m}^2$$
$$= 251 \ \mu\text{Wb/m}^2.$$

If the loop were replaced by, say, 10 turns of wire of the same mean diameter carrying the same current, the flux density at the centre would be 2510 μWb/m².

34. Force between Two Parallel Current-carrying Conductors.   Let A and B in Fig. 47 represent two parallel conductors carrying I_1 and I_2 amperes respectively and let the distance between their centres be d metres.   From expression (54), it follows that the flux density due to I_1 alone at a distance of d metres from the centre of A is $I_1\mu_0/2\pi d$ webers/square metre; and from Fig. 47, it is seen that conductor B is carrying I_2 amperes at right angles to the field set up by I_1 amperes in conductor A. Hence from expression (25),

$$\text{force per metre length} \brace \text{of conductor } B = \frac{I_1\mu_0}{2\pi d} \cdot I_2$$

$$= 2 \times 10^{-7} \times \frac{I_1 I_2}{d} \text{ newtons} \quad (58)$$

Similarly,

$$\text{force per metre} \brace \text{length of } A = 2 \times 10^{-7} \times \frac{I_1 I_2}{d} \text{ newtons}.$$

If the currents I_1 and I_2 are in the same direction, as in Fig. 47, there is a force of attraction between the conductors; but if the currents are in opposite directions, the conductors repel each other (see Art. 41 of *Principles of Electricity*). If $I_1 = I_2 = 1$ ampere and if $d = 1$ metre, it follows from expression (58) that the force

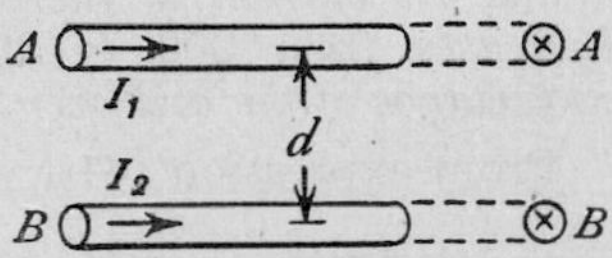

FIG. 47.—Two parallel current-carrying conductors situated in a non-magnetic medium.

per metre length of conductor is 2×10^{-7} newton (see definition of the ampere, Art. 2).

35. Self-Inductance. A circuit is said to be *inductive* or to possess *self-inductance* if an electric current in the circuit gives rise to magnetic flux linked with it.

The practical unit of self-inductance—or merely *inductance*—is the *henry* (H) and may be defined as the inductance of a circuit in which an e.m.f. of 1 volt is induced when the current varies at the rate of 1 ampere per second.

Hence, if L = inductance of a coil in henrys
and di = *increase* of current in amperes in dt second,

rate of increase of current = di/dt amperes/sec
and e.m.f. induced in coil = $-L di/dt$ volts . (59)

The minus sign indicates that the direction of the induced e.m.f. is opposite to that of the current.

If $d\Phi$=corresponding increase of flux in webers
and N=number of turns on coil,

rate of increase of flux=$d\Phi/dt$ webers/sec
and e.m.f. induced in coil=$-N(d\Phi/dt)$ volts . (60)

Equating (59) and (60), we have:

$$L\, di/dt = N(d\Phi/dt)$$

$$\therefore \quad L = N\frac{d\Phi}{di}$$

$$= \frac{\text{change of flux-linkages}}{\text{change of current}} \quad . \quad . \quad (61)$$

Example 15. *An iron ring is wound with* 300 *turns. When the current is increased from* 2 *to* 2·8 *A, the flux increases from* 200 *to* 224 *microwebers. Calculate the inductance of the coil over this range.*

From expression (61), we have

$$\text{inductance of coil} = \frac{300 \times (224 - 200)}{2\cdot8 - 2} \times 10^{-6}$$

$$= 0\cdot009 \text{ henry.}$$

Example 16. *Calculate the inductance of the coil referred to in Example* 15 *when the current is alternating and has a peak value of (a)* 2 *A and (b)* 2·8 *A.*

(a) When the current reverses from 2 to -2 A, the change of flux is 400 μWb, so that:

$$\text{inductance of coil} = \frac{300 \times 400 \times 10^{-6}}{4} = 0\cdot03 \text{ H.}$$

(b) When the current reverses from 2·8 to -2·8 A, the change of flux is 448 μWb, and

$$\text{inductance of coil} = \frac{300 \times 448 \times 10^{-6}}{5\cdot6} = 0\cdot024 \text{ H.}$$

These examples illustrate the importance of specifying the conditions for which the inductance of an iron-cored coil has been determined. This variation of the inductance is due to the variation of the relative permeability of the iron core, as explained in the next Article.

36. Inductance of a Coil in an A.C. Circuit. Let us consider a coil of N turns wound on a homogeneous core of uniform cross-sectional area. When the coil is carrying an *alternating current*, the flux varies between a maximum in one direction and the same value in the reverse direction; hence,

if Φ_m = maximum value of the flux, in webers,
  μ = corresponding absolute permeability = $\mu_r\mu_0$,
  a = cross-sectional area of magnetic circuit in square metres,
  l = mean length of magnetic circuit in metres
and I_m = maximum value of the current in amperes,

then   change of flux linkages when
  current changes from I_m to $-I_m$ $\Bigg\} = 2\Phi_m N$
and   change of current = $2I_m$.

Substituting in expression (61), we have:

$$L = \frac{2\Phi_m N}{2I_m} \quad \cdots \quad \text{(62)}$$

$$= \text{flux-linkages per ampere} \quad . \quad \text{(63)}$$

From (36), p. 43, $\Phi_m = I_m N \times \dfrac{\mu a}{l}$.

Substituting for Φ_m in (62),

$$L = N^2 \times \frac{\mu_r\mu_0 a}{l} \text{ henrys} \quad . \quad . \quad \text{(64)}$$

Hence, the inductance of a coil $\propto$ (no. of turns)^2
and $\propto$ relative permeability.

For air and other non-magnetic materials, the relative permeability is unity, so that the inductance of a coil having a non-magnetic core is independent of the current. In the case of an iron-cored coil, the permeability depends upon the value of the flux density, as already discussed in Art. 20; hence the reason why the inductance of an iron-cored coil should not be stated without specifying the value of the current at which that inductance was measured or calculated.

3*

37. Inductance of Two Parallel Wires. Let A and B in Fig. 48 be two conductors, each of radius r metres, spaced d metres apart in air; and suppose the conductors to be carrying I amperes in opposite directions. The distribution of the magnetic flux is represented by the dotted circles; and since the two conductors form one turn, the inductance is equal to the total flux between A and B per ampere of current in the conductors.

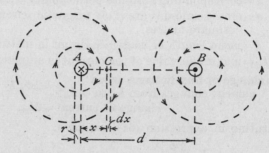

FIG. 48.—Inductance of two parallel conductors.

Consider a point C, distant x metres from the centre of A, on a line joining the centres of the conductors.

$$\text{Magnetizing force at } C \text{ due to current in } A \Big\} = \frac{I}{2\pi x}$$

and

$$\text{magnetizing force at } C \text{ due to current in } B \Big\} = \frac{I}{2\pi(d-x)}.$$

Since the currents in A and B are in opposite directions, the magnetizing forces at C are assisting each other,

$$\therefore \quad \text{resultant magnetizing force at } C \Big\} = \frac{I}{2\pi}\left(\frac{1}{x} + \frac{1}{d-x}\right)$$

and

$$\text{flux density at } C = \frac{\mu_0 I}{2\pi}\left(\frac{1}{x} + \frac{1}{d-x}\right).$$

$$\text{Flux across element of width } dx \text{ metre per metre length of line}\Big\} = \frac{\mu_0 I}{2\pi}\left(\frac{1}{x} + \frac{1}{d-x}\right)dx$$

∴ total flux in space between A and B per metre length of line

$$= \int_{r}^{d-r} \frac{\mu_0 I}{2\pi}\left(\frac{1}{x}+\frac{1}{d-x}\right)dx$$

$$= \frac{\mu_0 I}{2\pi}\Big[\ln x - \ln (d-x)\Big]_{r}^{d-r}$$

$$= \frac{\mu_0 I}{2\pi}\{\ln (d-r) - \ln r - \ln r + \ln (d-r)\}$$

$$= \frac{\mu_0 I}{\pi} \ln (d-r)/r \simeq \frac{\mu_0 I}{\pi} \ln d/r \text{ webers}$$

when d is large compared with r.

$$\text{Hence, inductance per metre} \atop \text{length of line} \Big\} = \frac{\mu_0}{\pi} . \ln d/r \text{ henrys (65)}$$

$$= \frac{4\pi \times 10^{-7} \times 2\cdot3 \log d/r}{\pi}$$

$$= 9\cdot2 \times 10^{-7} \log d/r \text{ henrys.}$$

This expression neglects the effect of the flux in each conductor, an effect that is relatively small when the conductor material is non-magnetic and the spacing between the wires is more than about 10 times the diameter of each wire.

38. Inductance of Two Concentric Cylinders. Suppose A and B in Fig. 49 to represent two concentric cylinders separated by an air space, A having an external radius of a metres and B an internal radius of b metres. If the cylinders

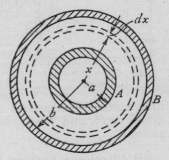

FIG. 49.—Inductance of two concentric cylinders.

carry I amperes in opposite directions, the resultant m.m.f. outside B is zero, whereas in the space between the cylinders, the magnetic effect of the current in B is zero and the flux is therefore due entirely to the current in A.* Hence, from expression (54),

$$\text{flux density at radius } x \text{ metres} = \frac{I\mu_0}{2\pi x} \text{ Wb/m}^2$$

and   flux in an element of thickness dx metre, per metre length $\Bigg\} = \dfrac{I\mu_0}{2\pi x} \cdot dx.$

Neglecting flux in cylinders, we have:

$$\text{total flux per metre length of cylinders} \Bigg\} = \int_{a}^{b} \frac{I\mu_0}{2\pi x} \cdot dx$$

$$= \frac{I\mu_0}{2\pi} \cdot \ln b/a \text{ webers}$$

and inductance per metre length of line $\Bigg\} = \dfrac{\mu_0 \ln b/a}{2\pi} \text{ henrys} \quad . \quad (66)$

$$= 4 \cdot 6 \times 10^{-7} \log b/a \text{ henrys.}$$

39. Current Growth in an Inductive Circuit connected across a D.C. Supply. Fig. 50 represents an inductive

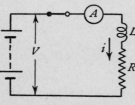

FIG. 50.—Inductive circuit.

circuit, having a resistance R ohms and a constant inductance L henrys, connected across a d.c. supply of V volts. The growth of the current is represented by the curve in Fig. 51, the delay being due to the e.m.f. induced by the growth of flux. By Lenz's Law, this e.m.f. opposes the increase of current; and the total voltage is absorbed partly in neutralizing the induced e.m.f. and partly in providing the voltage drop across R.

---

* If A is carrying a current I amperes towards the paper and B is carrying the same current outwards from the paper, then for a radius y greater than the external radius of B, the magnetizing force due to A alone is $I/(2\pi y)$ in a clockwise direction and that due to B alone is the same value anticlockwise. Hence, the resultant magnetizing force due to the currents in A and B is zero.

Suppose i amperes to be the current t seconds after the switch is closed, and di ampere to be the increase of current in dt second, as in Fig. 51. Then:

rate of increase of current $= di/dt$ amperes/second

and induced e.m.f. $= -L\ di/dt$ volts.

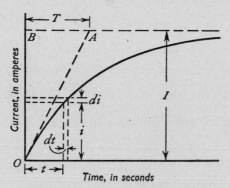

FIG. 51.—Growth of current in an inductive circuit.

Since total applied voltage $\left.\right\} = \left\{\right.$ p.d. across R + voltage to neutralize induced e.m.f.

$\therefore \qquad V = Ri + L\ di/dt \qquad . \quad . \quad . \quad (67)$

so that $\qquad V - Ri = L\ di/dt$

and $\qquad \dfrac{V}{R} - i = \dfrac{L}{R} \cdot \dfrac{di}{dt}.$

But $V/R =$ final value of current $=$ (say) I,

$\therefore \qquad \dfrac{R}{L}\ dt = \dfrac{di}{I - i}$

Integrating both sides, we have:

$$\frac{Rt}{L} = -\ln\ (I - i) + A$$

where $A =$ the constant of integration.

At the instant of closing the switch, $t=0$ and $i=0$, so that $A=\ln I$,

$$\therefore \qquad \frac{Rt}{L} = -\ln(I-i) + \ln I$$

$$= \ln \frac{I}{I-i} \qquad \cdots \cdots \quad (68)$$

Hence, $\qquad \dfrac{I-i}{I} = e^{-Rt/L}$

$$\therefore \qquad i = I\{1 - e^{-Rt/L}\} \quad \cdots \cdots \quad (69)$$

This exponential relationship is often referred to as the Helmholtz equation.

Immediately after the switch is closed, the rate of growth of the current is given by the slope of tangent OA drawn to the curve at the origin. If the current continued growing at this initial rate, it would attain its final value, I amperes, in T seconds, an interval that is termed the *time constant* of the circuit. From Fig. 51, it is seen that:

initial rate of growth of current $=I/T$ amperes/sec.

At the instant of closing the switch, $i=0$; hence from expression (67),

$$V = L \times \text{initial rate of growth of current,}$$

$\therefore$ initial rate of growth of current $= V/L$

hence, $\qquad I/T = V/L$

so that $\qquad T = LI/V = L/R$ seconds $\quad \cdots \quad (70)$

Substituting for R/L in (69), we have:

$$i = I(1 - e^{-t/T}) \quad \cdots \cdots \quad (71)$$

Example 17. *A coil having a resistance of 4 Ω and a constant inductance of 2 henrys is switched across a 20-V d.c. supply. Calculate* (a) *the time constant,* (b) *final value of the current and* (c) *the value of the current 1 second after the switch is closed.*

(a) Time constant $=L/R=2/4=0.5$ sec.

(b) Final value of current $=V/R=20/4=5$ A.

(c) Substituting $t=1$, $T=0\cdot5$ sec and $I=5$ A in (71),
$$i=5(1-e^{-1/0\cdot5})=5(1-e^{-2})$$
From mathematical tables, $e^{-2}=0\cdot1353$,
$$\therefore \qquad i=5(1-0\cdot1353)=4\cdot323 \text{ A.}$$

If such mathematical tables are not available, this section of the question can be solved by using expression (68) thus:
$$Rt/L=\ln I/(I-i)$$
$$=2\cdot303 \log I/(I-i)$$
$$\therefore \qquad \log I/(I-i)=\frac{4\times1}{2\times2\cdot303}=0\cdot8684$$
$$\therefore \qquad I/(I-i)=7\cdot386$$
so that $\qquad\qquad i=4\cdot323$ A.

40. Energy stored in an Inductive Circuit. If the current in a circuit having a constant inductance of L henrys increases by di ampere in dt second,
$$\text{induced e.m.f.} = -L \, di/dt \text{ volts}$$
and if i is the value of the current in amperes at that instant,
$$\left.\begin{array}{l}\text{energy absorbed by the magnetic}\\ \text{field during time } dt \text{ second}\end{array}\right\}=i \, L \cdot \frac{di}{dt} \cdot dt$$
$$=L \, i \, di \text{ joules.}$$

Hence total energy absorbed by the magnetic field when the current increases from 0 to I amperes
$$=L\int_0^I i \cdot di=L\times\tfrac{1}{2}\left[i^2\right]_0^I$$
$$=\tfrac{1}{2}LI^2 \text{ joules} \quad \cdots \cdots \quad (72)$$
From expression (64), $L=\dfrac{N^2\mu a}{l}$ for a homogeneous magnetic circuit of uniform cross-sectional area.
$$\therefore \quad \text{energy/cubic metre}=\tfrac{1}{2}I^2N^2 \cdot \frac{\mu}{l^2}=\tfrac{1}{2}\mu H^2$$
$$=\tfrac{1}{2}HB=\tfrac{1}{2}\cdot\frac{B^2}{\mu_r\mu_0} \text{ joules} \quad (72\text{A})$$

This expression has been derived on the assumption

that μ_r remains constant. In the case of ferrous materials, the variation of μ_r renders this expression inapplicable and the energy has to be determined graphically as already explained in Art. 27. For non-magnetic materials, $\mu_r = 1$ and the energy stored per cubic metre is $\frac{1}{2}B^2/\mu_0$ joules, the expression already derived in Art. 30.

41. Mutual Inductance. Two circuits are said to possess mutual inductance if an electric current in one circuit gives rise to magnetic flux linked with the other circuit. The practical unit of mutual inductance is the same as that of self-inductance, namely the *henry*; and two circuits have a mutual inductance of 1 henry if an e.m.f. of 1 volt is induced in one circuit when the current in the other circuit changes at the rate of 1 ampere per second.

If two circuits possess a mutual inductance of M henrys and if the current in one circuit increases by di ampere in dt second,

$$\left.\begin{array}{l}\text{e.m.f. induced in}\\ \text{secondary circuit}\end{array}\right\} = -M\,di/dt \text{ volts} \quad . \quad (73)$$

The minus sign indicates that the induced e.m.f. tends to circulate a current in the secondary circuit in such a direction as to oppose the increase of flux due to the increase of current in the primary circuit.

If $d\Phi$ is the increase of flux linked with the secondary circuit due to the increase of di ampere in the primary circuit,

$$\left.\begin{array}{l}\text{e.m.f. induced in}\\ \text{secondary circuit}\end{array}\right\} = -\frac{d\Phi}{dt} \times N_2 \text{ volts} \quad . \quad (74)$$

where N_2=number of secondary turns.

Equating (73) and (74),

$$M\,\frac{di}{dt} = \frac{d\Phi}{dt} \times N_2$$

$$\therefore M = \frac{N_2 \times d\Phi}{di}$$

$$= \frac{\text{change of flux-linkages with secondary}}{\text{change of current in primary}} \quad . \quad (75)$$

42. Mutual Inductance of Two Coils when the Primary is carrying an Alternating Current; Coefficient of Coupling.

Suppose the primary to be wound with N_1 turns and to be carrying an alternating current having a peak value of I_m amperes. Let S_1 be the reluctance * of the magnetic circuit of the primary winding for the peak value of the current. Then:

$$\text{maximum value of flux} = \Phi_m = \frac{I_m N_1}{S_1}$$

$$\therefore \qquad \Phi_m / I_m = N_1 / S_1.$$

But all this flux may not pass through the secondary; hence,

if $\qquad \dfrac{\text{maximum flux through secondary}}{\text{maximum flux through primary}} = (\text{say}) \ c$

$\therefore \qquad$ maximum flux through secondary $= c\Phi_m.$

When the current in the primary reverses from I_m to $-I_m$,

$$\text{change of flux through secondary} = 2c\Phi_m.$$

Hence, from (75),

$$M = \frac{2c\Phi_m N_2}{2I_m}$$

$$= \frac{c \, N_1 N_2}{S_1} \text{ henrys} \ . \quad . \quad . \quad . \quad (76)$$

From expression (64), it follows that:

$$\text{self-inductance of primary} = L_1 = \frac{N_1^2}{S_1} \ . \quad (77)$$

$$\text{self-inductance of secondary} = L_2 = \frac{N_2^2}{S_2} \ . \quad (78)$$

where $S_2 =$ reluctance of magnetic circuit of secondary.

* If the circuit is non-magnetic, the value of the reluctance is independent of the current; but if it contains iron, the value depends upon the maximum flux density and therefore upon the peak value of the current.

From (77) and (78),

$$\sqrt{(L_1 L_2)} = \frac{N_1 N_2}{\sqrt{(S_1 S_2)}} \quad . \quad . \quad . \quad (79)$$

and from (76) and (79),

$$\frac{M}{\sqrt{(L_1 L_2)}} = c\sqrt{\frac{S_2}{S_1}}$$

$$= coefficient\ of\ coupling \quad (80)$$

If $S_1 = S_2$, i.e. if the reluctances of the magnetic circuits of the two coils are equal, the coefficient of coupling is c, namely the fraction of the flux set up by the primary that passes through the secondary.

"Coefficient of coupling" is a term much used in radio work to denote the degree of coupling between two coils; thus, if the two coils are close together, most of the flux produced by current in one coil passes through the other and the coils are said to be *tightly* coupled. If the coils are well apart, only a small fraction of the flux is linked with the secondary, and the coils are said to be *loosely* coupled. In the case of coils wound on a closed-iron core, as in iron-cored transformers, almost all the flux produced by one coil is linked with the other and the coefficient of coupling is practically unity.

Example 18. *Calculate the mutual inductance between the solenoid and the search coil of Example 11. If the self-inductance of the solenoid is 2 mH and that of the search coil is 25 μH, find the coefficient of coupling between the two coils.*

For a long solenoid (Art. 28),

$$\text{flux density at centre} = \frac{IN\mu_0}{l} = \frac{800I \times 4\pi \times 10^{-7}}{1 \cdot 2}$$

$$= 0 \cdot 000838I \text{ Wb/m}^2$$

$$\therefore \text{ flux through search coil} = 0 \cdot 000838I \times \pi \times (0 \cdot 015)^2$$

$$= 0 \cdot 592I \times 10^{-6} \text{ weber.}$$

Since there is no iron in the solenoid, the change of flux is proportional to the change of current; hence, from (75),

$$\text{mutual inductance} = \frac{50 \times 0 \cdot 592I \times 10^{-6}}{I} = 29 \cdot 6 \times 10^{-6} \text{ H}$$

$$= 29 \cdot 6 \ \mu H.$$

In expression (80), the self and mutual inductances must be expressed in the same units,

$$\therefore \quad \text{coefficient of coupling} = \frac{29 \cdot 6}{\sqrt{(2000 \times 25)}} = 0 \cdot 132$$

Summary of Important Formulae in Chapter II

Force on a conductor $= BlI$ newtons . (25)

E.m.f. induced in conductor $= d\Phi/dt$ volts . (26)

E.m.f. induced in coil $= -N \cdot d\Phi/dt$ volts . (27)

Magnetomotive force $= NI$ ampere-turns . (28)

$$= \oint H \cdot dl \quad . \quad . \quad . \quad (30)$$

At any junction in a magnetic circuit, $\Sigma\Phi = 0$.

For a complete magnetic circuit, $\Sigma\text{m.m.f.} = \Sigma Hl$.

$$\text{Magnetic flux} = \Phi = \frac{\text{m.m.f}}{\text{reluctance}} \quad . \quad (29)$$

Flux density $= B = \Phi/a$.

$$B/H = \mu = \text{absolute permeability} \quad . \quad . \quad (33)$$

$$= \mu_0 \mu_r$$

$$\mu_0 = 4\pi \times 10^{-7} \quad . \quad . \quad . \quad . \quad . \quad . \quad (31)$$

$$\mu_r = \frac{B \text{ in a material}}{B \text{ in vacuum due to same magnetizing force}}.$$

$$\text{Ampere-turns/metre} = H = \frac{B}{\mu} = \frac{B}{\mu_0 \mu_r}$$

$$\left. \begin{array}{l} \text{Ampere-turns/metre for} \\ \text{non-magnetic medium} \end{array} \right\} = \frac{B \text{ (in Wb/m}^2)}{12 \cdot 57 \times 10^{-7}} \quad (32)$$

For a homogeneous magnetic circuit of uniform cross-section,

$$\text{reluctance} = \frac{l}{\mu a} \quad . \quad . \quad . \quad (37)$$

and $$\text{ampere-turns} = \Phi \cdot \frac{l}{\mu a} = \frac{Bl}{\mu}$$

For a composite magnetic circuit,

$$\Phi = \frac{NI}{\dfrac{l_1}{\mu_1 a_1} + \dfrac{l_2}{\mu_2 a_2}} + \quad . \quad . \quad . \quad (38)$$

$$\text{Leakage coefficient} = \frac{\text{total flux}}{\text{useful flux}} \quad \text{. . .} \quad (39)$$

$$\left.\begin{array}{c}\text{Hysteresis loss/cubic} \\ \text{metre/cycle}\end{array}\right\} = \left\{\begin{array}{l}\text{area of hysteresis loop,} \\ \quad\text{in joules} \quad \text{. . .} \quad (46)\end{array}\right.$$

$$\text{Hysteresis loss} = kvfB_{\max}^x \quad \text{. . . . .} \quad (47)$$

where x usually lies between 1·5 and 2·5.

Magnetizing force inside central portion of long solenoid

$$= I \times \text{turns/metre} \quad \text{. . .} \quad (48)$$

Permanent magnet has minimum volume when it is operated at the point where the product (BH) for the demagnetizing portion of the hysteresis loop is a maximum . . . . (51)

$$\left.\begin{array}{c}\text{Magnetic energy stored in} \\ \text{non-magnetic medium}\end{array}\right\} = \frac{B^2}{2\mu_0} \text{ joules/m}^3 \text{ . } \quad (52)$$

$$\left.\begin{array}{c}\text{Magnetic pull between two} \\ \text{iron surfaces}\end{array}\right\} = \frac{B^2 A}{2\mu_0} \text{ newtons . } \quad (53)$$

$$\left.\begin{array}{c}\text{Flux density around wire} \\ \text{carrying current}\end{array}\right\} = \frac{I\mu_0}{2\pi x} \quad \text{. .} \quad (54)$$

$$\left.\begin{array}{c}\text{Magnetizing force due to current} \\ \text{element (Laplace's Theorem)}\end{array}\right\} = \frac{I \cdot dx \cdot \cos\theta}{4\pi l^2} \quad (55)$$

$$= \frac{I \cos\theta \cdot d\theta}{4\pi r} \quad \text{. } \quad (56)$$

$$\left.\begin{array}{c}\text{Magnetizing force at centre} \\ \text{of circular loop}\end{array}\right\} = I/2r \quad \text{. .} \quad (57)$$

$$\left.\begin{array}{c}\text{Force between two} \\ \text{conductors carry-} \\ \text{ing current}\end{array}\right\} = \frac{2 \times 10^{-7} I_1 I_2}{d} \text{ newtons/m} \quad (58)$$

Self inductance (in henrys)

$$= L = \frac{\text{change of flux-linkages}}{\text{change of current}} \quad \text{. } \quad (61)$$

For an a.c. circuit,

$$L = \text{flux-linkages/ampere} \quad \text{. .} \quad (63)$$

For a homogeneous magnetic circuit of uniform section,

$$L = N^2 \cdot \frac{\mu_r \mu_0 a}{l} \text{ henrys} \quad \text{. . .} \quad (64)$$

Inductance of two parallel wires/metre length of line $\left.\right\} = \dfrac{\mu_0}{\pi}$. ln d/r henrys (65)

$$= 9 \cdot 2 \times 10^{-7} \log d/r$$

Inductance of concentric cylinders/metre $\left.\right\} = \dfrac{\mu_0}{2\pi}$. ln b/a henrys (66)

$$= 4 \cdot 6 \times 10^{-7} \log b/a$$

For R and L, in series, connected across a d.c. supply,

$$\text{instantaneous current} = i = I(1 - e^{-Rt/L}) \quad . \quad (69)$$
$$= I(1 - e^{-t/T}) \quad . \quad . \quad (71)$$

and $\qquad$ time constant $= T = L/R$ seconds . (70)

Magnetic energy stored in inductance $= \frac{1}{2}LI^2$ joules (72)

Mutual inductance

$$= M = \frac{\text{change of flux-linkages in secondary}}{\text{change of current in primary}} \quad . \quad (75)$$

For an a.c. circuit,

$$M = \frac{cN_1N_2}{S_1} \qquad . \quad . \quad . \quad . \quad . \quad . \quad . \quad (76)$$

Coefficient of coupling $= \dfrac{M}{\sqrt{(L_1 L_2)}}$. (80)

EXAMPLES II

Data of B–H, when not given in question, should be taken from Fig. 24.

1. A current-carrying conductor is situated at right angles to a uniform magnetic field having a density of $0 \cdot 3$ Wb/m². Calculate the force per metre length of the conductor when the current is 200 A.

2. Calculate the current in the conductor referred to in Q. 1 if the force per foot length of the conductor is $0 \cdot 5$ lb.

3. The coil of a moving-coil milliammeter has an effective length of 2 cm and a mean breadth of $1 \cdot 5$ cm and is wound with $60\frac{1}{2}$ turns. The airgap flux density is $0 \cdot 07$ Wb/m². Calculate the torque in newton-metres when the current is 15 mA.

4. Describe the main features of a moving-coil milliammeter and explain how it functions.

A certain milliammeter is to give a full-scale deflection for 15 mA. It has a resistance of 10 Ω, the area of the moving-coil is 6 cm² and there are 40 turns on it. The torque provided by the spring is $0 \cdot 4$ g.cm at full-scale deflection. What must be the flux density in the airgap?

What value of shunt resistance would be needed if it is required to measure 200 A? Why has such a shunt four terminals?

(App. El., L.U.)

5. A wire, 10 cm long, is moved at a uniform speed of 4 m/sec at right angles to its length and to a uniform magnetic field. Calculate the density of the field if the e.m.f. generated in the wire is 0·15 V.

If the wire forms part of a closed circuit having a total resistance of 0·04 Ω, calculate the force on the wire (a) in newtons and (b) in grams.

6. The flux through a 500-turn coil increases uniformly from zero to 200 μWb in 3 milliseconds. It remains constant for the fourth millisecond and then decreases uniformly to zero during the fifth millisecond. Draw to scale a graph representing the variation of the e.m.f. induced in the coil.

7. A mild-steel ring has a mean diameter of 16 cm and a cross-sectional area of 3 cm². Calculate (a) the ampere-turns to produce a flux of 400 μWb and (b) the corresponding values of the reluctance of the ring and of the relative permeability.

8. Sixty ring stampings, each 0·4 mm thick, 11 cm external and 9 cm internal diameter, are arranged in a stack. An airgap, 0·7 mm wide, is cut radially through the stack, which is then uniformly wound with 300 turns of wire. Calculate the current required to produce a flux density of 1·3 Wb/m² in the gap, assuming that 800 AT/m are required to produce this flux density in the iron. Neglect any magnetic leakage.

Calculate also the relative permeability of the iron at the above flux density.

9. An electromagnet has a magnetic circuit that can be regarded as comprising three parts in series, each of uniform cross-section, viz.:

(a) a length of 8 cm and cross-sectional area 0·5 cm²,
(b) a length of 6 cm and cross-sectional area 0·9 cm², and
(c) an airgap of length 0·5 mm and cross-sectional area 1·5 cm².

Parts (a) and (b) are of a material having a magnetic characteristic given by the following table:

H (ampere/metre) . .	100	210	340	500	800	1500
B (weber/metre²) . .	0·2	0·4	0·6	0·8	1·0	1·2

Determine the current necessary on a coil of 4000 turns wound on part (b) to produce in the airgap a flux density of 0·3 weber/m². Magnetic leakage may be neglected. (App. El., L.U.)

10. An electromagnet with its armature has an iron length of 40 cm and a cross-sectional area of 5 cm². There is a total airgap of 1·8 mm. Assuming a leakage coefficient of 1·2, calculate the ampere-turns required to produce a flux of 400 μWb in the armature. Points on the $B–H$ curve are as follows:

Flux density (Wb/m²) .	0·8	1·0	1·2
Magnetizing force (AT/m) .	800	1000	1600

11. A circular cast-steel lifting magnet has a cross-sectional area of 80 cm² and a mean magnetic path length of 60 cm. When it is used to lift certain steel plates, the reluctance of which is negligible, there is an effective gap of 0·8 mm at each pole. Calculate (a) the ampere-turns required to establish a flux of 10 milliwebers in the air-gaps and (b) the force in tons between the magnet and the plates. Assume a leakage coefficient of 1·15.

12. A magnetic circuit made of wrought iron is arranged as in Fig G. The centre limb has a cross-sectional area of 8 cm² and each of the side limbs has a cross-sectional area of 5 cm². Calculate the ampere-turns required to produce a flux of 1 milliweber in the centre limb, assuming the magnetic leakage to be negligible.

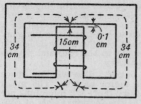

Fig. G.

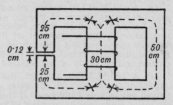

Fig. H.

13. A magnetic core made of Stalloy had the dimensions shown in Fig. H. There is an airgap 0·12 cm long in one side limb and a coil of 400 turns is wound on the centre limb. The cross-sectional area of the centre limb is 16 cm² and that of each side limb is 10 cm². Calculate the exciting current required to produce a flux of 1000 μWb in the airgap. Neglect any magnetic leakage and fringing.

14. A steel ring having a mean diameter of 35 cm and a cross-sectional area of 2·4 cm² is broken by a parallel-sided airgap of length 1·2 cm. Short pole pieces of negligible reluctance extend the effective cross-sectional area of the airgap to 12 cm². Taking the relative permeability of the steel as 700 and neglecting leakage, determine the current necessary in 300 turns of wire wound on the ring to produce a flux density in the gap of 0·25 weber/m².

Evaluate also the tractive force between the poles.

(App. El., L.U.)

15. A magnetic circuit in the form of an inverted U has an airgap between each pole and the armature of 0·05 cm. The cross-section of the magnetic circuit is 5 cm². Neglecting magnetic leakage and fringing, calculate the necessary exciting ampere-turns in order that the armature may exert a pull of 15 kg. The ampere-turns for the iron portion of the magnetic circuit may be taken as 20 per cent of those required for the double airgap. Prove the expression used for calculating the force. (N.C.T.E.C.)

16. A ring specimen of mild steel has a cross-sectional area of 6 cm² and a mean periphery of 25 cm. It is uniformly wound with two coils, A and B, having 80 and 300 turns respectively. Coil B is connected to a ballistic galvanometer having a constant of $1·2 \times 10^{-8}$ coulomb per division; the total resistance of this secondary circuit is 200,000 Ω. When a current of 2·2 A through coil A is reversed, the galvanometer gives a maximum deflection of 180 divisions. Neglecting the damping of the galvanometer, calculate the flux density in the iron. Prove any formula used.

If a radial saw-cut, 0·5 mm wide, is made in the ring, find the magnetizing current required in coil A to give the same flux density. Neglect any leakage and fringing of the flux. (App. El., L.U.)

17. A long solenoid is uniformly wound and in the centre of the solenoid is an iron rod which is in two halves and is 2 cm in diameter.

A secondary coil of 20 turns wound around the rod is connected to a ballistic galvanometer and the combined resistance of the secondary coil and the galvanometer is 150 Ω. When a certain current is reversed in the solenoid, the galvanometer deflection indicates that 50 microcoulombs flow around the secondary circuit. Calculate the force required to separate the two halves of the rod.

18. A coil M of 120 turns is wound uniformly over an iron ring having a mean circumference of 100 cm and a cross-sectional area of 5 cm². Another coil N of 15 turns, wound on the ring, is connected to a fluxmeter having a constant of 300 microweber-turns per division. When a current of 6 A through M is reversed, the fluxmeter deflection is 64 divisions. Calculate (a) the flux density in the ring and (b) the corresponding value of the relative permeability.

19. A 100-V lifting magnet dissipates 5 kW. The winding space available is 24 cm × 20 cm with a space factor of 0·6. The mean length per turn is 2 metres. If the resistivity (hot) is 2 microhms per cm cube, find: (a) the number of turns, (b) the sectional area of conductor, (b) the total exciting ampere-turns.   (U.L.C.I.)

Note.   Space factor $= \dfrac{\text{total cross-sectional area of copper}}{\text{total cross-sectional area available}}$

$$= \frac{aN}{\text{winding space available}}$$

where a = area of wire and N = number of turns. If l = mean length per turn, ρ = resistivity, V = applied voltage and I = current, $I = Va/(\rho l N)$.

20. The ascending and descending values of B and H for half the hysteresis curve for a sample of armature laminations are:

Ascending	B (Wb/m²)	.	0·1	0·25	0·5	0·6	0·75
	H (AT/m)	.	175	200	260	300	400
Descending	B .	.	0·7	0·6	0·54	0·34	0
	H .	.	230	60	0	−120	−170

Plot the hysteresis loop and determine the hysteresis loss in the specimen when the latter has an alternating flux of maximum density 0·75 Wb/m², if the frequency is 50 c/s and the volume of the specimen is 6000 cm³.

21. The hysteresis loop for a certain magnetic material is drawn to the following scales: 1 cm to 200 AT/m and 1 cm to 0·1 Wb/m². The area of the loop is 48 cm². Assuming the density of the material to be 7·8 g/cm³, calculate the hysteresis loss in watts/kg at 50 c/s.

22. The hysteresis loop for a certain iron ring is drawn to the following scales: 1 cm to 300 AT and 1 cm to 100 μWb. The area of the loop is 37 cm². Calculate the hysteresis loss per cycle.

23. A solenoid M, 120 cm long, and 8 cm diameter, is uniformly wound with 750 turns. A search coil N, 2·5 cm in diameter and wound with 30 turns, is mounted co-axially midway along the solenoid. Calculate the average e.m.f. induced in N when a current of 5 A through M is reversed in 0·2 second.

24. The demagnetization curve for a certain magnet steel is represented by the following data:

Demagnetizing force (AT/cm)	.	.	0	144	240	304	360	400	430
Flux density (Wb/m²)	.	.	.	0·6	0·5	0·4	0·3	0·2	0·1	0

Derive a graph showing the variation of (BH) with the flux density and estimate the values of B and H at which the product (BH) is a maximum.

25. Calculate the minimum dimensions of an Alcomax III magnet to maintain a flux of 400 μWb across an airgap, 5 mm long, having an effective cross-sectional area of 4 cm². Assume the data given on p. 64.

26. Calculate the relative minimum volumes of 6 per cent tungsten steel and Ticonal G to maintain a flux density of 0·6 Wb/m² across an airgap, 3mm long, having an effective cross-sectional area of 8 cm². Assume the data given on p. 64.

27. A flux density of 0·25 Wb/m² is to be provided in an airgap of length 3 mm and effective cross-sectional area 400 mm² by a permanent magnet bar of length 27 mm. The magnetic circuit is completed by iron pole pieces of total length 150 mm, cross-sectional area 100 mm² and relative permeability 800. Neglecting magnetic leakage and taking the demagnetization curve of the magnet material as:

B (Wb/m²)	0·6	0·5	0·4	0·3	0·2	0·1
H (A/m)	−16,000	−25,000	−31,000	−35,000	−37,000	−39,000

find the necessary cross-sectional area of the magnet bar.

(App. El., L.U.)

28. Each of the two airgaps of a moving-coil instrument is 2·5 mm long and has a cross-sectional area of 6 cm². If the flux density is 0·08 Wb/m², calculate the total energy stored in the magnetic field of the airgaps.

29. A long straight conductor, situated in air, is carrying a current of 500 A, the return conductor being far removed. Calculate (a) the magnetizing force and (b) the flux density at a radius of 8 cm.

30. Two long parallel conductors, spaced 4 cm between centres, are each carrying a current of 5000 A. Calculate the force (a) in newtons per metre and (b) in lb per yd length of each conductor.

31. Two long parallel conductors P and Q, situated in air and spaced 8 cm between centres, carry currents of 600 A in opposite directions. Calculate the values of the magnetizing force and of the flux density at points A, B and C in Fig. I, where the dimensions are given in cm. Calculate also the values of the same quantities at the same points if P and Q are each carrying 600 A in the same direction.

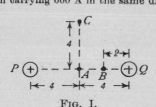

FIG. I.

32. A conductor is bent into a square, 15 cm × 15 cm, in air. Calculate the current required to produce a flux density of 100 μWb/m² at the centre of the square.

33. A conductor is bent to form a rectangle, 20 cm × 10 cm, in air. Calculate the flux density at the centre when the conductor is carrying a current of 50 A.

34. An insulated wire is bent to form a coil of 5 turns, close to one another. The coil has a diameter of 12 cm. Calculate the current required to produce a flux density of 700 $\mu Wb/m^2$ at the centre of the coil.

35. A wooden ring having a mean diameter of 25 cm and a cross-sectional area of 3 cm^2 is uniformly wound with 500 turns. Calculate the inductance of the coil and the average e.m.f. induced if a current of 2 A is reversed in 0·05 second.

36. An iron-cored choke is designed to have an inductance of 20 H when operating at a flux density of 1 Wb/m^2; the corresponding relative permeability for the iron core is 4000. Determine the number of turns in the winding, given that the magnetic flux path has a mean length of 22 cm in the iron core and of 1 mm in an airgap, and that its cross-section is 10 cm^2. Assume that flux leakage and fringing effects are negligible. Comment on these assumptions.   (App. El., L.U.)

37. A two-wire transmission line is 2 km long. The conductors are spaced 30 cm between centres, and each conductor has a diameter of 1·2 cm. Calculate the inductance of the line, neglecting the effect of the flux in the conductors.

38. A high-frequency feeder consists of 2 wires, each 2 mm in diameter, spaced 4 cm between centres, in air. Calculate the inductance per metre length of the feeder.

39. The inner conductor of a concentric cable has an external diameter of 3 mm and the outer conductor has an internal diameter of 12 mm. Calculate the inductance per metre length of cable. Calculate also the flux density at a radius of 5 mm when the cable is carrying a current of 20 A.

40. Discuss the factors which determine the self-inductance of a coil.
A coil having an inductance of 6 H and a resistance of 20 Ω is connected across a 50-V d.c. supply. Deduce from first principles the time taken for the current to grow to 1·5 A.   (App. El., L.U.)

41. Explain what is meant by the self-inductance of a coil and define the practical unit in which it is expressed. Upon what factors does the self-inductance of a coil depend?
A coil has a self-inductance of 2 H and a d.c. resistance of 200 Ω. It is switched suddenly across a 100-V d.c. supply of negligible internal resistance. Sketch the curve of current plotted against time and calculate the rate of rise of current, in amperes/second, at the instant of switching on and the value of the final steady current.   (U.E.I.)

42. A relay has a coil resistance of 20 Ω and an inductance of 0·5 H. It is energized by a direct voltage pulse which rises from 0 to 10 V instantaneously, remains constant for 0·25 sec and then falls instantaneously to zero. Draw a sketch, not necessarily to scale, showing the variation of the current in the coil to a time base. If the relay contacts close when the current is 200 mA (increasing) and open when it is 100 mA (decreasing), find the total time during which the contacts are closed.   (U.L.C.I.)

43. The field winding of a separately-excited d.c. generator has an inductance of 10 H and a resistance of 50 Ω and there is a discharge resistance of 50 Ω in parallel with the coil. The coil is energized by a d.c. supply at 200 V which is suddenly switched off. Plot a curve showing the value of the current in the field every 0·04 sec during a time interval of 0·2 sec after the instant the supply is switched off. Tabulate the values from which the curve is plotted.   (U.L.C.I.)

44. Explain what is understood by the term e.m.f. of self-induction. The current in a circuit consisting of an inductor of 0·1 H which has a resistance of 50 Ω, is increasing uniformly from zero at a rate of 5 A/sec. Draw to scale graphs of this current and of the voltage across the circuit for the first 1/100 of a second. If the coil is suddenly short-circuited at the end of this period, calculate the total energy which will have to be dissipated. (C. & G., Telecom. Prin. II)

45. A coil, having a resistance of 8 Ω and an inductance of 3 H, is connected across a 20-V d.c. supply. Calculate the energy stored in the magnetic field when the current has attained its final value.

46. A coil consists of two similar sections wound on a common core. Each section has an inductance of 0·06 H. Calculate the inductance of the coil when the sections are connected (a) in series, (b) in parallel.

47. A non-magnetic ring having a mean diameter of 30 cm and a cross-sectional area of 4 cm² is uniformly wound with two coils, A and B, one over the other. A has 90 turns and B has 240 turns. Calculate from first principles the mutual inductance between the coils. Neglect the space occupied by the windings.

Also, calculate the e.m.f. induced in B when a current of 6 A in A is reversed in 0·02 sec. With the aid of a diagram, indicate clearly the direction of this e.m.f. relatively to the initial direction of the current, giving the reason. (App. El., L.U.)

48. Define (i) the time constant of an inductive circuit and (ii) the mutual inductance between two circuits.

A coil of inductance 0·75 H and resistance 125 Ω is connected, by the closing of a switch, to a 250-V d.c. supply. Near to this coil is a second coil on open circuit, the mutual inductance between the two being 3 H. Determine the maximum e.m.f. induced in the second coil and the time at which it occurs. Determine also the current in the first coil at an instant 0·012 second after closing of the switch. Derive any formula used. (App. El., L.U.)

49. Define the unit of mutual inductance. A cylinder, 5 cm in diameter and 100 cm long, is uniformly wound with 3000 turns in a single layer. A second layer of 100 turns of much finer wire is wound over the first one, near its centre. Calculate the mutual inductance between the two coils. Derive any formula used.

(App. El., L.U.)

50. A solenoid P, 100 cm long and 10 cm in diameter, is uniformly wound with 600 turns. A search-coil Q, 3 cm in diameter and wound with 20 turns, is mounted co-axially midway along the solenoid. If Q is connected to a ballistic galvanometer, calculate the quantity of electricity through the galvanometer when a current of 6 A through the solenoid is reversed. The resistance of the secondary circuit is 0·1 MΩ. Find, also, the mutual inductance between the two coils.

51. When a current of 2 A through a coil P is reversed, a deflection of 43 divisions is obtained on a fluxmeter connected to a coil Q. If the fluxmeter constant is 150 microweber-turns/division, find the mutual inductance of coils P and Q. If the self-inductances of P and Q are 5 and 3 mH respectively, calculate the coefficient of coupling.

CHAPTER III

ELECTROSTATICS

43. Introductory. The terms used in Electrostatics and their relationships have been discussed in Chapter IX of *Principles of Electricity*; but the following summary of the principal terms may be helpful at this stage.

(a) An excess of positive or negative electricity on a body constitutes a *charge* of electricity, the *unit charge* being the *coulomb*. The negative charge on a single electron is $1 \cdot 602 \times 10^{-19}$ coulomb, and a current of 1 ampere in a conductor means that $6 \cdot 24 \times 10^{18}$ electrons per second are passing any given point.

(b) If a conductor carries I amperes for t seconds with a p.d. of V volts between two points A and B of the conductor,

$$\left.\begin{array}{l}\text{energy absorbed}\\ \text{in length } AB\end{array}\right\} = IVt = QV \text{ joules} \qquad . \quad . \quad (81)$$

$$= \text{charge in coulombs} \times \text{p.d. in volts.}$$

Conversely, the work done in moving a *positive* charge of Q coulombs from point A to point B is QV joules, where the potential of B is V volts *above* that of A.

The *electron-volt* is the work done in moving an electron from point A to point B where the potential of A is 1 volt above that of B.

$$1 \text{ electron-volt} = 1 \cdot 6 \times 10^{-19} \text{ joule.}$$

(c) A *capacitor* (or *condenser*) consists of two metal plates separated by an insulating material or dielectric; and the *unit of capacitance* is the *farad*, namely the capacitance which requires a p.d. of 1 volt to maintain a charge of 1 coulomb.

$$1 \text{ farad (F)} = 10^6 \text{ microfarads } (\mu F)$$
$$= 10^{12} \text{ micro-microfarads } (\mu\mu F) \text{ or}$$
$$\text{picofarads (pF).}$$

If $C =$ capacitance in farads,

       $V =$ p.d. across capacitor in volts

and $Q =$ charge on capacitor in coulombs,

$$Q = CV \qquad \ldots \quad (82)$$

(d) If capacitors having capacitances C_1, C_2, etc., are connected in parallel,

$$\text{total capacitance} = C_1 + C_2 + \ldots \qquad (83)$$

If the capacitors are connected in series, the resultant capacitance C is given by,

$$\frac{1}{C} = \frac{1}{C_1} + \frac{1}{C_2} + \ldots \quad \ldots \quad (84)$$

If two capacitors, having capacitances C_1 and C_2 respectively, are connected in series across a p.d. of V volts,

$$\text{p.d. across } C_1 = V \cdot \frac{C_2}{C_1 + C_2} \quad \ldots \quad (85)$$

and $$\text{p.d. across } C_2 = V \cdot \frac{C_1}{C_1 + C_2}$$

44. Electric Force and Electric Flux. The *electric force* or *electric field strength* in a dielectric is the *potential drop per unit length* or *electric potential gradient* and is expressed in volts/metre. For instance, if a p.d. of V volts is maintained across metal plates, M and N, in Fig. 52, separated d metres apart,

$$\left.\begin{array}{l}\text{electric force or electric field}\\\text{strength in dielectric}\end{array}\right\} = E^* = V/d \text{ volts/metre} \quad (86)$$

In the rationalized M.K.S. system, *one line of electric flux* is assumed to emanate from a positive charge of 1 coulomb and to enter a negative charge of 1 coulomb. Hence, if the charge on plates M and N of the capacitor shown in Fig 52 is Q coulombs,

electric flux between M and $N = \Psi = Q$ coulombs

and electric flux density $= D = Q/a$ coulombs/m^2 (87)

---

* The British Standards Institution recommends the use of E instead of $\mathscr{E}$ as the symbol for electric force.

where a=area of dielectric in square metres.

From expressions (86) and (87),

$$\frac{\text{electric flux density}}{\text{electric force}} = \frac{D}{E} = \frac{Q}{a} \div \frac{V}{d} = \frac{Q}{V} \cdot \frac{d}{a} = \frac{Cd}{a}$$

In electromagnetism, the ratio of the magnetic flux density in a vacuum to the magnetizing force is termed the permeability of free space. Similarly, in electrostatics, the ratio of the electric flux density in a vacuum to the electric force is termed the *permittivity of free space* and is represented by ϵ_0.* Hence, if the capacitor of Fig. 52 were in a glass enclosure G from which all the air has been removed,

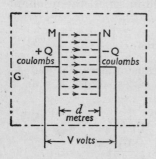

FIG. 52.—A parallel-plate capacitor.

$$\epsilon_0 = \frac{D}{E} = \frac{Cd}{a}$$

or $$C = \frac{\epsilon_0 a}{d} \qquad . \quad .(88)$$

The effect of filling the space between M and N with air at atmospheric pressure is to increase the capacitance by 0·06 per cent; hence, for all practical purposes, expression (88) can be applied to capacitors having air dielectric.

The value of ϵ_0 can be determined experimentally by charging a capacitor of known dimensions and air dielectric to a p.d. of V volts and then discharging it through a ballistic galvanometer having a known ballistic constant k coulombs/unit deflection. If the deflection is θ divisions,

$$Q = CV = k\theta$$

$$\therefore \qquad \epsilon_0 = \frac{k\theta}{V} \cdot \frac{d}{a}.$$

The value of ϵ_0 is $8 \cdot 85 \times 10^{-12}$ rationalized M.K.S. units.

* The British Standards Institution recommends the use of ϵ instead of κ as the symbol for permittivity.

Hence,

$$\frac{1}{\mu_0 \epsilon_0} = \frac{1}{4\pi \times 10^{-7} \times 8 \cdot 85 \times 10^{-12}} = 9 \cdot \times 10^{16} = (3 \times 10^8)^2$$

$$\therefore \frac{1}{\sqrt{(\mu_0 \epsilon_0)}} = 3 \times 10^8 \text{ m/sec}$$

= velocity of electromagnetic waves in free space.

45. Relative Permittivity or Dielectric Constant. The relative permittivity or dielectric constant of a material is the ratio of the capacitance of a capacitor having that material as dielectric to the capacitance of the same capacitor with a vacuum dielectric.

From (88), it follows that if the space between the metal plates of the capacitor in Fig. 52 is filled by a dielectric having a relative permittivity ϵ_r.

$$\text{capacitance} = C = \frac{\epsilon_r \epsilon_0 a}{d} \text{ farads} \quad . \quad . \quad . \quad . \quad (89)$$

$$= \frac{8 \cdot 85 \times 10^{-12} \epsilon_r a \text{ (square metres)}}{d \text{ (metres)}} \text{ farads}$$

and charge due to a p.d. of V volts $\Big\} = Q = CV = \dfrac{\epsilon_r \epsilon_0 a V}{d}$ coulombs

$$\therefore \frac{\text{electric flux density}}{\text{electric force}} = \frac{D}{E} = \frac{Q}{a} \div \frac{V}{d} = \epsilon_r \epsilon_0$$

$$= \epsilon = \text{absolute permittivity} \quad (90)$$

This expression is similar in form to expression (33) deduced for the magnetic circuit, namely:

$$\frac{\text{magnetic flux density}}{\text{magnetizing force}} = \frac{B}{H} = \mu = \mu_r \mu_0.$$

Expression (90) is also similar in form to expression (2) for a passive conductor, namely:

$$\frac{\text{current density in amperes/metre}^2}{\text{potential gradient in volts/metre}} = \text{conductivity}.$$

Values of the relative permittivity of some of the most

important insulating materials are given in the following table:

Material	Relative permittivity
Air . .	1·0006
Paper (dry)	2–2·5
Bakelite .	4·5–5·5
Glass . .	5–10
Rubber .	2–3·5
Mica .	3–7
Porcelain .	6–7

46. Capacitance of Multi-Plate Capacitor. Suppose a capacitor to consist of n parallel plates, alternate plates being connected together.

Let $a =$ area of *one* side of each plate in square metres,

   $d =$ thickness of dielectric in metres,

and $\epsilon =$ absolute permittivity of the dielectric,

   $= \epsilon_r \epsilon_0$

then $$C = \frac{\epsilon(n-1)a}{d} \text{ farads} \quad . \quad . \quad (91)$$

47. Capacitance of and Potential Gradient in a Parallel-plate Capacitor with Composite Dielectric. Suppose the

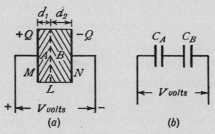

FIG. 53.—Parallel-plate capacitor with two dielectrics.

space between metal plates M and N to be filled by dielectrics A and B of thickness d_1 and d_2 metres respectively, as shown in Fig. 53. The boundary L between the two dielectrics is an *equipotential surface*, i.e. all points on this surface are at the same potential, so that if a very thin metal foil were inserted between A and B, it would not alter the electric field in the dielectrics. Hence the latter may be regarded as equivalent to two capacitors, C_A and C_B, connected in series as in Fig. 53. If the dielectric constants of A and B are ϵ_1 and ϵ_2 respectively and if the cross-sectional area of the dielectrics is a square metres, then:

$$C_A = \frac{\epsilon_1 \epsilon_0 a}{d_1} \quad \text{and} \quad C_B = \frac{\epsilon_2 \epsilon_0 a}{d_2}$$

and
$$\left.\begin{array}{l}\text{total capacitance between} \\ \text{plates } M \text{ and } N\end{array}\right\} = \frac{C_A C_B}{C_A + C_B}.$$

Let Q = charge in coulombs due to p.d. of V volts then Q/a = electric flux density, in coulombs/m², in A and B.

Let E_1 and E_2 = electric forces (or potential gradients) in A and B respectively.

$$\therefore \quad \left.\begin{array}{l}\text{electric force or potential} \\ \text{gradient in } A\end{array}\right\} = E_1 = \frac{D}{\epsilon_1 \epsilon_0} = \frac{Q}{\epsilon_1 \epsilon_0 a}$$

and
$$\left.\begin{array}{l}\text{electric force or potential} \\ \text{gradient in } B\end{array}\right\} = E_2 = \frac{D}{\epsilon_2 \epsilon_0} = \frac{Q}{\epsilon_2 \epsilon_0 a}.$$

Hence,
$$\frac{E_1}{E_2} = \frac{\epsilon_2}{\epsilon_1} \quad \cdots \quad (92)$$

i.e., for dielectrics having the same cross-sectional area in series, the potential gradients are inversely proportional to their dielectric constants.

Example 19. *A capacitor consists of two metal plates, each 40 cm × 40 cm, spaced 6 mm apart. The space between the metal plates is filled with a glass plate 5 mm thick and a layer of paper 1 mm thick. The dielectric constants of the glass and paper are 8 and 2 respectively. Calculate (a) the capacitance, neglecting any fringing flux, and (b) the potential gradient in each dielectric in kilovolts/mm due to a p.d. of 10 kV between the metal plates.*

4

(a) Fig. 54 (a) shows a cross-section (not to scale) of the capacitor; and in Fig. 54 (b), C_p represents the capacitance of the paper layer between M and the

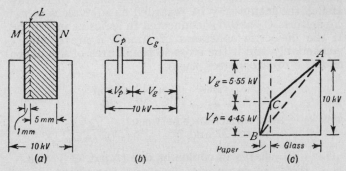

FIG. 54.—Diagrams for Example 19.

equipotential surface L and C_g represents that of the glass between L and N. From expression (89), we have:

$$C_p = \frac{8 \cdot 85 \times 10^{-12} \times 2 \times 0 \cdot 4 \times 0 \cdot 4}{0 \cdot 001} = 2 \cdot 83 \times 10^{-9} \text{ F}$$

and $C_g = \dfrac{8 \cdot 85 \times 10^{-12} \times 8 \times 0 \cdot 4 \times 0 \cdot 4}{0 \cdot 005} = 2 \cdot 265 \times 10^{-9}$ F.

If C is the resultant capacitance between M and N,

$$\frac{1}{C} = \frac{10^9}{2 \cdot 83} + \frac{10^9}{2 \cdot 265} = 0 \cdot 7955 \times 10^9$$

$$\therefore \qquad C = 1 \cdot 257 \times 10^{-9} \text{ F} = 0 \cdot 001257 \ \mu\text{F}.$$

(b) Since C_p and C_g are in series across 10 kV, it follows from expression (85) that the p.d., V_p, across the paper is given by:

$$V_p = \frac{10 \times 2 \cdot 265}{2 \cdot 83 + 2 \cdot 265} = 4 \cdot 45 \text{ kV}$$

and $\qquad V_g = 10 - 4 \cdot 45 = 5 \cdot 55$ kV

These voltages are represented graphically in Fig 54 (c).

$$\left.\text{Potential gradient in the} \atop \text{paper dielectric}\right\} = \frac{4 \cdot 45}{1} = 4 \cdot 45 \text{ kV/mm}$$

$$\text{and} \left.\text{potential gradient in the} \atop \text{glass dielectric}\right\} = \frac{5 \cdot 55}{5} = 1 \cdot 11 \text{ kV/mm}.$$

These potential gradients are represented by the slopes of AC and CB for the glass and paper respectively in Fig. 54 (c). Had the dielectric between plates M and N been homogeneous, the potential gradient would have been $10/6 = 1 \cdot 67$ kV/mm, as represented by the slope of the dotted line AB in Fig. 54 (c). It will therefore be seen that the effect of using a composite dielectric of two materials having different dielectric constants is to increase the potential gradient in the material having the lower dielectric constant. This effect has very important applications in high-voltage work.

48. Comparison of Electrostatic and Electromagnetic Terms. It may be helpful to compare the terms and symbols used in electrostatics with the corresponding terms and symbols used in electromagnetism:

Electrostatics		Electromagnetism	
Term	Symbol	Term	Symbol
Electric flux . .	Ψ	Magnetic flux . .	Φ
Electric flux density .	D	Magnetic flux density	B
Electric force . .	E	Magnetizing force .	H
Electromotive force .	E	Magnetomotive force	F
Electric potential difference . .	V	Magnetic potential difference . .	—
Permittivity of free space . . .	ϵ_0	Permeability of free space . . .	μ_0
Relative permittivity	ϵ_r	Relative permeability	μ_r
Absolute permittivity $= \dfrac{\text{electric flux density}}{\text{electric force}}$		Absolute permeability $= \dfrac{\text{magnetic flux density}}{\text{magnetizing force}}$	
i.e. $\epsilon_0 \epsilon_r = \epsilon = D/E$		i.e $\mu_0 \mu_r = \mu = B/H$	

49. Types of Capacitors. Capacitors may be divided into the following five main groups according to the nature of the insulating medium or dielectric:

(a) *Air capacitors.* This type usually consists of one set of fixed plates and another set of movable plates, and is mainly used for radio work where it is required to vary the capacitance.

(b) *Paper capacitors.* The electrodes consist of metal foils interleaved with paper impregnated with wax or oil and rolled into a compact form.

(c) *Mica capacitors.* This type consists either of alternate layers of mica and metal foil clamped tightly together or of thin films of silver sputtered on the two sides of a mica sheet. Owing to its relatively high cost, this type is mainly used in high-frequency circuits when it is necessary to reduce the loss to a minimum.

(d) *Ceramic capacitors.* The electrodes consist of metallic coatings (usually silver) on the opposite faces of a thin disc or plate of ceramic material such as the hydrous silicate of magnesia or talc—somewhat similar to that used by tailors for marking cloth. This type of capacitor is mainly used in high-frequency circuits subject to a very wide variation of temperature.

(e) *Electrolytic capacitors.* The type most commonly used consists of two aluminium foils, one with an oxide film and one without, the foils being interleaved with a material such as paper saturated with a suitable electrolyte, for example, ammonium borate. The aluminium oxide film is formed on the one foil by passing it through an electrolytic bath of which the foil forms the positive electrode. The finished unit is assembled in a container —usually of aluminium—and hermetically sealed. The oxide film acts as the dielectric; and as its thickness in a capacitor suitable for a working voltage of 100 V is only about 15×10^{-6} cm, a very large capacitance is obtainable in a relatively small volume.

The main disadvantages of the electrolytic capacitor are (a) the insulation resistance is comparatively low and (b) it is only suitable for circuits when the voltage applied to the capacitor never reverses its direction. Electrolytic capacitors are mainly used where very

large capacitances are required, e.g. for reducing the
ripple in the voltage wave obtained
from a rectifier (Art. 162).

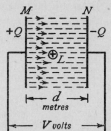

FIG. 55.—An isolated
charge in an electric
field.

**50. Force on an Isolated Charge in
an Electric Field.** Suppose L in
Fig. 55 to be a very small metal
sphere carrying a positive charge of
q coulombs situated in the electric
field between plates M and N
separated by an air dielectric, M
being positive relative to N. Since
like charges repel and unlike charges
attract each other, there is a force
acting on L urging it towards N.
If the plates are d metres apart and if the p.d. between
them is V volts,

$$\left.\begin{array}{l}\text{electric force (or potential} \\ \text{gradient) in the dielectric}\end{array}\right\} = E = V/d \text{ volts/metre.}$$

If L is moved a distance dx metre towards the positive
plate M, the increase of potential is $E \cdot dx$ volts. Hence
it follows from expression (81) that:

$$\left.\begin{array}{l}\text{work done on charge} \\ \text{(in joules)}\end{array}\right. = \left.\begin{array}{l}\text{charge} \\ \text{(coulombs)}\end{array}\right. \times \left.\begin{array}{l}\text{increase of potential} \\ \text{(volts)}\end{array}\right.$$

i.e.   force on charge $\times dx = qE \cdot dx$
        (in newtons)

$\therefore$ force on charge $= qE$ newtons
                    $= E$ newtons/coulomb   (93)

Example 20. *An electron has a velocity of 10^7 m/sec
at right angles to the electric field between the deflecting
plates of a cathode-ray tube (Art. 179). If the plates are
0·8 cm apart and 2 cm long (Fig. 56) and if the p.d.
between the plates is 50 V, calculate the distance through
which the electron is deflected sideways during its movement
through the electric field. Assume an electron to have a
mass of $9·1 \times 10^{-31}$ kg and to carry a charge of $1·6 \times 10^{-19}$
coulomb and neglect any fringing of the electric flux.*

$$\left.\begin{array}{l}\text{Electric force (or electric field} \\ \text{strength) between plates}\end{array}\right\} = \frac{50}{0·008} = 6250 \text{ V/m}$$

From expression (93),

force on electron $= 6250 \times 1 \cdot 6 \times 10^{-19} = 10^{-15}$ newton.

Time taken to travel through electric field $\Big\} = 0 \cdot 02/10^7 = 2 \times 10^{-9}$ sec.

But   force $=$ mass $\times$ acceleration

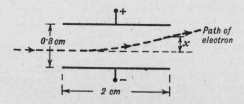

FIG. 56.—Diagram for Example 20.

$\therefore$ transverse acceleration $= \dfrac{10^{-15}}{9 \cdot 1 \times 10^{-31}} = 1 \cdot 1 \times 10^{15}$ m/sec^2

and final transverse velocity of electron $\Big\} =$ acceleration $\times$ time

$= 1 \cdot 1 \times 10^{15} \times 2 \times 10^{-9}$

$= 2 \cdot 2 \times 10^6$ m/sec

and transverse movement of electron $\Big\} = \Big($ average transverse velocity $\Big) \times$ time

$= \tfrac{1}{2} \times 2 \cdot 2 \times 10^6 \times 2 \times 10^{-9}$

$= 0 \cdot 0022$ m $= 2 \cdot 2$ mm,

i.e. the electron is deflected through a distance of $2 \cdot 2$ mm towards the positive plate, as represented by x in Fig. 56.

51. Electric Field due to an Isolated Charge. Suppose a small metal sphere, far removed from any other metal body, to have a positive charge of Q coulombs and suppose the surrounding medium to have an absolute permittivity ϵ. There will be Q lines of electric flux radiating uniformly in all directions, as indicated in Fig. 57; and since the electric field is symmetrical in all directions, the equipotential surfaces must be spheres having their centres at the centre of the charge, as indicated by the dotted circles in Fig 57.

Let us consider an equipotential spherical surface of radius r metres. Since the area of this sphere is $4\pi r^2$ square metres,

electric flux density at radius $r = \dfrac{Q}{4\pi r^2}$ coulombs/metre^2

and electric force or potential gradient at radius r $\Bigg\} = E = D/\epsilon$

$$= \frac{Q}{4\pi r^2 \epsilon} \text{ volts/metre (94)}$$

From this expression it follows that for two concen-

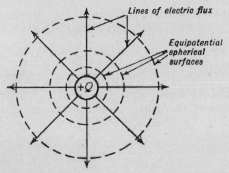

FIG. 57.—Electric field due to an isolated charge.

tric spherical surfaces of radii x and $(x+dx)$ metres respectively,

p.d. between the two equipotential spheres $\Bigg\} = \dfrac{Q \cdot dx}{4\pi x^2 \epsilon}$ volts

∴ p.d. between equipotential spheres of radii a and b metres ($b > a$) $\Bigg\} = \displaystyle\int_a^b \frac{Q \cdot dx}{4\pi x^2 \epsilon}$

$$= \frac{Q}{4\pi\epsilon}\left[-\frac{1}{x}\right]_a^b$$

$$= \frac{Q}{4\pi\epsilon}\left(\frac{1}{a} - \frac{1}{b}\right) \text{ volts}$$

Hence, the capacitance between two concentric metal spheres of external radius a and internal radius b metres respectively (where $b > a$)

$$= \frac{Q}{\text{p.d. between spheres}}$$

$$= \frac{4\pi\epsilon}{1/a - 1/b} \text{ farads} \quad . \quad . \quad . \quad (94\text{A})$$

$$\simeq 4\pi\epsilon a \text{ when } b \gg a$$

52. Force between Concentrated Electric Charges.
Suppose A in Fig 58 to represent a small metal sphere carrying a charge Q_1 coulombs in a medium having an absolute permittivity ϵ. From expression (94),

$$\left.\begin{array}{l}\text{electric force at radius } r \\ \text{due to charge } Q_1 \text{ alone}\end{array}\right\} = \frac{Q_1}{4\pi r^2 \epsilon}.$$

If another small metal sphere B, carrying a charge Q_2 coulombs, is placed at a point r metres from the centre of A, as in Fig. 58, it follows from expression (93) that:

$$\text{force on } B = Q_2 \times \text{electric force at radius } r$$

$$= \frac{Q_1 Q_2}{4\pi r^2 \epsilon} \text{ newtons} \quad . \quad . \quad . \quad (95)$$

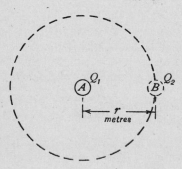

There must also be an equal force acting on A. If the charges are both positive or both negative, they repel each other; but if the charges are unlike, they attract each other. The relationship represented by expression (95) is often referred to as Coulomb's Law.

FIG. 58.—Force between concentrated electric charges.

53. Electric Field due to a Charged Cylindrical Conductor. Let us consider a long conductor of radius r metres, carrying a positive charge of Q coulombs per metre length in a medium having an absolute permittivity ϵ. Hence, there are Q lines of electric flux per metre length of conductor radiating uniformly, as shown in Fig. 59. The equipotential surfaces are concentric cylinders around the conductor; and for an equipotential surface of radius x metres,

$$\left.\begin{array}{l}\text{area of surface per metre}\\\text{length of conductor}\end{array}\right\}=2\pi x \text{ metre}^2$$

$$\therefore \qquad \text{flux density at radius } x = \frac{Q}{2\pi x} \text{ coulombs/metre}^2$$

$$\left.\begin{array}{l}\text{and electric force or potential}\\\text{gradient at radius } x\end{array}\right\}=\frac{Q}{2\pi x \epsilon} \text{volts/metre} \quad (96)$$

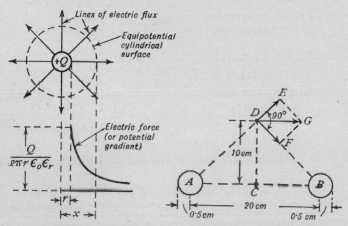

FIG. 59.—Electric field due to a charged cylindrical conductor.

FIG. 60. Diagram for Example 21.

Hence the potential gradient has a maximum value of $Q/(2\pi r \epsilon)$ volts/metre at the surface of the conductor and varies inversely as the distance, as shown by the graph in Fig. 59.

Example 21. *Two long conductors, A and B, each having a diameter of 1 cm, are spaced 20 cm between centres in air, as in Fig 60. If the charges per metre*

4*

length on A and B are +0·1 and −0·1 microcoulomb respectively, calculate the potential gradient at (a) *a point C midway between A and B,* (b) *a point D, 10 cm above C and* (c) *at the surface of A, on a line joining the centres of A and B.*

(a) From expression (96),

$$\text{potential gradient at } C \atop \text{due to } A \text{ alone} \Big\} = \frac{10^{-7}}{2\pi \times 0 \cdot 1 \times 8 \cdot 85 \times 10^{-12}}$$

$$= 18{,}000 \text{ V/m from } A \text{ towards } B$$

$$\text{and potential gradient} \atop \text{at } C \text{ due to } B \atop \text{alone} \Big\} = 18{,}000 \text{ V/m from } A \text{ towards } B.$$

$$\therefore \quad \text{total potential} \atop \text{gradient at } C \Big\} = 36{,}000 \text{ V/m}$$

$$= 360 \text{ V/cm.}$$

(b) $\text{Distance between} \atop D \text{ and centre of } A \Big\} = 10\sqrt{2} = 14 \cdot 14 \text{ cm}$

$$\therefore \quad \text{potential gradient} \atop \text{at } D \text{ due to } A \atop \text{alone} \Big\} = \frac{10^{-7}}{2\pi \times 0 \cdot 1414 \times 8 \cdot 85 \times 10^{-12}}$$

$$= 12{,}700 \text{ V/m in direction } DE$$

$$\text{and potential gradient} \atop \text{at } D \text{ due to } B \atop \text{alone} \Big\} = 12{,}700 \text{ V/m in direction } DF.$$

Since *DE* and *DF* are at right angles to each other,

$$\text{resultant potential} \atop \text{gradient at } D \Big\} = DG = \sqrt{2} \times 12{,}700$$

$$= 18{,}000 \text{ V/m.}$$

(c) $\text{Potential gradient} \atop \text{at surface of } A \text{ due} \atop \text{to } A \text{ alone} \Big\} = \frac{10^{-7}}{2\pi \times 0 \cdot 005 \times 8 \cdot 85 \times 10^{-12}}$

$$= 360{,}000 \text{ V/m from } A \text{ towards } B$$

$$\text{and potential gradient} \atop \text{at point on surface of} \atop A \text{ nearest } B, \text{ due to } B \atop \text{alone} \Big\} = \frac{10^{-7}}{2\pi \times 0 \cdot 195 \times 8 \cdot 85 \times 10^{-12}}$$

$$= 9230 \text{ V/m from } A \text{ towards } B$$

$\therefore$ total potential gradient on surface of A facing B $\Bigg\}$ $=369{,}230$ V/m

$\qquad\qquad\qquad = 3692$ V/cm.

54. Capacitance of Two Parallel Wires.

Suppose A and B in Fig. 61 to represent two parallel wires, each of radius r metres, spaced d metres between centres in a medium of absolute permittivity ϵ. Also, suppose $+Q$ and $-Q$ to be the charges in coulombs/ metre on A and B respectively due to a p.d. of V volts.

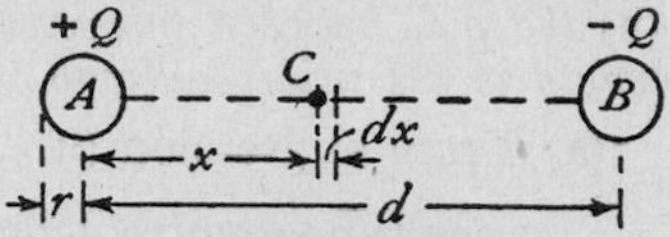

FIG. 61.—Capacitance of parallel wires.

Taking a point C, x metres from the centre of A, on a line joining the centres of A and B, we have from expression (96):

electric force at C due to A alone $\Big\}$ $=\dfrac{Q}{2\pi x\epsilon}$ volts/m

and electric force at C due to B alone $\Big\}$ $=\dfrac{Q}{2\pi(d-x)\epsilon}$ volts/m

$\therefore$ total electric force at $C=\dfrac{Q}{2\pi\epsilon}\left(\dfrac{1}{x}+\dfrac{1}{d-x}\right)$ volts/m.

P.d. across an element of width dx metre $\Big\}$ $=\dfrac{Q\cdot dx}{2\pi\epsilon}\left(\dfrac{1}{x}+\dfrac{1}{d-x}\right)$ volts

$\therefore$ total p.d. between A and B $\Big\}$ $=\displaystyle\int_{r}^{d-r}\dfrac{Q}{2\pi\epsilon}\left(\dfrac{1}{x}+\dfrac{1}{d-x}\right)dx$

i.e. $\qquad V=\dfrac{Q}{2\pi\epsilon}\Big[\ln x-\ln(d-x)\Big]_{r}^{d-r}$

$\qquad\qquad =\dfrac{Q}{\pi\epsilon}\cdot\ln(d-r)/r$ volts

$\therefore$ capacitance per metre length $\Big\}$ $=\dfrac{Q}{V}=\dfrac{\pi\epsilon}{\ln(d-r)/r}$ farads

$\qquad\qquad =\dfrac{12\cdot1\times10^{-12}\epsilon_r}{\log(d-r)/r}$ farads $\quad$ (97)

If d is less than about $10r$, expression (97) is not quite correct, owing to the attraction between the positive and negative charges on A and B causing their effective distance apart to be slightly less than d. The correction for this effect is beyond the scope of this volume.

Example 22. *Calculate* (a) *the capacitance per metre length of the conductors referred to in Example 21 and* (b) *the p.d. between the conductors if the charge per metre length is* 0·1 *microcoulomb.*

(a) From expression (97),

$$\text{capacitance/metre length} = \frac{12\cdot1\times10^{-12}}{\log(19\cdot5/0\cdot5)}$$
$$= 7\cdot6\times10^{-12}\ \text{F} = 7\cdot6\ \text{pF}.$$

(b) P.d. between con-⎫
ductors　　　　　　⎭ $= \dfrac{\text{charge/metre length}}{\text{capacitance/metre length}}$

$$= \frac{0\cdot1\times10^{-6}}{7\cdot6\times10^{-12}} = 13{,}160\ \text{V}.$$

55. Capacitance of Concentric Cylinders.

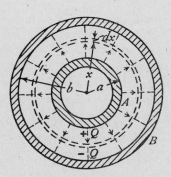

FIG. 62.—Capacitance of concentric cylinders.

Suppose A and B in Fig. 62 to represent two concentric metal cylinders, A having an external radius a metres and B an internal radius b metres; and suppose the cylinders to be separated by an insulator having an absolute permittivity ϵ. Let Q be the charge in coulombs/metre of axial length of the cylinders due to a p.d. of V volts between them. Hence the number of radial lines of electric flux between A and B is Q per metre length,

∴　electric flux density at⎫
　　radius x metres　　　⎭ $= \dfrac{Q}{2\pi x}$ coulombs/metre²

and electric force or potential⎫
　gradient at radius x　　　⎭ $= \dfrac{Q}{2\pi x \epsilon}$ volts/metre　(98)

$\therefore$ p.d. across element of $\left.\begin{array}{c} \\ \end{array}\right\} = \dfrac{Q \cdot dx}{2\pi x \epsilon}$ volts
  thickness dx metre

and total p.d. between A $\left.\begin{array}{c} \\ \end{array}\right\} = \displaystyle\int_{a}^{b} \dfrac{Q \cdot dx}{2\pi x \epsilon}$ volts
  and B

i.e. $\qquad\qquad\qquad V = \dfrac{Q \ln b/a}{2\pi \epsilon}$

and capacitance per metre $\left.\begin{array}{c} \\ \end{array}\right\} = \dfrac{Q}{V} = \dfrac{2\pi \epsilon}{\ln b/a}$ farads
  length

$$= \dfrac{24 \cdot 2 \times 10^{-12} \epsilon_r}{\log b/a} \text{ farads} \quad (99)$$

56. Potential Gradient in Dielectric between Concentric Cylinders.

From expression (98),

potential gradient at $\left.\begin{array}{c} \\ \end{array}\right\} = \dfrac{Q}{2\pi x \epsilon}$ volts/metre
  radius x metres

But $\qquad\qquad Q = V \times$ capacitance/metre length

$\therefore$ potential gradient $\left.\begin{array}{c} \\ \end{array}\right\} = V \cdot \dfrac{2\pi \epsilon}{\ln b/a} \cdot \dfrac{1}{2\pi x \epsilon}$
  at radius x metres

$$= V/(x \ln b/a) \quad . \quad . \quad . \quad (100)$$

Hence the potential gradient in the dielectric is inversely proportional to the radius and is therefore a maximum at the surface of the inner conductor,

i.e. maximum potential gradient

$$= \dfrac{V}{2 \cdot 3 \, a \log b/a} \text{ volts/metre} \quad . \quad . \quad (101)$$

Example 23. *The conductor of a single-core, paper-insulated, lead-sheathed cable has a diameter of 0·25 inch. The dielectric has a thickness of 0·25 inch and a relative permittivity of 3·5. Calculate (a) the capacitance per mile of the cable and (b) the maximum potential gradient in the dielectric when a p.d. of 10 kV is maintained between the conductor and the lead sheath.*

(a) 1 mile $= 1760 \times 0 \cdot 9144 = 1609$ metres.

Also, $a = 0 \cdot 125$ inch and $b = 0 \cdot 125 + 0 \cdot 25 = 0 \cdot 375$ inch,

$\therefore \qquad\qquad \log b/a = \log 3 = 0 \cdot 477.$

From (99), capacitance per mile of cable

$$=\frac{24 \cdot 2 \times 10^{-12} \times 3 \cdot 5 \times 1609}{0 \cdot 477}$$

$$=0 \cdot 2857 \times 10^{-6} \text{ F}=0 \cdot 2857 \text{ } \mu\text{F}$$

(b) From (101), maximum potential gradient

$$=\frac{10,000}{2 \cdot 3 \times 0 \cdot 125 \times 0 \cdot 0254 \times 0 \cdot 477}$$

$$=2,870,000 \text{ V/m}=28 \cdot 7 \text{ kV/cm.}$$

57. Charging and Discharging Currents of a Capacitor. If the p.d. across a capacitor having a capacitance of C farads is *increased* by dv volt in dt second, and if dq coulomb is the corresponding increase of charge, then:

$$dq=C \cdot dv$$

If the charging current at that instant is i amperes, then:

$$dq=i \cdot dt$$

Hence $i \cdot dt=C \cdot dv$

and $i=C \cdot dv/dt$

$$=C \times \text{rate of increase of p.d.} \quad . \quad (102)$$

If the capacitor is being discharged and if the p.d. falls by dv volt in dt second, the discharge current is given by:

$$i=C \cdot dv/dt \quad . \quad (103)$$

Since dv is now negative, the current is also negative.

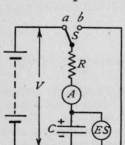

FIG. 63.—Charging of a capacitor.

58. Variation of Current and P.D. when a Capacitor is connected in series with a High Resistance across a D.C. Supply. Fig. 63 shows a circuit arrangement whereby a capacitor C can be charged through a high resistance R and a microammeter A from a d.c. source of V volts. An electrostatic voltmeter, ES, is connected across the capacitor. By moving switch S from a to b, the capacitor can be discharged through the

same high resistance, an effect that will be considered in
Art. 59.

Suppose the p.d. across C, t seconds after switching S
over to a, to be v volts, and the corresponding charging
current to be i amperes, as indicated in Fig. 64.   Also,

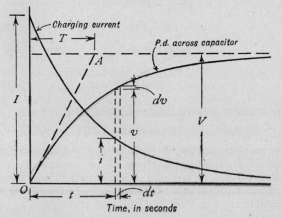

FIG. 64.—Variation of current and p.d. during charging.

suppose the p.d. to increase from v to $(v+dv)$ volts
in dt second; then, from (102),

$$i = C \cdot dv/dt$$

and corresponding p.d. across $R = Ri = RC \cdot dv/dt$.

But $V =$ p.d. across $C+$p.d. across R

$$= v + RC \cdot dv/dt \quad . \quad . \quad . \quad (104)$$

$\therefore$ $V - v = RC \cdot dv/dt$

so that $\dfrac{dt}{RC} = \dfrac{dv}{V-v}.$

Integrating both sides, we have:

$$t/RC = -\ln (V - v) + A$$

where $A =$ the constant of integration.

When $t=0$, $v=0$,

$\therefore$ $$A = \ln V$$

so that $$\frac{t}{RC} = \ln \frac{V}{V-v}$$

$\therefore$ $$\frac{V}{V-v} = e^{t/RC}$$

and $$v = V(1 - e^{-t/RC}) \quad . \quad . \quad (105)$$

Also, $$i = C \cdot dv/dt = CV \cdot \frac{d}{dt}(1 - e^{-t/RC})$$

$$= \frac{V}{R} e^{-t/RC} \quad . \quad . \quad . \quad (106)$$

At the instant of switching on, $t=0$ and $e^{-0}=1$,

$\therefore$ initial value of current $= V/R = $ (say) I.

This result is really obvious from the fact that at the instant of switching on there is no charge on C and therefore no p.d. across it. Consequently the whole of the applied voltage must momentarily be absorbed by R.

Substituting for V/R in (106), we have:

instantaneous charging current $= i = I e^{-t/RC}$ (107)

If the p.d. across the capacitor continued increasing at the initial rate, it would be represented by OA, the tangent drawn to the initial part of the curve. If T be the *time constant* in seconds, namely the time required for the p.d. across C to increase from zero to its final value if it continued increasing at its initial rate, then:

initial rate of increase of p.d. $= V/T$ volts/sec (108)

But it follows from (104) that at the instant of closing the switch on a, $v=0$, then:

$$V = RC \cdot dv/dt$$

$\therefore$ initial rate of in-$\left.\begin{array}{c} \text{crease of p.d.} \end{array}\right\} = dv/dt = V/RC \quad . \quad (109)$

Equating (108) and (109), we have:

$$V/T = V/RC$$

$\therefore$ $$T = RC \text{ seconds} \quad . \quad . \quad (110)$$

Hence we can rewrite (105) and (107) thus:

$$v = V(1 - e^{-t/T}) \quad . \quad . \quad . \quad (111)$$

and
$$i = I e^{-t/T} \quad . \quad . \quad . \quad . \quad (112)$$

Comparison of expressions (71) and (111) shows that the shape of the voltage growth across a capacitor is similar to that of the current growth in an inductive circuit.

59. Discharge of a Capacitor through a High Resistance. Having charged capacitor C in Fig. 63 to a p.d. of V volts, let us now move switch S over to b and thereby

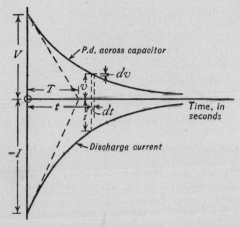

FIG. 65.—Variation of current and p.d. during discharge.

discharge the capacitor through R. The pointer of microammeter A is immediately deflected to a maximum value in the negative direction, and then the readings on both the microammeter and the voltmeter ES (Fig. 63) decrease to zero as indicated in Fig. 65.

Suppose the p.d. across C to be v volts t seconds after S has been moved to b, and the corresponding current to be i amperes, as in Fig. 65, then:

$$i = -v/R \quad . \quad . \quad . \quad (113)$$

The negative sign indicates that the direction of the discharge current is the reverse of that of the charging current.

Suppose the p.d. across C to change by dv volt in dt second,

$$\therefore \qquad\qquad i = C \cdot dv/dt \quad \dotfill \quad (114)$$

Since dv is now negative, i must also be negative, as already noted. Equating (113) and (114), we have:

$$-v/R = C \cdot dv/dt$$

so that $\qquad\qquad \dfrac{dt}{RC} = -\dfrac{dv}{v}.$

Integrating both sides, we have:

$$t/RC = -\ln v + A.$$

When $t=0$, $v=V$, so that $A = \ln V$.

Hence $\qquad t/RC = \ln V/v$

so that $\qquad V/v = e^{t/RC}$

and $\qquad\qquad v = Ve^{-t/RC} = Ve^{-t/T} \quad \dotfill \quad (115)$

Also, $\qquad i = -v/R = -\dfrac{V}{R}e^{-t/RC} = -Ie^{-t/T} \quad . \quad (116)$

where $I = $ initial value of the discharge current $= V/R$.

Example 24. *A capacitor having a capacitance of 8 μF is connected in series with a resistance of $0 \cdot 5$ $M\Omega$ across a 200-V d.c. supply. Calculate: (a) the time constant, (b) the initial charging current, (c) the time taken for the p.d. across the capacitor to grow to 160 V, and (d) the current and the p.d. across the capacitor 4 seconds after it is connected to the supply.*

(a) From (110), time constant $= 0 \cdot 5 \times 10^6 \times 8 \times 10^{-6}$
$$= 4 \text{ seconds.}$$

(b) Initial charging current $= \dfrac{V}{R} = \dfrac{200}{0 \cdot 5 \times 10^6}$ ampere
$$= 400 \text{ microamperes.}$$

(c) From (111), $\qquad 160 = 200(1 - e^{-t/4})$
$$\therefore \qquad\qquad e^{-t/4} = 0 \cdot 2.$$

From mathematical tables, $t/4 = 1 \cdot 61$

$\therefore$ $t = 6 \cdot 44$ seconds.

Or alternatively, $e^{t/4} = 1/0 \cdot 2 = 5.$

$\therefore$ $\dfrac{t}{4} \cdot \log e = \log 5.$

But $e = 2 \cdot 718$, $\therefore t = \dfrac{4 \times 0 \cdot 699}{0 \cdot 4343} = 6 \cdot 44$ seconds.

(d) From (111) $v = 200(1 - e^{-4/4}) = 200(1 - 0 \cdot 368)$
$$= 200 \times 0 \cdot 632 = 126 \cdot 4 \text{ V.}$$

It will be seen that the time constant can be defined as the time required for the p.d. across the capacitor to grow from zero to $63 \cdot 2$ per cent of its final value.

From (112),

$$\left. \begin{matrix} \text{corresponding} \\ \text{current} \end{matrix} \right\} = i = 400 \cdot e^{-1} = 400 \times 0 \cdot 368$$

$$= 147 \text{ microamperes.}$$

60. Energy stored in a Charged Capacitor. Suppose the p.d. across a capacitor of capacitance C farads to be increased from v to $(v + dv)$ volts in dt second. From (102), the charging current, i amperes, is given by:

$$i = C \cdot dv/dt.$$

$$\left. \begin{matrix} \text{Instantaneous value of power to} \\ \text{capacitor} \end{matrix} \right\} = iv \text{ watts}$$

$$= vC \cdot dv/dt \text{ watts,}$$

$$\left. \begin{matrix} \text{and energy supplied to capacitor} \\ \text{during interval } dt \end{matrix} \right\} = vC \cdot \frac{dv}{dt} \cdot dt$$

$$= Cv \cdot dv \text{ joules.}$$

Hence energy supplied to capacitor when p.d. is increased from 0 to V

$$= \int_0^V Cv \cdot dv = \tfrac{1}{2} C \left[v^2 \right]_0^V$$
$$= \tfrac{1}{2} C V^2 \text{ joules} \quad \cdot \quad \cdot \quad \cdot \quad \cdot \quad (117)$$

For a capacitor with dielectric of thickness d metres and area a square metres,

$$\left.\begin{array}{c}\text{energy per cubic}\\ \text{metre}\end{array}\right\} = \frac{1}{2} \cdot \frac{CV^2}{ad} = \frac{1}{2} \cdot \frac{\epsilon a}{d} \cdot \frac{V^2}{ad}$$

$$= \tfrac{1}{2}\epsilon(V/d)^2 = \tfrac{1}{2}\epsilon E^2$$

$$= \tfrac{1}{2}DE = \tfrac{1}{2}D^2/\epsilon \text{ joules} \quad . \quad (118)$$

These expressions are similar to expressions (72A) for the energy stored per cubic metre of a magnetic field.

61. Force of Attraction between Oppositely Charged Surfaces. Let us consider two parallel plates M and N (Fig. 66) immersed in a homogeneous fluid, such as air or oil, having an absolute permittivity ϵ. Suppose the area of the dielectric to be a square metres and the distance between M and N to be x metres. If the p.d. between the plates is V volts, then from (118),

$$\left.\begin{array}{c}\text{energy per cubic metre}\\ \text{of dielectric}\end{array}\right\} = \tfrac{1}{2}\epsilon(V/x)^2 \text{ joules.}$$

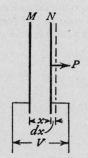

FIG. 66.—Attraction between charged parallel plates.

Suppose plate M to be fixed and N to be movable, and let P be the force of attraction, in newtons, between the plates. Let us next disconnect the charged capacitor from the supply and then pull plate N outwards through a distance dx metre. If the insulation of the capacitor is perfect, the charge on the plates remains constant. This means that the electric flux density and therefore the potential gradient in the dielectric must remain unaltered, the constancy of the potential gradient being due to the p.d. between plates M and N increasing in proportion to the distance between them. It follows from expression (118) that the energy per cubic metre of the dielectric remains constant. Consequently, all the energy in the *additional* volume of the dielectric must be derived from the work done when the force P

newtons acts through distance dx metre, namely $P \cdot dx$ joules,

i.e. $P \cdot dx = \frac{1}{2}\epsilon(V/x)^2 \cdot a \cdot dx$

$\therefore$ $P = \frac{1}{2}\epsilon a(V/x)^2$ newtons   .   .   .   (119)

        $= \frac{1}{2}\epsilon a \times$ (potential gradient in volts/metre)^2

Example 25. *Two parallel metal discs, each 10 cm in diameter, are spaced 1 mm apart, the dielectric being air. Calculate the force in grams on each disc when the p.d. between them is 1 kV.*

Area of one side of each plate $\Big\}$ $= 0 \cdot 7854 \times (0 \cdot 1)^2 = 0 \cdot 007854$ m^2.

From expression (119),

     force $= \frac{1}{2} \times 8 \cdot 85 \times 10^{-12} \times 0 \cdot 007854 \times (1000/0 \cdot 001)^2$

           $= 0 \cdot 0348$ newton

           $= \dfrac{0 \cdot 0348 \times 1000}{9 \cdot 81} = 3 \cdot 55$ grams.

62. Dielectric Strength. If the p.d. between the opposite sides of a sheet of solid insulating material is increased beyond a certain value, the material breaks down. Usually this results in a tiny hole or puncture through the dielectric so that the latter is then useless as an insulator.

The potential gradient necessary to cause breakdown of an insulating medium is termed its *dielectric strength* and is usually expressed in kilovolts/mm. The value of the dielectric strength of a given material decreases with increase of thickness, and the table* on page 118 gives the approximate dielectric strengths of some of the most important materials.

Summary of Important Formulae in Chapter III

         Q(coulombs) $= C$(farads) $\times V$(volts)   .   (82)

For capacitors in parallel,

            $C = C_1 + C_2 + \ldots$.   .   .   (83)

* See *Dictionary of Applied Physics*, Vol. II, p. 117.

Material	Thickness (mm)	Dielectric strength (kV/mm)
Air (at normal pressure and temperature)	0·2	5·75
	0·6	4·92
	1	4·36
	6	3·27
	10	2·98
Mica	0·01	200
	0·1	115
	1·0	61
Glass (density 2·5) . . .	1	28·5
	5	18·3
Ebonite	1	50
Paraffin-waxed paper . .	0·1	40–60

For capacitors in series,

$$\frac{1}{C} = \frac{1}{C_1} + \frac{1}{C_2} + \cdots \quad . \quad . \quad . \quad (84)$$

For C_1 and C_2 in series,

$$V_1 = V \cdot \frac{C_2}{C_1 + C_2} \quad . \quad . \quad . \quad (85)$$

Electric force or potential gradient in dielectric $\Big\} = E = V/d$. (86)

Electric flux density $= D = Q/a$. (87)

Absolute permittivity $= D/E = \epsilon = \epsilon_0 \epsilon_r$. (90)

Permittivity of free space $= \epsilon_0 = 8 \cdot 85 \times 10^{-12}$

$$\frac{1}{\sqrt{(\mu_0 \epsilon_0)}} = 3 \times 10^8 \text{ m/sec}$$

$=$ velocity of electromagnetic waves in free space.

1 microfarad $= 10^{-6}$ farad

1 picofarad $= 10^{-12}$ farad.

Capacitance of parallel-plate capacitor with n plates $\Big\} = \dfrac{\epsilon(n-1)a}{d}$. (91)

For two dielectrics, A and B, of same area, in series,

$$\frac{\text{electric force or potential gradient in } A}{\text{electric force or potential gradient in } B} = \frac{\text{dielectric constant of } B}{\text{dielectric constant of } A} \quad (92)$$

Force on isolated charge in electric field $\Big\} = E$ newtons/coulomb (93)

Potential gradient at radius r from isolated charge $\Big\} = \dfrac{Q}{4\pi r^2 \epsilon}$ volts/metre (94) $\checkmark$

Force between charges (Coulomb's Law) $\Big\} = \dfrac{Q_1 Q_2}{4\pi r^2 \epsilon}$ newtons . (95)

Potential gradient at radius x from charged cylinder $\Big\} = \dfrac{Q}{2\pi x \epsilon}$ volts/metre (96)

Capacitance of two concentric spheres $\Big\} = \dfrac{4\pi\epsilon}{1/a - 1/b}$ farads . . (94A)

Capacitance of two parallel wires/metre length of line $\Big\} = \dfrac{12 \cdot 1 \times 10^{-12} \epsilon_r}{\log (d-r)/r}$ farads (97)

Capacitance of concentric cylinders/metre $\Big\} = \dfrac{24 \cdot 2 \times 10^{-12} \epsilon_r}{\log b/a}$ farads (99)

Potential gradient in dielectric between concentric cylinders $\Big\} = \dfrac{V}{2 \cdot 3x \log b/a}$ (100)

Charging current of capacitor $= dq/dt = C \cdot dv/dt$ (102)

For R and C in series across d.c. supply,

$$v = V(1 - e^{-t/RC}) \quad . \quad . \quad (105)$$

and $\qquad i = Ie^{-t/RC} \quad . \quad . \quad . \quad (107)$

Time constant $= T = RC \quad . \quad . \quad . \quad (110)$

For C discharged through R,

$$v = Ve^{-t/RC} \quad . \quad . \quad (115)$$

and $\qquad i = -Ie^{-t/RC} \quad . \quad . \quad (116)$

Energy stored in capacitor $= \frac{1}{2}CV^2$ joules . (117)

Energy per cubic metre of dielectric $\Big\} = \frac{1}{2}\epsilon E^2 = \frac{1}{2}DE$

$$= \frac{1}{2}D^2/\epsilon \text{ joules} \quad . \quad . \quad (118)$$

$$\left.\begin{array}{c}\text{Electrostatic \quad attraction}\\ \text{between parallel plates}\end{array}\right\} = \tfrac{1}{2}\epsilon a (V/x)^2 \text{ newtons} \quad (119)$$

EXAMPLES III

1. A capacitor consists of two metal plates, each having an area of 600 cm^2, spaced 2 mm apart. The whole of the space between the plates is occupied by a sheet of insulating material having a relative permittivity of 5. A p.d. of 400 V is maintained between the two plates. Calculate: (a) the capacitance in picofarads, (b) the charge in microcoulombs, (c) the electric flux density and the electric force in the dielectric.

2. A condenser consists of two metal plates, each 10 cm square, placed parallel and 3 mm apart. The space between the plates is occupied by a plate of insulating material 3 mm thick. The condenser is charged to 300 V.

(a) The metal plates are isolated from the 300-V supply and the insulating plate is removed. What is expected to happen to the voltage between the metal plates?

(b) If the metal plates are moved to a distance of 6 mm apart, what is the further effect on the voltage between them?
Assume throughout that the insulation is perfect.

(Joint Section A)

3. A slab of insulating material, 4 mm thick, is inserted between the plates of a parallel-plate capacitor. To restore the capacitance to its original value it is necessary to increase the spacing between the plates by 2 mm. Calculate the relative permittivity of the slab.

4. Explain what is meant by electric stress in a dielectric and state the factors upon which it depends.

Two parallel metal plates of large area are spaced at a distance of 1 cm from each other in air, and a potential difference of 5000 V is maintained between them. If a sheet of glass, 0·5 cm thick and having a relative permittivity (or dielectric constant) of 6, is introduced between the plates, what will be the maximum electric stress and where will it occur?

(App. El., L.U.)

5. Define the permittivity of a dielectric medium. The oil dielectric to be employed in a parallel-plate condenser has a permittivity of 2·3 and the maximum working potential gradient in the oil is not to exceed 1000 V/mm. Calculate, after deriving an expression for the capacitance of a parallel-plate condenser, the approximate plate area required for a capacitance of 0·0003 μF, the maximum working voltage being 10,000 V.

(App. El., L.U.)

6. A certain capacitor has a capacitance of 3 μF. A capacitance of 2·5 μF is required by combining this capacitance with another. Calculate the capacitance of the second capacitor and state how it must be connected to the first.

7. A capacitor A is connected in series with two capacitors B and C connected in parallel. If the capacitances of A, B and C are 4, 3 and 6 μF respectively, calculate the equivalent capacitance of the combination.

If a p.d. of 20 V is maintained across the whole circuit, calculate the charge on the 3-μF capacitor.

8. A capacitor consists of two metal plates, each 40 cm × 30 cm, spaced 6 mm apart. A plate of glass, 3 mm thick, is placed between the metal plates, across which there is a p.d. of 5 kV. Calculate (a) the capacitance of the condenser and (b) the potential gradients in the glass and in the air in kV/mm. Assume the relative permittivity of the glass to be 7.

9. Define (a) permittivity and (b) farad.

Calculate the capacitance in microfarads of a condenser having nine parallel plates separated by mica sheets 0·2 mm thick. The area of one side of each plate is 12 cm² and the relative permittivity of mica is 5. Prove any formula employed.

If this condenser were charged to a p.d. of 10 V and the mica sheet then removed without altering the spacing of the plates, what would be the p.d. across the condenser terminals? Assume the insulation resistance to be infinite.   (App. El., L.U.)

10. Calculate the capacitance between a pair of metal plates, each 30 cm × 50 cm, if they are separated by the following layers of insulating material:

first layer, 2 mm thick, having relative permittivity of 4,
second ,, , 3 mm   ,, ,   ,,   ,,   ,,   2,
third ,, , 1 mm   ,, ,   ,,   ,,   ,,   3.

If a p.d. of 600 V is maintained between the plates, calculate the p.d. across and the potential gradient in each layer.

11. Prove that the energy stored in a condenser of capacitance C farads charged to a potential difference of V volts is $\frac{1}{2}CV^2$ joules.

A 10-μF condenser is charged from a 200-V battery 250 times per second and completely discharged through a 5-Ω resistor during the interval between charges. Determine:

(a) The power taken from the battery.
(b) The average value of the current in the 5-Ω resistor.

(Joint Section A)

12. Find an expression for the energy stored in a condenser of capacitance C farads charged to a p.d. of V volts.

A condenser having a capacitance of 3 μF is charged to a p.d. of 200 V and then connected in parallel with another condenser having a capacitance of 2 μF. Calculate the p.d. across the parallel condensers and the energy stored in the condensers before and after being connected in parallel. Account for the difference.   (App. El., L.U.)

13. Two capacitors, having capacitances of 4 and 6 μF respectively, are connected in series across a 120-V d.c. supply. Calculate (a) the p.d. across each capacitor, (b) the energy stored on each capacitor and (c) the equivalent capacitance of the two capacitors.

14. A capacitor is charged to a p.d. of 50 V and then discharged through a ballistic galvanometer having a constant of $1·6 \times 10^{-10}$ coulomb per division. If the first deflection or "throw" of the galvanometer is 124 divisions, what is the value of the capacitance?

If the capacitor consists of two metal plates, each 30 cm × 30 cm spaced 2 mm apart in air, calculate the value of ϵ_0.

15. If there are 4×10^{16} electrons passing per second between the cathode and anode of a vacuum diode and if the p.d. between the electrodes is 120 V, calculate (a) the current in mA, (b) the energy dissipated in 10 minutes (i) in joules and (ii) in electron-volts.

16. The anode current in a certain vacuum triode is 4 mA when the p.d. between the anode and cathode is 90 V. Calculate (a) the

number of electrons per second reaching the anode and (b) the energy absorbed in 5 minutes (i) in electron-volts, (ii) in joules.

17. A 6-μF capacitor is charged to 400 V. Calculate (a) the flux in the dielectric and (b) the energy stored. Find also the number of electrons added to one plate of the capacitor during the charging period and the time taken to charge the capacitor if the charging current remains constant at 20 μA.

18. A concentrated charge of 0·003 microcoulomb is situated between two parallel plates, 8 mm apart. A p.d. of 500 V is maintained between the plates. Calculate the force on the charge.

19. An electron has a velocity of 2×10^7 m/sec at right angles to the electric field between the deflecting plates of a cathode-ray tube. If the plates are 6 mm apart and 2·5 cm long and if the p.d. between the plates is 80 V, calculate the distance through which the electron is deflected sideways during its movement through the electric field. Mass of electron $= 9·1 \times 10^{-31}$ kg, and charge on electron $= 1·6 \times 10^{-19}$ C.

20. A charge of 0·5 μC is isolated in a dielectric having a relative permittivity of 4. Calculate the electric flux density and the potential gradient at a distance of 20 cm from the centre of the charge. Calculate also the p.d. between two equipotential surfaces 20 and 30 cm respectively from the centre of the charge.

21. A charge of 8×10^{-10} coulomb is uniformly distributed over the surface of a metal sphere of radius 2 cm, situated in air. Calculate (a) the electric force and the electric flux density at the surface of the sphere and (b) the p.d. between the surface of the sphere and a point 8 cm from the centre of the sphere.

22. A metal sphere of 6-cm diameter is placed in the centre of a hollow sphere having an internal diameter of 10 cm. If the space between the spheres is filled with a dielectric having a relative permittivity of 3, calculate the capacitance between the spheres.
If a p.d. of 200 V is maintained between the spheres, calculate the potential gradient at a point 4 cm from the centre of the spheres.

23. Two charges of +2 microcoulombs each are situated 15 cm apart in a dielectric having a relative permittivity of 4. Calculate the force between them.

24. A charge of +10 microcoulombs is situated 30 cm from a charge of −4 microcoulombs in a medium having a dielectric constant of 2. Calculate the force between them.

25. Calculate the charge per metre length of a long conductor in air to produce a potential gradient of 300 V/m at a distance of 10 cm from the centre of the conductor.

26. A long copper wire, 0·6 cm diameter, is situated in air and is remote from any other metal body. If the wire has a charge of 0·01 microcoulomb per metre length, calculate (a) the potential gradient and the electric flux density at the surface of the wire and (b) the p.d. between the surface and a point 2 cm from the centre of the wire.

27. A p.d. of 2 kV is maintained between conductors P and Q shown in Fig. I, p. 89. Calculate the values of the electric force and of the electric flux density at points A, B and C. The conductors are situated in air and each conductor has a diameter of 1 cm.

28. An electron is situated between two parallel plates and just outside the negative plate. The plates are spaced 0·5 cm apart in air

and a p.d. of 400 V is maintained between them. Calculate the force on the electron.

If the electron, starting from rest, travels unimpeded to the positive plate, calculate (a) the kinetic energy of the electron when it reaches the positive plate and (b) the time taken.

29. A two-wire transmission line is 2 km long. The conductors are spaced 30 cm between centres and each conductor has a diameter of 1·2 cm. Calculate the capacitance of the line.

30. A high-frequency feeder consists of two wires, each 2 mm in diameter, spaced 4 cm between centres, in air. Calculate the capacitance per metre length of the feeder.

31. The inner conductor of a concentric cable has an external diameter of 3 mm and the outer conductor has an internal diameter of 10 mm. If the dielectric constant of the insulation is 2·8, calculate the capacitance per metre length of the cable.

If a p.d. of 500 V is maintained between the two conductors, calculate the values of the electric force and of the electric flux density (a) at the surface of the inner conductor and (b) at the inner surface of the outer conductor.

32. Each of two coaxial cylinders forming an air-dielectric condenser has an axial length of 75 cm. The outside diameter of the inner cylinder is 5 mm and the inside diameter of the outer is 12 mm. Determine the capacitance of the condenser in $\mu\mu$F, and state the shape and position of the equipotential surface having a potential midway between those of the two cylinders. Derive any formula used.

(App. El., L.U.)

33. A single-phase, lead-sheathed cable, 10 km long, has a conductor diameter of 6 mm. Calculate the thickness of the insulation required to limit the maximum dielectric stress to 8 kV (r.m.s.) per mm when the p.d. between the conductor and the sheath is 38 kV (r.m.s.) at 50 c/s. Calculate also the value of the charging current, assuming the dielectric constant to be 2·8.

34. A single-phase concentric cable has two layers of different dielectrics, each 3 mm thick. The relative permittivity of the inner layer is 3·8 and that of the outer layer 2·7. The diameter of the inner conductor is 4 mm. The cable is connected to a 20-kV, 50-c/s supply. Calculate (a) the capacitance of the cable, (b) the charging current, (c) the maximum potential gradient in each dielectric. The length of the cable is 3 miles.

If the dielectrics were interchanged, what would be the potential gradient at the surface of the conductor?

35. A single-phase, lead-sheathed cable, 2 miles long, has a conductor diameter of 0·3 in, and the thickness of the insulation is 0·2 in. If the resistivity of the dielectric is 2×10^8 megohm-inches, calculate the insulation resistance of the cable.

Note. For an element of radius x, thickness dx and length l, resistance $= dR = \rho \cdot dx/(2\pi x l)$,

$$\therefore \quad R = \int_a^b \frac{\rho \cdot dx}{2\pi x l} = \frac{\rho}{2\pi l} \ln b/a = \frac{2\cdot 3\rho}{2\pi l} \log b/a.$$

36. A single-core cable, 4 miles long, has an insulation resistance of 97 megohms. The core diameter is 1 cm and the diameter over the insulation is 2 cm. Calculate the resistivity of the insulating material.

37. A capacitor having a capacitance of 100 μF is charged and discharged thus:

Steady charging current of 10 mA from 0 to 3 seconds,
,,   ,,   ,,   ,, 5 ,, ,,   3 to 5   ,,
Zero current   ,, ,,   5 to 6   ,,
Steady discharge ,,   ,, 5 ,, ,,   6 to 12 ,,
,,   ,,   ,,   ,, 2 ,, ,, 12 to 17 ,,

Draw graphs to scale showing how the current and the p.d. across the capacitor vary with time.

38. Derive an expression for the stored electrostatic energy of a charged condenser.

A 10-μF condenser in series with a 10,000-ohm resistance is connected across a 500-V d.c. supply. The fully-charged condenser is disconnected from the supply and discharged by connecting a 1000-ohm resistance across its terminals. Calculate:

(a) the initial value of the charging current,
(b) the initial value of the discharge current,
(c) the amount of heat in calories dissipated in the 1000-Ω resistance.

(App. El., L.U.)

39. Derive an expression for the current flowing at any instant after the application of a constant voltage V to a circuit consisting of a capacitance C in series with a resistance R.

Determine, for the case in which $C = 0.01$ μF, $R = 100,000$ Ω and $V = 1000$ V, the voltage to which the condenser has been charged when the charging current has decreased to 90 per cent of its initial value, and the time taken for the current to decrease to 90 per cent of its initial value. (App. El., L.U.)

40. A condenser of 2 μF capacitance is joined in series with a 2 MΩ resistance to a d.c. supply of 100 V. Draw a current-time graph and explain what happens in the period after the circuit is made if the condenser is initially uncharged.

Calculate the current flowing and the energy stored in the condenser at the end of an interval of 4 seconds from the start.

(N.C.T.E.C.)

41. A capacitor is charged from a d.c. source through a resistance of 0.4 MΩ. If the p.d. reaches 0.75 of its final value in half a second, calculate the value of the capacitance and justify any formula used.

(U.L.C.I., Adv. El. Tech.)

42. A capacitor of 0.1 μF capacitance, charged to a potential difference between plates of 100 V, is discharged through a resistor of 1 MΩ. Calculate:

(a) the initial value of the discharge current,
(b) its value 0.1 second later,
(c) the initial rate of decay of the capacitor voltage,
(d) the energy dissipated in the resistor.

Using the above data, sketch the variation of discharge current with time. (C. & G., Telecom. Prin. II)

43. A condenser having a capacitance of 20 μF is found to have an insulation resistance of 50 megohms, measured between the terminals. If this condenser is charged off a d.c. supply of 230 V, find the time required after disconnection from the supply for the p.d. across the condenser to fall to 60 V. Prove any formula used.

(App. El., L.U.)

44. Define the time constant of a circuit containing capacitance and resistance in series.

When a condenser, charged to a p.d. of 400 V, is connected to a voltmeter having a resistance of 25 MΩ, the voltmeter reading is observed to have fallen to 50 V at the end of an interval of 2 minutes. Evaluate the capacitance of the condenser, deriving any expressions used.   (App. El., L.U.)

45. A circuit consisting of a 6-μF capacitor, an electrostatic voltmeter and a high resistance in parallel is connected across a 140-V d.c. supply.   It is then disconnected and the reading on the voltmeter falls to 70 V in 127 seconds.   When the test is performed without the high resistance, the time for the same fall in voltage in 183 seconds.   Calculate the value of the high resistance.

46. A 200-$\mu\mu$F capacitor is charged to a p.d. of 50 V.   The dielectric has a cross-sectional area of 300 cm^2 and a relative permittivity of 2·5. Calculate the energy stored per cubic metre of the dielectric.

47. A parallel-plate capacitor with the plates 2 cm apart is immersed in oil having a relative permittivity of 3.   The plates are charged to a p.d. of 25 kV.   Calculate the force between the plates in newtons per square metre of plate area and the energy stored in joules per cubic metre of the dielectric.

48. A capacitor consists of two metal plates, each 60 cm × 50 cm, spaced 1 mm apart.   The space between the metal plates is occupied by a dielectric having a relative permittivity of 6, and a p.d. of 3 kV is maintained between the plates.   Calculate (a) the capacitance in picofarads, (b) the electric force and the electric flux density in the dielectric and (c) the total force of attraction, in grams, between the plates.

CHAPTER IV

D.C. GENERATORS AND MOTORS

63. Introductory. The construction and the characteristics of d.c. generators and motors have been dealt with in *Principles of Electricity*, so that in this chapter we shall confine our attention to such matters as equalizing connections for lap windings, armature reaction, commutation, parallel operation of d.c. generators, the grading of starting resistance for shunt motors, the losses in and the efficiency of d.c. machines.

64. Equalizing or Equipotential Connections for Lap Windings. In Art. 118 of *Principles of Electricity* it was shown that a lap winding has as many paths in parallel as there are poles; and from Fig. 164 of *Principles of Electricity*, it can be seen that the conductors of any one path are distributed under two *adjacent* poles only. Consequently any difference in the reluctance of the magnetic circuits, such as unequal airgap lengths, produces an inequality in the flux per pole and therefore in the e.m.f. generated per circuit.

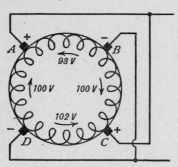

FIG. 67.—Lap-wound armature.

Let us consider a fourpole lap-wound armature which, for the purpose of this discussion, can be represented as in Fig. 67. Suppose the e.m.f.'s generated in the four paths to have the values and directions shown. It will be evident that in each of the parallel circuits ABC and ADC through the winding there is a resultant e.m.f. of 2 V acting as in Fig. 68(a) and circulating a current I_1 through the conductor bridging the positive brushes A and C. Similarly, Fig. 68 (b) shows a current I_1 circulating through the negative brushes B and D.

If the armature is supplying a current I to an external load (Fig. 68 (c)) and if the armature e.m.f.'s had been

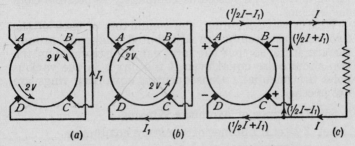

FIG. 68.—Circulating currents in brush connections.

equal, the current at each brush would have been $\frac{1}{2}I$. But with the conditions shown in Fig. 67, the current at brushes A and B is $(\frac{1}{2}I - I_1)$, and that at C and D is $(\frac{1}{2}I + I_1)$, as indicated in Fig. 68 (c). Since the armature winding and the brush connections have a low resistance, I_1 may be very large and brushes C and D may become so overloaded that excessive sparking may occur at those brushes.

This trouble is overcome by connecting together points on the winding which ought to be at the same potential. For in-

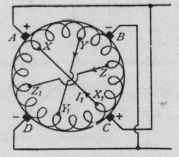

FIG. 69.—Equalizing connections.

stance, tappings X and X_1 (Fig. 69) are symmetrically situated in relation to the positive brushes and would be at the same potential if all the e.m.f.'s were equal. If the e.m.f.'s are as indicated in Fig. 67, current I_1 is diverted from the brushes and flows through the equalizing connection XX_1. In Fig. 69, YY_1 and ZZ_1 are two other equalizing connections equally spaced round the winding. Actually there may be six to twelve of these connections—usually in the form of rings—so as to ensure that in all positions of the armature the circulating current is diverted as completely as possible from the brushes.

With a wave winding, the conductors of each of the two parallel circuits are distributed uniformly around the armature, so that the total e.m.f.'s generated in the two circuits are equal even if the fluxes in the various poles are unequal. Consequently, equalizing rings are not necessary.

65. Resistance of Armature Winding.

Let Z =total number of armature conductors,

p =number of *pairs* of poles,

c =number of parallel circuits

$\quad$ =2 for a wave winding

$\quad$ =2p for a lap winding,

l =total length of one armature conductor,

a =cross-sectional area of conductor

and $\quad \rho$ =resistivity of the conductor,

then $\quad$ resistance of one conductor $=\rho l/a$.

No. of conductors in series per circuit $= Z/c$,

$\therefore \qquad$ resistance of one circuit $=\dfrac{Z}{c} \cdot \dfrac{\rho l}{a}$.

Since there are c circuits in parallel,

$\therefore \qquad$ resistance of winding $= R_a = \dfrac{Z}{c^2} \cdot \dfrac{\rho l}{a}$.

66. Armature Reaction.

By armature reaction is meant the effect of armature ampere-turns upon the value and the distribution of the magnetic flux entering and leaving the armature core.

Let us, for simplicity, consider a two-pole machine having an armature with eight slots and two conductors per slot, as shown in Fig. 70. The curved lines between the conductors and the commutator segments represent the front end-connections and those on the outside of the armature represent the back end-connections. The armature winding—like all modern d.c. windings—is of the double-layer type, the end-connections of the outer layer being represented by full lines and those of the inner layer by dotted lines. This type of winding has been fully discussed in Chap. XIV of *Principles of Electricity*.

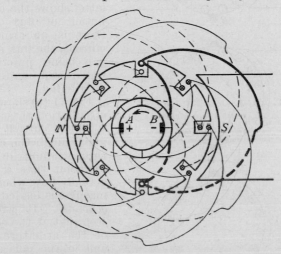

Fig. 70.—A two-pole armature winding.

Brushes A and B are placed so that they are making contact with conductors which are moving midway between the poles and have therefore no e.m.f. induced in them. Suppose the armature to be driven anti-clockwise; the direction of the e.m.f.'s generated in the various conductors is represented by the dots and crosses. By following the directions of these e.m.f.'s it is found that brush A is positive and B negative. In diagrams where the end-connections are omitted, it is usual to show the brushes midway between the poles, as in Fig. 71.

In general, an armature has ten to fifteen slots per pole,

5

so that the conductors are more uniformly distributed round the armature core than is suggested by Fig. 70; and for simplicity we may omit the slots and consider the conductors uniformly distributed as in Fig 71 (a). The latter shows the distribution of flux when there is no armature current, the flux in the gap being practically radial and uniformly distributed.

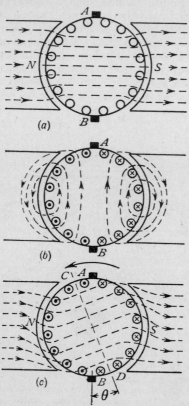

(a)

(b)

(c)

FIG. 71.—Flux distribution due to (a) poles alone, (b) armature current alone, (c) poles and armature current.

Fig. 71 (b) shows the distribution of the flux set up by current flowing through the armature winding in the direction that it will actually flow when the machine is loaded as a *generator*. It will be seen that at the centre of the armature core and in the pole shoes the direction of this flux is at right angles to that due to the field winding; hence the reason why the flux due to the armature current is termed the *cross flux*.

Fig. 71 (c) shows the resultant distribution of the flux due to the combination of the fluxes in Fig. 71 (a) and (b); thus over the leading *

* The pole tip which is first met during revolution by a point on the armature or stator surface is known as the *leading pole tip* and the other as the *trailing pole tip*.

halves of the pole-faces the cross-flux is in opposition to the main flux, thereby reducing the flux density, whereas over the trailing halves the two fluxes are in the same direction, so that the flux density is strengthened. Apart from the effect of magnetic saturation, the increase of flux over one half of the pole-face is the same as the decrease over the other half, and the total flux per pole remains practically unaltered. Hence the effect of armature reaction is to twist or distort the flux in the direction of rotation.

One important consequence of this distortion of the flux is that the magnetic neutral axis is shifted through an angle θ from AB to CD; in other words, with the machine on no load and the flux distribution of Fig. 71 (a), conductors are moving parallel to the magnetic flux and therefore generating no e.m.f. when they are passing axis AB. When the machine is loaded as a generator and the flux distorted as in Fig. 71 (c), conductors are moving parallel to the flux and generating no e.m.f. when they are passing axis CD.

An alternative and in some respects a better method of representing the effect of armature current is to draw a developed diagram of the armature conductors and poles, as in Fig. 72 (a). Suppose the direction of the current in the conductors to be as shown by the dots and crosses.

In an actual armature, the two conductors forming one turn are situated approximately a pole pitch apart, as in Fig. 70; but *as far as the magnetic effect of the currents in the armature conductors is concerned*, the end connections could be arranged as shown by the dotted lines in Fig. 72 (a). From the latter, it will be seen that the conductors situated between the vertical axes CC_1 and DD_1 act as if they formed concentric coils producing a magnetomotive force having its maximum value along axis AA_1. Similarly, the currents in the conductors to the left of axis CC_1 and to the right of DD_1 produce a magnetomotive force that is a maximum along axis BB_1. Since the conductors are assumed to be distributed uniformly around the armature periphery, the distribution of the m.m.f. is represented by the chain-dotted line * in Fig. 72 (b). These lines pass through zero at points C_1 and D_1 midway between the brushes.

Let $I = total$ armature current in amperes,

$\therefore$ current per conductor $= I/c$

no. of conductors per pole $= Z/(2p)$

$\therefore$ no. of ampere-conductors per pole $\Big\} = \dfrac{I}{c} \cdot \dfrac{Z}{2p}.$

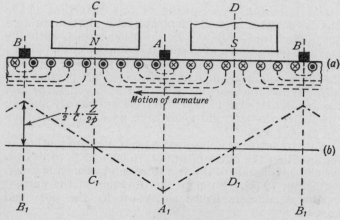

FIG. 72.—Distribution of armature m.m.f.

Since two armature conductors constitute one turn,

$\therefore$ no. of armature ampere-turns per pole $\Big\} = \dfrac{1}{2} \cdot \dfrac{I}{c} \cdot \dfrac{Z}{2p}$ (120)

This expression represents the armature m.m.f. at each brush axis.

The effect of the armature ampere-turns upon the distribution of the magnetic flux is represented in Fig. 73. The dotted lines in Fig. 73 (a) represent the distribution

* The m.m.f. is assumed to be positive when the direction of the flux produced by it is from the airgap into the core (Fig. 73).

of the magnetic flux in the airgap on *no load*. The corresponding variation of the flux density over the

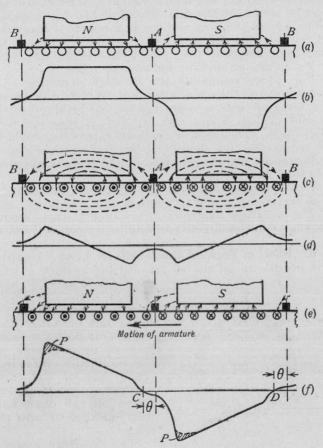

FIG. 73.—Distribution of main flux, cross-flux and resultant flux.

periphery of the armature is represented by the ordinates of Fig. 73 (b). Fig. 73 (c) and (d) represent the cross-flux due to the armature ampere-turns alone, the armature current being assumed in the direction in which it flows when the machine is loaded as a generator. It will be seen that the flux density in the gap increases from zero at the centre of the pole-face to a maximum at the pole-tips and then decreases rapidly owing to the increasing length of the path of the fringing flux, until it is a minimum midway between the poles.

Fig. 73 (e) represents the machine operating as a generator, and the distribution of the flux density around the armature core is approximately the resultant of the graphs of Fig. 73 (b) and (d), and is represented in Fig. 73 (f). The effect of magnetic saturation would be to reduce the flux density at the trailing pole-tips, as indicated by the shaded areas P, and thereby to reduce the total flux per pole.

It will also be seen from Fig. 73 (f) that the points of zero flux density, and therefore of zero generated e.m.f. in the armature conductors, have been shifted through an angle θ in the direction of rotation to points C and D.

67. Effect of Forward Brush Shift (or Lead).

Suppose the brushes to be shifted forward by an angle θ from

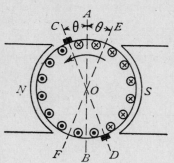

FIG. 74.—Effect of forward brush shift.

axis AB to axis CD, as in Fig. 74. Draw EF making the same angle θ on the other side of AB. Then with anti-clockwise rotation of the armature, *all* the conductors on the left-hand side of CD carry current outwards and all those on the other side carry current towards the paper.

The armature ampere-turns can now be divided into two groups:

(a) Those due to conductors in angles COE and FOD, shown separately in Fig. 75 (a). From the latter, it is obvious that these conductors are carrying current in such a direction as to try to set up a flux in opposition to that produced by the field winding, and their effect is to reduce the flux through the armature.   Hence the ampere-turns due to these conductors are referred to as *demagnetizing* or *back* ampere-turns.

(b) Those due to conductors in angles *COF* and *EOD* and shown separately in Fig. 75 (b).   The ampere-turns

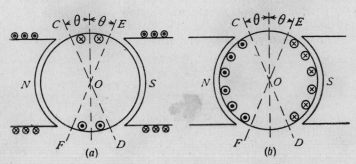

Fig. 75.—Demagnetizing and distorting armature ampere-turns.

due to the current in these conductors are responsible for the distortion of the flux and are therefore termed the *distorting* or *cross* ampere-turns.

68. Calculation of Demagnetizing and Distorting Ampere-turns.

Let θ =brush shift in electrical degrees (i.e. the span corresponding to 2 pole-pitches is regarded as 360 electrical degrees)

=$p \times$ brush shift in angular degrees.

From expression (120),

$$\left.\begin{array}{l}\text{no. of armature ampere-}\\\text{turns per pole}\end{array}\right\} = \frac{1}{2} \cdot \frac{I}{c} \cdot \frac{Z}{2p}$$

From Fig. 75 (a) it is seen that for every 360 electrical degrees there are 4θ electrical degrees containing conductors that are responsible for the demagnetizing ampere-turns,

$$\therefore \quad \left.\begin{matrix} \text{no. of demagnetizing} \\ \text{ampere-turns/pole} \end{matrix}\right\} = \left(\begin{matrix} \text{total ampere-} \\ \text{turns/pole} \end{matrix}\right) \times \frac{4\theta}{360}$$

$$= \frac{1}{2} \cdot \frac{I}{c} \cdot \frac{Z}{2p} \cdot \frac{4\theta}{360} \quad (121)$$

Since all the armature ampere-turns which do not produce demagnetization are responsible for distortion of the flux,

$\therefore$ no. of distorting ampere-turns/pole

$$= \left(\begin{matrix} \text{total ampere-} \\ \text{turns/pole} \end{matrix}\right) - \left(\begin{matrix} \text{demagnetizing} \\ \text{amp-turns/pole} \end{matrix}\right)$$

$$= \frac{1}{2} \cdot \frac{I}{c} \cdot \frac{Z}{2p}\left(1 - \frac{4\theta}{360}\right) \quad \cdot \quad \cdot \quad (122)$$

An alternative method is to express the demagnetizing and distorting ampere-turns in terms of the number of commutator segments through which the brushes have been moved from the geometric neutral. Thus,
if $C =$ total number of commutator segments
and $s =$ brush shift in terms of the segments,
no. of commutator segments per pair of poles $= C/p$

and no. of segments per electrical degree $= \dfrac{C}{360p}$

$\therefore$ no. of segments for θ electrical degrees $= \dfrac{C\theta}{360p}$

i.e. $$s = \frac{C\theta}{360p}$$

so that $$\frac{\theta}{360} = \frac{sp}{C}.$$

Substituting for $\theta/360$ in expression (121), we have:

$$\left.\begin{matrix} \text{No. of demagnetizing} \\ \text{ampere-turns/pole} \end{matrix}\right\} = \frac{1}{2} \cdot \frac{I}{c} \cdot \frac{Z}{2p} \cdot \frac{4sp}{C}$$

$$= \frac{IZ}{c} \cdot \frac{s}{C} \quad \cdot \quad \cdot \quad (123)$$

and $$\left.\begin{matrix} \text{no. of distorting} \\ \text{ampere-turns/pole} \end{matrix}\right\} = \frac{IZ}{c}\left\{\frac{1}{4p} - \frac{s}{C}\right\} \quad (124)$$

69. Armature Reaction in a D.C. Motor. The direction of the armature current in a d.c. motor is *opposite* to that of the generated e.m.f., whereas in a generator the current is in the *same* direction as the generated e.m.f. It follows that in a d.c. motor the flux is distorted backwards; and the brushes have to be shifted backwards if they are to be on the magnetic neutral axis when the machine is loaded. A backward shift in a motor gives rise to demagnetizing ampere-turns and the reduction of flux tends to cause an increase of speed; in fact, this method—commutation permitting—may be used to compensate for the effect of the IR drop in the armature, thereby maintaining the speed of a shunt motor practically constant at all loads.

70. Compensating Winding. It has already been explained in Art. 66 that the effect of armature reaction is to alter the distribution of the flux density under the pole face, as shown in Fig. 73. If the load fluctuates rapidly over a wide range, the sudden shifting backwards and forwards of the flux may induce a sufficiently high e.m.f.* in an armature coil to produce an arc across the top of the mica sheet separating the commutator segments to which the coil is connected. Such an arc may then extend to adjacent segments until it ultimately results in a flash-over between the brushes. Hence, machines subject to sudden fluctuation of load may have to be fitted with a *compensating winding*. The latter is placed in slots in the pole-shoes and connected in series with the armature winding in such a way that the ampere-turns of the compensating winding are equal and opposite to those due to the armature conductors that are opposite the pole face, as shown in Fig. 76 (a) and (b).

The combined effect of currents in the armature and compensating windings of a d.c. generator is to skew the flux in the airgap as indicated in Fig. 76 (c), but to leave the density of the flux unaltered. The pull exerted on the armature teeth by the skewed flux has a tangential component tending to oppose the rotation of the

---

* This e.m.f. is a maximum in coils that are approximately midway between the brushes.

5*

core. In the case of a motor, the flux is skewed in the opposite direction, thereby exerting on the teeth a pull having a tangential component responsible for the rotation of the armature.

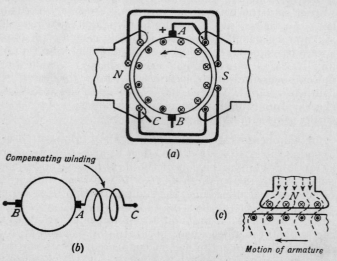

Fig 76.—Arrangement and connection of a compensating winding.

From expression (120),

$$\left.\begin{array}{c}\text{no. of armature ampere-turns} \\ \text{per pole}\end{array}\right\} = \frac{1}{2} \cdot \frac{I}{c} \cdot \frac{Z}{2p}.$$

Hence, for a uniform flux density under the pole face,

$$\left.\begin{array}{c}\text{no. of ampere-turns/pole} \\ \text{for compensating winding}\end{array}\right\} = \frac{1}{2} \cdot \frac{I}{c} \cdot \frac{Z}{2p} \cdot \frac{\text{pole arc}}{\text{pole pitch}} \quad (125)$$

$$\simeq 0.7 \times \text{armature ampere-turns/pole}.$$

Owing to its high cost, a compensating winding is fitted only to relatively large machines subject to sudden fluctuations of load, e.g. rolling-mill motors.

71. Commutation. The e.m.f. generated in a conductor of a d.c. armature is an alternating e.m.f. and the current in a conductor is in one direction when the conductor is moving under a N-pole and in the reverse direction when it is moving under a S-pole. This reversal of current in a coil has to take place while the two commutator segments to which the coil is connected are being short-circuited by a brush, and the process is termed *commutation*. It has to take place in a very small fraction of a second—usually about 1/500 second. The reversal of, say, 100 A in an inductive circuit in such a short time is likely to present difficulty and may cause considerable sparking at the brushes.

For simplicity in considering the variation of current

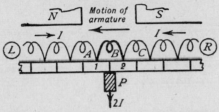

FIG. 77.—Portion of armature winding.

in the short-circuited coil we can represent the coils and the commutator segments as in Fig. 77, where the two ends of any one coil are connected to adjacent segments, as in a lap winding.

If the current per conductor is I and if the armature is moving from right to left, then—assuming the brush to be positive—coil C is carrying current from right to left (R to L), whereas coil A is carrying current from L to R. We shall therefore examine the variation of current in coil B which is connected to segments 1 and 2.

The current in coil B remains at its full value from R to L until segment 2 begins to make contact with brush P, as in Fig. 78 (a). As the area of contact with segment 2 increases, current i_1 flowing to the brush via segment 2 increases and current $(I - i_1)$ through coil B decreases. If the current distribution between segments

1 and 2 were determined by the areas of contact only, the current through coil B would decrease linearly, as shown by line M in Fig. 79. It follows that when the brush is making equal areas of contact with segments 1 and 2, current through B would be zero; and further movement of the armature would cause the current through B to grow in the reverse direction.

Fig. 78 (b) represents the position of the coils near the end of the period of short-circuit. The current from segment 1 to P is then i_2 and that flowing from left to right through B is $(I - i_2)$. The short-circuit is ended when segment 1 breaks contact with P, and the current through coil B should by that instant have attained its full value from L to B. Under these conditions there

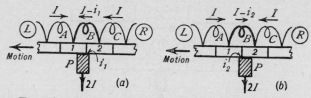

FIG. 78.—Coil B near the beginning and the end of commutation.

should be no sparking at the brush, and this linear variation of the current in the short-circuited coil is referred to as *straight-line* or *linear commutation*.

It was explained in Art. 66 that the armature current gives rise to a magnetic field; thus, Fig. 71 (b) shows the flux set up by the armature current alone. From the direction of this cross-flux and assuming anti-clockwise rotation, we can deduce that an e.m.f. is generated towards the paper in a conductor moving in the vicinity of brush A, namely in the direction in which current was flowing in the conductor before the latter was short-circuited by the brush. The same conclusion may be derived from a consideration of the resultant distribution of flux given in Fig. 73 (f), where a conductor moving in the region of brush A is generating an e.m.f. in the same direction as that generated when the conductor was

moving under the preceding main pole. This generated
e.m.f., being due to armature reaction,* is termed
reactance voltage and is responsible for delaying the

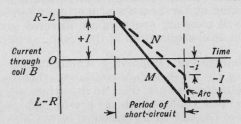

FIG. 79.—Variation of current in the
short-circuited coil.

reversal of the current in the short-circuited coils as
shown by curve N in Fig. 79. The result is that when
segment 1 is due to break contact with the brush, as in

FIG. 80.—Flux due to
current   in   short-
circuited coil alone.

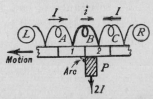

FIG. 81.—Arcing when segment
leaves brush.

Fig. 81, the current through coil B has grown to some
value i (Fig. 79); and the remainder, namely $(I-i)$, has

* In many textbooks the flux due to current in the short-
circuited coil alone is considered. This flux is assumed to pass
across the slot and thereby surround the short-circuited conductors, as in Fig. 80; and the reactance voltage is regarded
as being due to the reversal of this flux. The result is the
same as that derived above; but as we have already derived
the distribution of the resultant flux (Fig. 73 (e) and (f)), it is
thought that a method based upon this conclusion is preferable,
since it is more in accordance with what is actually happening
in the machine.

to pass between segment 1 and the brush in the form of an arc. This arc is rapidly drawn out and the current through B grows quickly from i to I, as shown in Fig. 79.

It is this reactance voltage that is mainly responsible for sparking at the brushes of d.c. machines, and most methods of reducing sparking are directed towards the reduction or neutralization of the reactance voltage.

72. Methods of Improving Commutation. (a) *By increasing the brush-contact resistance.* Let us consider the conditions shown in Fig. 78 (b), where segment 1 is about to break contact with the brush; and suppose that the area of contact with segment 2 is, say, 20 times that with segment 1. Let us also, for simplicity, neglect any reactance voltage generated in coil B.

If $r =$ resistance of contact between segment 2 and brush,

then $20r =$ resistance of contact between segment 1 and brush.

Let $R =$ resistance of coil B.

From Fig. 78 (b) it will be seen that:

p.d. between 1 and $P =$ p.d. across $B +$
p.d. between 2 and P

i.e. $i_2 \times 20r = (I - i_2)R + (2I - i_2)r$

∴ $i_2 = I \cdot \dfrac{R + 2r}{R + 21r}.$

Let us consider the effect of varying the value of r relative to that of R; thus if $r = R$, then:

$$i_2 = 0 \cdot 136I.$$

If $r = 0 \cdot 1R$, $i_2 = 0 \cdot 39I$,

and if $r = 0 \cdot 01R$, $i_2 = 0 \cdot 841I.$

It will therefore be evident that if the brush contact resistance is made very low, for example by using copper gauze brushes, a large current is still flowing from the leading segment to the brush even when the area of contact has decreased to a very small value. This means that the current density becomes very high and an arc is easily formed as the segment leaves the brush. By the use of carbon brushes the contact resistance is considerably increased and commutation greatly improved. Various grades of carbon brushes possessing different contact resistances are manufactured; and the most suitable grade for a particular machine is very largely a matter of experiment.

(b) *By shifting the brushes forward in a generator and backward in a motor.* If the brushes of a generator were moved forward to the magnetic neutral zones C and D in Fig. 73 (f), the short-circuited coils would not be generating any e.m.f. and the reversal of the current in a short-circuited coil would then be determined by the relative resistances of that coil and of the areas of contact of the brush and the segments, as already explained for method (a). In general, however, it is desirable to move the brushes a little further forward than the magnetic neutral zone in order that

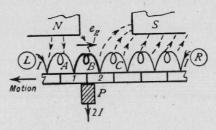

Fig. 82.—Brush ahead of magnetic neutral axis.

the short-circuited coil may be cutting the fringing flux of the main pole immediately in front, as shown in Fig. 82. The e.m.f., e_g, generated in B is then of assistance in hastening or forcing the reversal of current in that coil.

The disadvantage of this method is that for best commutation the brushes have to be shifted for every variation of load. Also, the larger the forward shift of the brushes of a generator or the backward shift for a motor, the greater are the demagnetizing ampere-turns.

(c) *By using commutating poles.* Instead of moving the brushes of a generator forward beyond the magnetic neutral zone so as to generate in the short-circuited coil an e.m.f. which assists the reversal of the current, we can obtain the same effect by inserting auxiliary poles between the main poles. These auxiliary poles are termed *commutating poles* or *interpoles*, and their polarity must be the same as that of the main pole immediately ahead, as in Fig. 83. The brushes are fixed on the geometric neutral axis, and the exciting winding of the commutating poles is connected in series with the armature winding in order that the flux set up in these poles may be proportional to the current to be commutated.

The e.m.f., e_g, generated in that part of the short-circuited coil that is opposite the face of the compole must be sufficient to neutralize the e.m.f. generated by

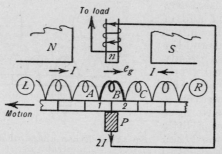

FIG. 83.—Commutating pole.

the cross-flux in the remainder of the coil and to provide the surplus e.m.f. necessary to hasten or force the reversal of the current. Since the value of e_g should be proportional to the armature current and since the flux in the compoles is proportional to the armature current, it follows that if the value of e_g is satisfactory on full load, it is automatically satisfactory at all loads between no load and full load.

Fig. 84 shows the connections of the compole and shunt windings for a two-pole generator driven anti-clockwise. It will be seen that the compole and armature ampere-turns are in opposition to one another; consequently the number of ampere-turns on the compoles must be sufficient to neutralize the armature ampere-turns and to provide the extra ampere-turns required to send the necessary flux through the magnetic circuit of the compoles. In practice, the number of compole ampere-turns per pole is about $1 \cdot 2$ to $1 \cdot 3$ times the number of armature ampere-turns per pole.

Fig. 85 shows the effect of commutating poles upon the distribution of the magnetic flux in a d.c. generator; thus, in Fig. 85 (b), the chain-dotted line represents the distribution of the armature m.m.f. and the uniformly

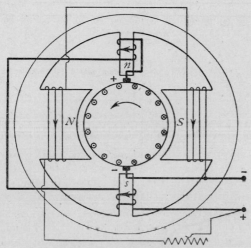

FIG. 84.—Connections of a shunt generator with compoles.

dotted line represents the m.m.f. due to the commutating poles. The dotted line in Fig. 85 (c) represents the distribution of flux on no load and is similar to that already given in Fig. 73 (b); and the full line in Fig. 85 (c) represents the flux distribution when the machine is running as a loaded d.c. generator. It will be seen that flux distortion under the main poles is not affected by the presence of commutating poles.

It is useful to note that once a compole winding has been correctly connected to the armature, it will always remain correct; and it is a useful exercise to examine the effect of the compole when (a) the machine is changed from a generator to a motor and (b) the direction of rotation is reversed. In the latter case it is useful to consider the reversal of (i) the shunt winding and (ii) the

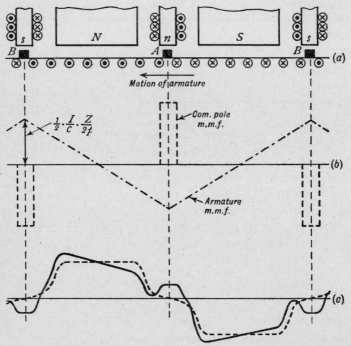

FIG. 85.—Distribution of flux in a generator with compoles.

armature plus the compole windings (the connection between the armature and the compoles remaining unaltered).

73. Parallel Operation of Shunt Generators. Let us assume that shunt generator P (Fig. 86) is connected across busbars BB and supplying the load and that it is desired to connect shunt generator Q in parallel. The engine driving Q is run up to its rated speed, switch S_2 is closed and a voltmeter V is connected across switch S_1. The excitation of Q is varied by means of R until the reading on V is zero and S_1 is then closed.

The current supplied from an armature depends upon

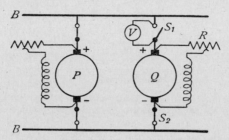

FIG. 86.—Paralleling of shunt generators.

the difference between the generated e.m.f. and the terminal voltage. Thus:

if E_P and E_Q =generated e.m.f.'s of P and Q respectively,

$\quad I_P$ and I_Q =armature currents of P and Q respectively,

$\quad R_P$ and R_Q =armature resistances of P and Q respectively,

$\quad N_P$ and N_Q =armature speeds of P and Q respectively,

$\quad \Phi_P$ and Φ_Q =flux per pole of P and Q respectively

and $\qquad V$ =terminal voltage,

then $\qquad E_P = k_P N_P \Phi_P$ and $E_Q = k_Q N_Q \Phi_Q$

where k_P and k_Q =constants for P and Q respectively.

But $\qquad I_P = \dfrac{E_P - V}{R_P}$ and $I_Q = \dfrac{E_Q - V}{R_Q}$

$$\therefore \quad \frac{I_Q}{I_P} = \frac{k_Q N_Q \Phi_Q - V}{k_P N_P \Phi_P - V} \cdot \frac{R_P}{R_Q}$$

Hence the busbar voltage can be maintained constant and the load transferred from P to Q by increasing the excitation or the speed (or both) of Q and by reducing the excitation or the speed (or both) of P.

Let us next consider the effect of operating two shunt generators in parallel and let us assume that their open-circuit voltages have been adjusted to the same value OA (Fig. 87). Also suppose the external or load characteristics of the two machines to be represented by lines P and Q in Fig. 87. Then, when the current supplied by generator P is OC, the terminal voltage is OB; and since this terminal

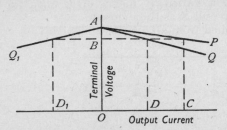

FIG. 87.—Distribution of load between two shunt generators.

voltage is common to the two machines, the current supplied by generator Q is represented by OD. It follows that if the characteristics are linear and if the two generators have the same no-load voltage and the same percentage voltage regulation, they will share the total load in the ratio of their full-load outputs.

It is sometimes more convenient to draw one of the load characteristics on the left-hand side of the vertical axis, as shown by AQ_1 in Fig. 87. Then, for terminal voltage OB, CD_1 represents the total load current.

74. Parallel Operation of Compound Generators.

Let us consider two *over-compound* generators P and Q (Fig. 88); and suppose P to be connected across busbars BB supplying load current OA (Fig. 89) and that it is required to connect Q in parallel.

We will first consider the case with switch S_3 *open*. After Q's engine has been run up to its rated speed, switch S_1 is closed and R_2 adjusted to give zero reading on voltmeter V. The e.m.f. OC (Fig. 89) of Q should then be equal to the terminal voltage AB of P. Immediately switch S_2 is closed, it is found that the overload devices protecting the machines are tripped by excessive currents. This instability is due to the fact that it is impossible to adjust the e.m.f. of Q to be *precisely* equal to the terminal voltage of P, and the slightest difference between these two voltages produces a series of reactions that result in the currents becoming excessive. For instance, if the e.m.f. of Q is slightly less than the terminal voltage of P, a current flows through Q in opposition to its generated e.m.f. Consequently the ampere-turns of the series winding D are opposing those of the shunt winding F; hence the flux and the generated e.m.f. of Q are reduced, thereby allowing a larger current to flow

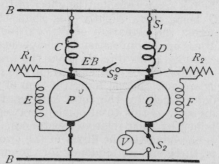

Fig. 88.—Paralleling of compound generators.

through Q. Dynamo P is now having to supply the original load current and the current taken by Q, which is now running as a motor. Consequently the flux and the terminal voltage of P are increased, thus increasing still further the current through Q.

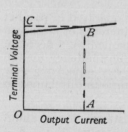

Fig. 89.—External characteristic of over-compound generator.

These reactions, which take a relatively long time to describe, follow one another extremely quickly until the currents are sufficiently large to operate the overload protective devices fitted to switch S_2 and to the corresponding switch of generator P.

Let us next consider the effect of closing switch S_3 before paralleling generator Q. By means of S_3 the junctions between the armature and series windings of each machine are connected together by an *equalizing bar* EB having a very low resistance compared with the resistance of the series windings C and D. Consequently, when S_1 is closed, the total load current is divided between C and D in the inverse ratio of their resistances.

After Q's engine has been brought up to its rated speed and the reading on V adjusted to zero, switch S_2 is closed. Let us again consider the effect of the e.m.f. generated in Q being very slightly less than the terminal voltage across the armature of P. Current flows through Q's armature in opposition to the generated e.m.f.; but this current comes directly from the armature of P via the equalizer EB. The currents in the series windings C and D are not affected, since the sum of these two currents is determined by the total load on the busbars and the division of this total current between C and D is determined by their relative resistances. Consequently there is no change in the fluxes of the two machines and there is, therefore, no tendency for the currents in Q and P to increase any further. In fact the tendency will be for the electrical power supplied to the armature of Q to speed up that machine and thus increase its generated e.m.f., whereas the increased load on P will slow down its engine and thereby cause its e.m.f. and therefore its armature current to be reduced. Hence, with the aid of the equalizing bar EB, stable operation of over-compound dynamos is possible.

Under-compound dynamos can be operated in parallel without an equalizing bar, since an increase of armature current in such a machine is accompanied by a decrease of the terminal voltage and there is no tendency for the current to increase any further. An equalizing bar should always be used with level-compound dynamos to prevent any risk of instability.

75. Grading of the Starting Resistance for a Shunt Motor. Fig. 90 shows the essential connections of a shunt motor and its starter. For simplicity, the latter is shown with only four contact-studs. When the starter arm A is moved to stud 1, the armature current instantly grows to I_1 (Fig. 91), the value of which is given by:

$$I_1 = V/R_1 \qquad . \quad . \quad . \quad (126)$$

where $R_1 =$ total resistance of armature and starter.

I_1 represents the maximum permissible current at starting and is usually about $1.5 \times$ full-load current. As the armature accelerates, its back e.m.f. grows and the armature current decreases, as indicated by curve ab. When the current has fallen to some prearranged value I_2, arm A is moved to stud 2, thereby cutting out sufficient

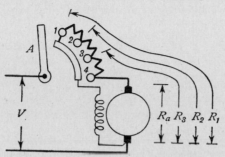

FIG. 90.—Starter for shunt motor.

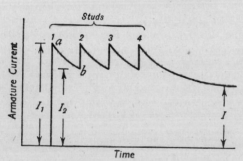

FIG. 91.—Variation of starting current.

resistance to allow the current to rise once more to I_1. Since the shunt current is constant, the back e.m.f., E_1, remains constant while A is being moved from stud 1 to stud 2.

$$\therefore \qquad V = E_1 + I_2 R_1$$
and
$$V = E_1 + I_1 R_2$$

$$\therefore \qquad I_1 R_2 = I_2 R_1, \quad \text{so that} \quad \frac{I_1}{I_2} = \frac{R_1}{R_2}.$$

Similarly, if E_2 be the back e.m.f. when A is being moved from stud 2 to stud 3, then:

$$V - E_2 = I_2 R_2 = I_1 R_3$$

so that
$$\frac{I_1}{I_2} = \frac{R_2}{R_3}.$$

If E_3 be the back e.m.f. when A is being moved from 3 to 4,

$$V - E_3 = I_2 R_3 = I_1 R_a$$

so that
$$\frac{I_1}{I_2} = \frac{R_3}{R_a}$$

Hence,
$$\frac{R_1}{R_2} = \frac{R_2}{R_3} = \frac{R_3}{R_a} = \frac{I_1}{I_2} = (\text{say})\ k.$$

$\therefore$
$$R_3 = k R_a$$
$$R_2 = k R_3 = k^2 R_a$$

and
$$R_1 = k R_2 = k^3 R_a.$$

If $n =$ number of *contact studs* on starter,

then
$$R_1 = k^{n-1} R_a \quad . \quad . \quad . \quad . \quad . \quad (127)$$

Example 26. *Calculate the resistance steps for the starter of a 5 b.h.p., 230-V shunt motor, assuming that the starter is provided with six studs and that the maximum starting current is not to exceed 1·5 times the full-load current. The full-load efficiency of the motor is 86 per cent and the resistances of the armature and shunt circuits are 0·5 and 300Ω respectively.*

$$\text{Full-load current} = \frac{5 \times 746}{230 \times 0.86} = 18.85 \text{ A.}$$

$\therefore$ maximum permissible$\left.\vphantom{\begin{matrix}a\\b\end{matrix}}\right\}$
starting current $\quad = 1.5 \times 18.85$

$$= 28.27 \text{ A.}$$

$$\text{Shunt current} = \frac{230}{300} = 0.77 \text{ A}$$

$\therefore$ maximum permissible$\left.\vphantom{\begin{matrix}a\\b\end{matrix}}\right\}$
armature current $\quad = 28.27 - 0.77 = 27.5 \text{ A}$

From equation (126), $R_1 = \dfrac{230}{27.5} = 8.36\ \Omega.$

Since $n=6$, it follows from expression (127) that:

$$8 \cdot 36 = k^5 \times 0 \cdot 5$$
$$\therefore \qquad k^5 = 16 \cdot 72$$
and
$$5 \log k = 1 \cdot 223$$
$$\therefore \qquad \log k = 0 \cdot 2446$$
and
$$k = 1 \cdot 756*$$

Hence,
$$R_2 = 8 \cdot 36/1 \cdot 756 = 4 \cdot 76 \ \Omega,$$
$$R_3 = 4 \cdot 76/1 \cdot 756 = 2 \cdot 71 \ \Omega,$$
$$R_4 = 2 \cdot 71/1 \cdot 756 = 1 \cdot 54 \ \Omega,$$
$$R_5 = 1 \cdot 54/1 \cdot 756 = 0 \cdot 878 \ \Omega$$
and
$$R_a = 0 \cdot 878/1 \cdot 756 = 0 \cdot 5 \ \Omega.$$

It is advisable to work out this last step as it forms a check on the arithmetic.

Hence
$$\text{resistance of 1st step} = R_1 - R_2$$
$$= 8 \cdot 36 - 4 \cdot 76 = 3 \cdot 6 \ \Omega,$$
$$\text{resistance of 2nd step} = R_2 - R_3$$
$$= 4 \cdot 76 - 2 \cdot 71 = 2 \cdot 05 \ \Omega,$$
$$\text{resistance of 3rd step} = R_3 - R_4$$
$$= 2 \cdot 71 - 1 \cdot 54 = 1 \cdot 17 \ \Omega,$$
$$\text{resistance of 4th step} = R_4 - R_5$$
$$= 1 \cdot 54 - 0 \cdot 878 = 0 \cdot 662 \ \Omega$$
and
$$\text{resistance of 5th step} = R_5 - R_a$$
$$= 0 \cdot 878 - 0 \cdot 5 = 0 \cdot 378 \ \Omega.$$

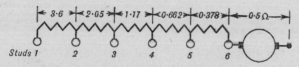

Fig. 92.—Values of the resistance steps.

These values are shown on the corresponding steps in Fig. 92.

* With $k = 1 \cdot 756$, the minimum value of the armature current during starting is $15 \cdot 67$ A, whereas the full-load armature current is $18 \cdot 08$ A. If the motor has to start against full-load torque, it is necessary to use a larger number of studs.

76. Losses in Generators and Motors. The losses in d.c. machines can be classified thus:

i. *Armature losses.*

(a) I^2R loss in armature winding.

(b) Iron loss in armature core due to hysteresis and eddy currents. Hysteresis loss has been discussed in Art. 27 and is dependent upon the quality of the iron. It is proportional to the frequency and is approximately proportional to the square of the flux. The eddy-current loss is due to circulating currents set up in the iron laminations due to the magnetic flux being cut by the core. Since the e.m.f.'s induced in the core are proportional to the frequency and the flux, it follows that the eddy-current loss is proportional to (frequency $\times$ flux)^2. Also, in *Principles of Electricity*, Art. 123, it was shown that the eddy-current loss is proportional to the square of the thickness of the laminations.

ii. *Commutator losses.*

(a) Loss due to the contact resistance between the brushes and the segments. This loss is dependent upon the quality of the brushes. For carbon brushes, the p.d. between a brush and the commutator is usually about 1 V over a wide range of current, so that the total contact-resistance loss, in watts, is approximately $2 \times$ total armature current.

(b) Loss due to friction between the brushes and the commutator. This loss depends upon the total brush pressure, the coefficient of friction and the peripheral speed of the commutator.

iii. *Excitation losses.*

(a) Loss in the shunt circuit (if any) equal to the product of the shunt current and the terminal voltage. In shunt generators this loss increases a little between no load and full load; but in level-compound generators and in shunt and compound motors it remains approximately constant.

(b) Losses in series, compole and compensating windings (if any). These losses are proportional to the square of the armature current.

iv. *Bearing friction and windage losses.* The bearing friction loss is roughly proportional to the speed, but the windage loss, namely the power absorbed in setting up circulating currents of air, is proportional to the cube of the speed. The windage loss is very small unless the machine is fitted with a cooling fan.

v. *Stray load loss.* It was shown in Art. 66 that the effect of armature reaction is to distort the flux, the flux densities at certain points of the armature being increased; consequently the iron loss is also increased. It is rather difficult to estimate this stray loss.* It is usually neglected and this accounts for the value of the efficiency calculated by the Swinburne method (Art. 79 (b)) being a little higher than that obtained from the input and output powers of the machine.

77. Efficiency of a D.C. Machine. (a) *Generator.*

If R_a =total resistance of armature circuit (including the brush-contact resistance and the resistance of series and compole windings, if any),

I =output current,

I_s =shunt current

and I_a =armature current $= I + I_s$,

then total loss in armature circuit $= I_a^2 R_a$.

If V =terminal voltage,

loss in shunt circuit $= I_s V$.

This includes the loss in the shunt regulating resistance.

If C =sum of iron, friction and windage losses,

$$\text{total losses} = I_a^2 R_a + I_s V + C$$

but output power $= IV$

∴ input power $= IV + I_a^2 R_a + I_s V + C$

and efficiency $= \dfrac{IV}{IV + I_a^2 R_a + I_s V + C}$ (128)

* A method of calculating this loss is given by the author in the *Journal of the Institution of Electrical Engineers,* February 1925.

(b) *Motor*.

If I =input current and I_s =shunt current, then
$$\text{armature current} = I_a = I - I_s.$$

Using the symbols given above for a generator, we have:
$$\text{total losses} = I_a^2 R_a + I_s V + C$$

but
$$\text{input power} = IV$$

$\therefore$
$$\text{output power} = IV - I_a^2 R_a - I_s V - C$$

and
$$\text{efficiency} = \frac{IV - I_a^2 R_a - I_s V - C}{IV} \qquad (129)$$

78. Approximate Condition for Maximum Efficiency.
Let us assume (a) that the shunt current is negligible
compared with the armature current at load corresponding to maximum efficiency and (b) that the shunt,
iron and friction losses are independent of the load;
then from expression (128),

$$\text{efficiency of a generator} = \frac{IV}{IV + I^2 R_a + I_s V + C}$$
$$= \frac{V}{V + I R_a + \frac{1}{I}(I_s V + C)}.$$

This efficiency is a maximum when the denominator is a
minimum, namely when:

$$\frac{d}{dI}\left\{ V + I R_a + \frac{1}{I}(I_s V + C) \right\} = 0$$

i.e.
$$R_a - \frac{1}{I^2}(I_s V + C) = 0$$

$\therefore$
$$I^2 R_a = I_s V + C \qquad . \quad (130)$$

i.e. the efficiency of the generator is a maximum when
the load is such that the variable loss is equal to the constant loss.

Precisely the same conclusion can be derived for a
motor from expression (129).

79. Determination of Efficiency. (a) *By direct
measurement of input and output powers*. In the case of
small machines the output power can be measured by
some form of mechanical brake such as that shown in

Fig. 93, where a belt (or ropes) on an air- or water-cooled pulley has one end attached via a spring balance S to the floor and has a weight W suspended at the other end.

If W and S are in pounds, the net pull on the belt due to friction at the pulley is $(W-S)$ lb.

If $r=$effective radius of brake in feet, and $N=$speed of pulley in r.p.m., then:

$$\text{output power}=\frac{2\pi N(W-S)r}{33,000}\text{ h.p.}$$

$$=\frac{2\pi N(W-S)r \times 746}{33,000}\text{ watts}\quad(131)$$

If $V=$supply voltage, and $I=$current taken by motor in amperes,

$$\text{input power}=IV\text{ watts}$$

and
$$\text{efficiency}=\frac{2\pi N(W-S)r \times 746}{33,000 \times IV}\ .\quad(132)$$

The size of machine that can be tested by this method

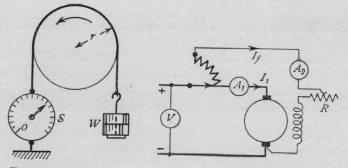

FIG. 93.—Brake test on a motor.   FIG. 94.—Measurement of no-load loss.

is limited by the difficulty of dissipating the heat generated at the brake.

(b) *By separate measurement of the losses (Swinburne's Method).* Let us for simplicity consider the case of a shunt generator or motor. The machine is run as a motor on no load with the supply voltage V adjusted to the rated voltage, namely the voltage stamped on the nameplate. The speed is adjusted to its rated value by means of shunt regulator R (Fig. 94). If I_1 and I_s be the readings on ammeters A_1 and A_2 respectively,

$$\text{input power to armature} = I_1 V \text{ watts}$$
and
$$\text{shunt loss} = I_s V \text{ watts}$$

The input power to the armature supplies: (i) iron loss in core; (ii) friction loss at bearings and commutator; (iii) windage loss; and (iv) a very small $I^2 R$ loss due to the resistance of the armature circuit. This $I^2 R$ loss can be calculated; but usually it is negligible compared with the other losses.

The resistance of the armature circuit (including the interpole windings, if any) is determined by disconnecting one end of the shunt circuit, as in Fig. 95, and noting the

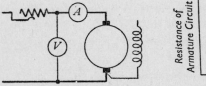

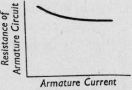

FIG. 95.—Measurement of armature resistance.

FIG. 96.—Variation of armature resistance with current.

voltages across the armature for various values of current with the armature stationary. The resistance decreases slightly with increase of armature current, as shown in Fig. 96. This effect is due to the brush contact resistance being approximately inversely proportional to the current.

If the windings are at room temperature when these measurements are being made, the resistance at normal working temperature should be calculated. Thus, if the resistance be R_1 at room temperature of, say, $15°C$, if $50°C$ be the temperature rise of the windings after the machine has been operating on full load for 3 or 4 hours, then from Art. 5 we have:

$$\text{resistance at } 65°C = R_1 \times \frac{234 \cdot 5 + 65}{234 \cdot 5 + 15}$$
$$= 1 \cdot 2 R_1.$$

If $I =$ line current at which the efficiency is to be calculated,

$$\left.\begin{array}{c}\text{corresponding armature}\\\text{current}\end{array}\right\} = I_a = I + I_s, \text{ as a generator,}$$

$$= I - I_s, \text{ as a motor.}$$

If $R_a =$ resistance of armature circuit at working temperature for current I_a (Fig. 96),

corresponding loss in armature circuit $= I_a^2 R_a$.

Since iron, friction and windage losses $= I_1 V$

and   shunt loss $= I_s V$

$\therefore$ total losses $= I_a^2 R_a + (I_1 + I_s) V$.

If the machine is a generator, output power $= IV$.

$\therefore$ input power $= IV + I_a^2 R_a + (I_1 + I_s) V$

and $$\text{efficiency} = \frac{IV}{IV + I_a^2 R_a + (I_1 + I_s) V} \quad (133)$$

If the machine is a motor, input power $= IV$.

$\therefore$ output power $= IV - I_a^2 R_a - (I_1 + I_s) V$

and $$\text{efficiency} = \frac{IV - I_a^2 R_a - (I_1 + I_s) V}{IV} \quad (134)$$

The main advantages of the Swinburne method are: (i) the power required to test a large machine is comparatively small and (ii) the data enable the efficiency to be calculated at any load.

The main disadvantages are: (i) no account is taken of the stray losses (Art. 76), and (ii) the test does not enable the performance of the machine on full load to be checked; for instance, it does not indicate whether commutation on full load is satisfactory and whether the temperature rise is within the specified limit.

(c) *Regenerative or Hopkinson Method for Two Similar Shunt Machines.* The two machines to be tested are mechanically coupled to each other and are connected electrically as shown in Fig. 97. With switch S open machine M is started up as a motor by means of starter St. The excitation of G is adjusted to give zero reading on voltmeter V_1 and S is then closed. Current I_1 is adjusted to any desired value by increasing the excita-

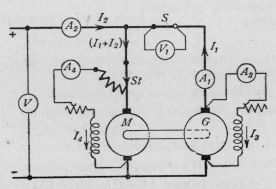

Fig. 97.—Regenerative or Hopkinson test.

tion of G or reducing the excitation of M, and the corresponding readings on the ammeters are noted. If V be the supply voltage, then:

$$\text{output power of } G = I_1 V$$

and

$$\text{input power to } M = (I_1 + I_2)V.$$

An approximate value of the efficiency can be derived by assuming the efficiencies of the two machines to be equal; thus, if η (pronounced "eta") be the efficiency of each machine,

$$\text{output power of } M = \eta(I_1 + I_2)V$$
$$= \text{input power to } G$$

$\therefore$　output power of $G = \eta \times \text{input power to } G$
$$= \eta^2(I_1 + I_2)V.$$

Hence $\eta^2(I_1+I_2)V=I_1V$

$\therefore$ $$\eta=\sqrt{\left(\frac{I_1}{I_1+I_2}\right)} \quad . \quad . \quad (135)$$

The armature current of M may be 15 to 30 per cent greater than that of G so that the armature I^2R loss in M is considerably greater than that in G. On the other hand, the excitation of G is appreciably greater than that of M so that the excitation and iron losses in G are correspondingly greater than those in M. Most of these differences can be allowed for by calculating the efficiencies thus:

If R_a=resistance of the armature circuit of each machine, and if I_3 and I_4=shunt currents of G and M respectively,

armature I^2R loss in $G=(I_1+I_3)^2R_a$

and   armature I^2R loss in $M=(I_1+I_2-I_4)^2R_a$.

Also, loss in shunt circuit of $G=I_3V$

and   loss in shunt circuit of $M=I_4V$.

But total losses in G and M=power supplied from mains

$$=I_2V$$

$\therefore$ iron, friction and windage losses in G and M

$$=I_2V-\{(I_1+I_3)^2R_a+(I_1+I_2-I_4)^2R_a+(I_3+I_4)V\}$$
$$=\text{(say) } C.$$

We shall now make the only assumption necessary with this method, namely that these losses are equally divided between the two machines.

$\therefore$ iron, friction and windage losses per machine $=\tfrac{1}{2}C$.

For the generator,

total losses $=(I_1+I_3)^2R_a+I_3V+\tfrac{1}{2}C=\text{(say) } P_g$

and output power $=I_1V$

$\therefore$ efficiency of $G=\dfrac{I_1V}{I_1V+P_g}$ $. \quad . \quad . \quad . \quad . \quad . \quad (136)$

6

For the motor,

$$\text{total losses} = (I_1 + I_2 - I_4)^2 R_a + I_4 V + \tfrac{1}{2} C = \text{(say) } P_m$$

and input power $= (I_1 + I_2) V$

$$\therefore \text{ efficiency of } M = \frac{(I_1 + I_2) V - P_m}{(I_1 + I_2) V} \qquad \cdot \quad \cdot \quad \cdot \quad (137)$$

The advantages of the Hopkinson method are: (i) the total power required to test two machines is small compared with the power of each machine; (ii) the machines can be tested under full-load conditions so that the commutation and the temperature rise can be checked; and (iii) the efficiency is being determined under load conditions so that the stray loss is being taken into account.

The main disadvantage is the necessity for two practically identical machines to be available.

Example 26. *A 100-kW, 460-V shunt generator was run as a motor on no load at its rated voltage and speed. The total current taken was 9·8 A, including a shunt current of 2·7 A. The resistance of the armature circuit (including interpoles) at normal working temperature was 0·11 Ω. Calculate the efficiencies at* (a) *full load and* (b) *half load.*

(a) Output current at full load $= \dfrac{100 \times 1000}{460} = 217 \cdot 5$ A,

$\therefore$ armature current at full load $= 217 \cdot 5 + 2 \cdot 7 = 220 \cdot 2$ A.

$\left.\begin{array}{l}\text{Copper loss in armature} \\ \text{circuit at full load}\end{array}\right\} = (220)^2 \times 0 \cdot 11 = 5325$ W.

Loss in shunt circuit $= 2 \cdot 7 \times 460 = 1242$ W.

Armature current on no load $= 9 \cdot 8 - 2 \cdot 7 = 7 \cdot 1$ A,

$\left.\begin{array}{l}\therefore \text{ input power to armature} \\ \text{on no load}\end{array}\right\} = 7 \cdot 1 \times 460 = 3265$ W.

$\left.\begin{array}{l}\text{But loss in armature circuit} \\ \text{on no load}\end{array}\right\} = (7 \cdot 1)^2 \times 0 \cdot 11 = 5 \cdot 5$ W.

This loss is less than 0·2 per cent of the input power and could therefore have been neglected.

Hence, iron, friction and windage losses $=3260$ W,

and total losses at full load $=5325+1242+3260=9827$W
$$=9\cdot83 \text{ kW}.$$

Input power at full load $=100+9\cdot83=109\cdot8$ kW

and efficiency at full load $=\dfrac{100}{109\cdot8}=0\cdot911$ per unit*

$$=91\cdot1 \text{ per cent}.$$

(b) Output current at half load $\Big\}=108\cdot7$ A,

$\therefore$ armature current at half load $\Big\}=108\cdot7+2\cdot7=111\cdot4$ A

and copper loss in armature circuit at half load $\Big\}=(111\cdot4)^2\times0\cdot11=1365$ W

$\therefore$ total losses at half load $=1365+1242+3260=5867$ W
$$=5\cdot87 \text{ kW}.$$

Input power at half load $=50+5\cdot87=55\cdot87$ kW

and efficiency at half load $\Big\}=\dfrac{50}{55\cdot87}=0\cdot895$ per unit

$$=89\cdot5 \text{ per cent}.$$

Example 28. *Two* 1000-*kW,* 500-*V shunt dynamos were tested by the Hopkinson method. When the output current of the generator was* 2000 *A, the input current from the*

---

* Per-unit value $=\dfrac{\text{actual value (in any unit)}}{\text{basic or rated value (in same unit)}}$

Thus, if the rated voltage of a system is 200 V, a voltage of 190 V is $190/200=0\cdot95$ p.u.; or if an ammeter is reading $5\cdot2$ A when the correct value is 5 A, the error is $(5\cdot2-5)/5 =0\cdot04$ p.u. It will be obvious that the percentage value is 100 times the per-unit value.

The main advantage of using per-unit instead of percentage values is that multiplying or dividing the per-unit value of one quantity by the per-unit value of another quantity gives the result in per-unit value; thus, if, in a d.c. circuit, the voltage and current respectively are $0\cdot9$ and $0\cdot8$ p.u. of the basic values, the power is $0\cdot72$ of the basic value. Had we used percentage values, the product would have been 7200—a meaningless value. Per-unit values are frequently used in electric transmission and distribution calculations.

supply mains (I_2 in Fig. 97) was 380 A, and the shunt currents of the generator and motor were 10·4 and 8·8 A respectively. The resistance of the armature circuit of each machine was 0·006 Ω. Calculate the efficiency of the generator at full load by assuming (a) equal efficiencies and (b) equal iron and friction losses.

$$\left. \begin{array}{l} \text{Output current of} \\ \text{generator on full} \\ \text{load} \end{array} \right\} = \frac{1000 \times 1000}{500} = 2000 \text{ A.}$$

(a) From expression (135),

$$\text{efficiency on full load} = \sqrt{\left(\frac{2000}{2000 + 380} \right)}$$
$$= 0·9165 \text{ per unit}$$
$$= 91·65 \text{ per cent.}$$

$$\left. \begin{array}{l} \text{(b) Armature} \\ \text{current of } G \end{array} \right\} = 2000 + 10·4 = 2010 \text{ A}$$

$$\left. \begin{array}{l} \therefore \text{ copper loss in arma-} \\ \text{ture circuit of } G \end{array} \right\} = (2010)^2 \times 0·006 = 24,250 \text{ W}$$
$$= 24·25 \text{ kW.}$$

$$\left. \begin{array}{l} \text{Loss in shunt circuit} \\ \text{of } G \end{array} \right\} = 10·4 \times 500 = 5200 \text{ W}$$
$$= 5·2 \text{ kW.}$$

$$\text{Armature current of } M = 2000 + 380 - 8·8 = 2371·2 \text{ A}$$

$$\left. \begin{array}{l} \therefore \text{ copper loss in arma-} \\ \text{ture circuit of } M \end{array} \right\} = (2371)^2 \times 0·006 = 33,750 \text{ W}$$
$$= 33·75 \text{ kW.}$$

$$\left. \begin{array}{l} \text{Loss in shunt circuit} \\ \text{of } M \end{array} \right\} = 8·8 \times 500 = 4400 \text{ W}$$
$$= 4·4 \text{ kW.}$$

$$\left. \begin{array}{l} \text{But total losses in } G \\ \text{and } M \end{array} \right\} = 380 \times 500 = 190,000 \text{ W}$$
$$= 190 \text{ kW}$$

$$\left. \begin{array}{l} \therefore \text{ iron and friction} \\ \text{losses in } G \text{ and } M \end{array} \right\} = 190 - (24·25 + 5·2 + 33·75 + 4·4)$$
$$= 122·4 \text{ kW}$$

so that

$$\left.\begin{array}{l}\text{iron and friction losses}\\\text{in each machine}\end{array}\right\}=61\cdot2 \text{ kW}$$

$$\left.\begin{array}{l}\text{Hence total losses in}\\G \text{ on full load}\end{array}\right\}=24\cdot25+5\cdot2+61\cdot2$$

$$=90\cdot65 \text{ kW}.$$

$$\left.\begin{array}{l}\text{Input power to } G \text{ on}\\\text{full load}\end{array}\right\}=1000+90\cdot65=1090\cdot65 \text{ kW}$$

$$\therefore \left.\begin{array}{l}\text{efficiency on full}\\\text{load}\end{array}\right\}=\frac{1000}{1090\cdot65}=0\cdot9169 \text{ per unit}$$

$$=91\cdot69 \text{ per cent}.$$

In this example, the two methods happen to give practically the same result.

Summary of Important Formulae in Chapter IV

$$\left.\begin{array}{l}\text{Armature ampere-}\\\text{turns/pole}\end{array}\right\}=\frac{1}{2}\cdot\frac{I}{c}\cdot\frac{Z}{2p} \quad \cdot \quad \cdot \quad (120)$$

where $p=$no. of *pairs* of poles.

$$\left.\begin{array}{l}\text{Demagnetizing}\\\text{ampere-turns/pole}\end{array}\right\}=\frac{1}{2}\cdot\frac{I}{c}\cdot\frac{Z}{2p}\cdot\frac{4\theta}{360} \quad (121)$$

$$=\frac{IZ}{c}\cdot\frac{s}{C} \quad \cdot \quad \cdot \quad (123)$$

where $\theta=$brush lead in *electrical* degrees
and $s=$brush lead in segments.

$$\left.\begin{array}{l}\text{Distorting ampere-}\\\text{turns/pole}\end{array}\right\}=\frac{1}{2}\cdot\frac{I}{c}\cdot\frac{Z}{2p}\left(1-\frac{4\theta}{360}\right) \cdot \quad (122)$$

$$=\frac{IZ}{c}\left(\frac{1}{4p}-\frac{s}{C}\right) \quad \cdot \quad \cdot \quad (124)$$

$$\left.\begin{array}{l}\text{Ampere-turns/pole for}\\\text{compensating winding}\end{array}\right\}=\frac{1}{2}\cdot\frac{I}{c}\cdot\frac{Z}{2p}\cdot\frac{\text{arc}}{\text{pitch}} \quad \cdot \quad (125)$$

For a shunt motor starter,

$$R_1=k^{n-1}R_a \quad \cdot \quad \cdot \quad \cdot \quad (127)$$

where $n=$ no. of contact studs,

$$k=\frac{\text{maximum current during starting}}{\text{minimum current during starting}}$$

and $R_a=$ resistance of armature circuit.

Also, $$k=\frac{R_1}{R_2}=\frac{R_2}{R_3}=\ldots=\frac{R_{n-1}}{R_a}$$

Efficiency of dynamo $=\dfrac{IV}{IV+I_a^2R_a+I_sV+C}$ (128)

where $C=$ iron, friction and windage losses.

Efficiency of motor $=\dfrac{IV-I_a^2R_a-I_sV-C}{IV}$ (129)

For maximum efficiency,

variable loss $=$ constant loss . (130)

For brake test,

efficiency $=\dfrac{2\pi N(W-S)r\times746}{33,000\times IV}$. (132)

For Swinburne test,

efficiency of dynamo $=\dfrac{IV}{IV+I_a^2R_a+(I_1+I_s)V}$ (133)

efficiency of motor $=\dfrac{IV-I_a^2R_a-(I_1+I_s)V}{IV}$ (134)

where $I_1=$ armature current on no load.

For Hopkinson test,

$$\left.\begin{array}{c}\text{approximate value}\\\text{of efficiency}\end{array}\right\}=\sqrt{\left(\dfrac{I_1}{I_1+I_2}\right)}\quad.\quad(135)$$

where $I_1=$ output current of generator and $I_2=$ current from supply mains.

EXAMPLES IV

1. Give reasons for the use of equalizing rings in a simple lap-wound d.c. armature. Why are such rings not fitted to wave-wound armatures?

An armature for an eight-pole machine has 320 single-turn coils. Construct a table showing the coils to be tapped for connections to be made to 5 equidistant equalizing rings. (U.L.C.I.)

2. A 300-kW, 500-V, eight-pole, d.c. generator has 768 armature conductors, lap-wound. Calculate the number of demagnetizing and cross ampere-turns/pole when the brushes are given a lead of 5 electrical degrees from the geometric neutral. Neglect the effect of the shunt current.

3. A 30-h.p., 440-V, four-pole, d.c. motor has an armature wave-wound with 846 conductors and the commutator has 141 segments. The full-load efficiency is 88 per cent and the shunt current is 1·2 A. If the brushes are shifted backwards through 1½ segments from the geometric neutral, calculate (a) the demagnetizing ampere-turns/pole and (b) the distorting ampere-turns/pole on full load.

4. A four-pole motor has a wave-wound armature with 888 conductors. The brushes are displaced backwards through 5 angular degrees from the geometric neutral. If the total armature current is 90 A, calculate (a) the cross and the back ampere-turns/pole and (b) the additional field current to neutralize this demagnetization, if the field winding has 1200 turns/pole.

5. Calculate the number of turns/pole required for the commutating poles of the d.c. generator referred to in Q.2, assuming the compole ampere-turns/pole to be about 1·3 times the armature ampere-turns/pole and the brushes to be in the geometric neutral.

6. An eight-pole generator has a lap-wound armature with 640 conductors. Ratio of pole arc/pole pitch is 0·7. Calculate the ampere-turns/pole for a compensating winding to give uniform airgap density when the total armature current is 900 A.

7. If the number of ampere-turns/pole required to send the necessary flux through the magnetic circuit of the interpoles in Q.6 is 25 per cent of the armature ampere-turns/pole, calculate the total ampere-turns/pole for the interpoles, assuming that the machine is fitted with a compensating winding having the ampere-turns/pole calculated in Q.6.

8. A non-interpole d.c. motor having a simple lap winding has a commutator 9 inches in diameter containing 100 segments, the mica insulation between adjacent segments being 0·04 inch thick. Find the time of commutation of one coil if the thickness of a brush is ¾ in, and the motor runs at 650 r.p.m.

State the reasons why the current in a coil may not be completely reversed within this time of commutation. Make a sketch showing where interpoles should be fitted in the motor to improve the commutation. Indicate clearly the polarity of the interpoles and main poles and the direction of rotation. (U.L.C.I.)

9. Describe the process of commutation in a d.c. generator and explain briefly how satisfactory commutation may be obtained over the normal working range.

A four-pole, d.c. machine running at 1500 r.p.m. has a commutator of 12-inch diameter. If the current per brush arm is 150 A, the thickness of the brush 0·5 inch and the self-inductance of each armature coil 0·07 mH, calculate the average e.m.f. of self-inductance in each coil during commutation. (App. El., L.U.)

10. Explain the operation of paralleling two similar d.c. shunt generators. Under what conditions is the external load automatically shared in proportion to their ratings when a number of shunt dynamos are connected in parallel?

Two shunt dynamos operating in parallel have each an armature resistance of 0·02 Ω. The combined external load current is 2500 A.

If the generated e.m.f.'s of the machines are 560 V and 550 V respectively, calculate the bus-bar voltage and the output in kilowatts of each machine.   (C. & G., El. Eng. Pract., Int.)

11. Two shunt generators A and B operate in parallel and their load characteristics may be taken as straight lines.   The voltage of generator A falls from 240 V at no load to 220 V at 200 A, while that of B falls from 245 V at no load to 220 V at 150 A.   Determine the current which each machine supplies to a common load of 300 A and the bus-bar voltage at this load.   Explain clearly how the load may be equalised between the two generators.   (N.C.T.E.C.)

12. In a certain substation there are 5 d.c. shunt generators in parallel, each having an armature resistance of $0 \cdot 1$ Ω, running at the same speed and excited to give equal induced e.m.f.'s.   Each generator supplies an equal share of a total load of 250 kW at a terminal voltage of 500 V into a load of fixed resistance.   If the field current of one generator is raised by 4 per cent, the others remaining unchanged, calculate the power output of each machine and their terminal voltage under these conditions.   Assume that the speeds remain constant and that the flux of each machine is proportional to the field current.
(U.E.I.)

13. Describe, with a diagram of connections, how a shunt generator may be connected to bus-bars to which other generators are already connected.   Carefully explain the effect of varying (a) the field current, and (b) the speed, of *one* of the generators.

Two shunt generators operate in parallel and supply a total load of 800 A.   Generator A gives 240 V at no load and 225 V at 500 A output.   Generator B gives 245 V at no load and 225 V at 400 A output.   Assuming their load characteristics to be straight lines, determine, either graphically or by calculation, the current supplied by each generator and the common bus-bar voltage.   (N.C.T.E.C.)

14. A 300-kW dynamo is to operate in parallel with a 400-kW dynamo over-compounded to give 500 V on no load and 540 V on full load.   The series winding of the 400-kW dynamo has a resistance of $0 \cdot 0012$ Ω.   Calculate (a) the percentage voltage regulation and (b) the resistance of the series winding of the 300-kW dynamo.   Assume the shunt currents to be negligible.

15. Determine the number of sections and the resistance of each section of a starter for a 240-V d.c. shunt motor having an armature resistance of $0 \cdot 6$ Ω.   The current is not to exceed 40 A and the starter handle is to be moved on to the next stud when the current falls to $0 \cdot 75$ of this value.   Prove any formula employed.
(C. & G., El. Eng. Pract., Int.)

16. Describe the method of starting a d.c. motor.   Give a sketch showing the essentials of a starter suitable for a shunt motor and explain the functions of the various parts.

A d.c. 220-V shunt motor has an armature resistance of $0 \cdot 1$ Ω and a shunt field resistance of 100 Ω.   With all the starting resistance in circuit and armature stationary, the current taken from the mains is to be 50 A.   Calculate the resistance required in the starter.   If the starter arm is moved from the first to the second stud when the current has fallen to 40 A, calculate the value to which the current will rise if the resistance thereby cut out is 1 Ω.   Calculate also the corresponding e.m.f. developed by the motor.   (App. El., L.U.)

17. Describe, with the aid of a circuit diagram, a starter suitable for a 230-V, 5 b.h.p. shunt motor.   Explain the action of the protective devices fitted to the starter you describe.

A 200-V shunt motor has an armature resistance of $\frac{1}{2}$ Ω and the maximum armature current at starting on the first stud is limited by the starter resistance to 40 A. When the current has fallen to 30 A, the starter handle is moved to the next stud and the current rises to 50 A. Calculate the total resistance of the starter on the first and second studs.

If the no-load armature current and speed are 2·5 A and 1000 r.p.m., estimate the motor speed at the instant the starter handle is moved from the first to the second stud. (E.M.E.U.)

18. Give a complete diagram of connections for a d.c. shunt motor starter showing the usual protective devices and explain the function of each part.

Calculate the resistance of each section of an eight-section starter for a 460-V shunt motor. The resistance of the armature of the motor is 0·75 Ω and the maximum armature current during starting is not to exceed 50 A. (App. El., L.U.)

19. A shunt generator gives a full-load output of 6 kW at a terminal potential difference of 200 V. The armature and field resistances are 0·5 Ω and 50 Ω respectively. If the mechanical and iron losses combined amount to 500 W, calculate the horsepower required at the driving shaft on full load and the full-load efficiency. (U.L.C.I.)

20. Give the advantages and disadvantages of shunt, series and compound d.c. generators.

A compound-wound generator with "long" shunt gives 240 V at full-load output of 100 A. The resistances of the various windings of the machine are: armature (including brush contact), 0·1 Ω; series field, 0·02 Ω; interpole field, 0·025 Ω; shunt field (including regulating resistance), 100 Ω. The iron loss at full load is 1000 watts; windage and friction losses total 500 watts. Calculate the efficiency of the generator at full load. (App. El., L.U.)

21. Tabulate the various types of losses occurring in a loaded d.c. machine, and indicate how they vary with the load current.

A 400-V shunt motor takes a line current of 42 A when developing its full-load output of 18 h.p. The field resistance is 200 Ω and the armature resistance 1 Ω. Contact drop can be taken as 2 V. Calculate the various losses in the machine at full load, and find the efficiency and output of the motor when the line current is 22 A. (U.L.C.I.)

22. Explain what you understand by the "constant losses" in a shunt motor. A 6½-horsepower, 200-V, shunt motor has a full-load current of 30 A. The armature circuit resistance is $\frac{1}{2}$ Ω and the shunt field resistance is 200 Ω. Determine the "constant loss" for this motor and hence find the input current when the output is one-half of full-load output. (E.M.E.U.)

23. Explain the reasons for the occurrence of "eddy current" losses in the armatures of d.c. machines and describe the measures taken to minimize these losses.

The armature of a certain four-pole d.c. motor has an armature eddy-current loss of 300 W when running at a given speed and field excitation. If the speed is increased by 10 per cent and the field excitation is increased by 20 per cent, calculate the new value of eddy-current loss. Assume that the magnetic circuit is unsaturated and neglect magnetic leakage. (U.L.C.I.)

24. Describe how you would perform a brake test on a d.c. motor. Deduce from first principles the expression for the brake horse-power.

In such a test, the effective load on the brake pulley was 84 lb, the
6*

effective diameter of the pulley 25 in, and the speed 720 r.p.m. The motor took 49 A at 220 V. Calculate the brake-horsepower and the efficiency at this load. (U.L.C.I.)

25. State what can be learnt on test by running a shunt motor on no load.

A 500-V shunt motor takes a total current of 5 A when running unloaded. The resistance of the armature circuit is 0·25 Ω and the field resistance is 125 Ω. Calculate the output and the efficiency when the motor is loaded and taking an input current of 100 A. State any assumptions made in the calculation. (U.L.C.I.)

26. A 500-V shunt motor takes 4 A on no load, of which 1 A is the field current. Resistance of armature (including brushes) = 0·5 Ω. Calculate the losses occurring in the machine when taking 40 A from the line at normal voltage. Find also the output of the motor in h.p. and its efficiency. What is the value of the line current for which the efficiency is a maximum? (N.C.T.E.C.)

27. Enumerate the various losses which take place in a shunt motor when it is running on no load.

A 230-V shunt motor, running on no load and at normal speed, takes an armature current of 2·5 A from 230-V mains. The field-circuit resistance is 230 Ω and the armature circuit resistance is 0·3 Ω. Calculate the motor output and efficiency when the total current taken from the mains is 35 A.

If the motor is used as a 230-V shunt generator, find the efficiency and input power for an output current of 35 A. (E.M.E.U.)

28. In a test on a d.c. shunt generator whose full-load output is 200 kW at 250 V, the following figures are obtained:

   (a) When running light as a motor at full speed, the line current was 36 A, the field current 12 A and the supply voltage 250.

   (b) With the machine at rest, a p.d. of 6 V produced a current of 400 A through the armature circuit.

Explain how these results may be utilized to obtain the efficiency of the generator, and obtain the efficiency at full load and half load. Neglect voltage drop at the brushes. (U.E.I.)

29. Discuss the various no-load losses occurring in a shunt machine. When running on no load, a 400-V shunt motor takes 5 A. Armature resistance is 0·5 Ω, field resistance 200 Ω. Estimate the h.p. output and the efficiency of the motor when running on full load and taking 50 A from the line (neglecting contact drop). Find also the percentage change in speed, no load to full load. (U.L.C.I.)

30. A 5-h.p., 105-V, 1200 r.p.m. shunt motor when run light at normal speed takes an armature current of 3 A at 102 V, normal voltage being applied to the field winding. The field and armature resistances are 95 Ω and 0·1 Ω respectively. Calculate the probable output horsepower and efficiency of the motor when operating at 105 V and taking a line current of 40 A. Allow 2 volts drop at the brushes. Comment upon the assumptions made in calculating the result. (N.C.T.E.C.)

31. Sketch and explain the shape of the efficiency-current curve of a shunt motor. How can this curve be obtained without running the motor on load?

A 500-V shunt motor takes a current of 5 A when running light. The field current is 1 A and the armature circuit resistance 0·25 Ω. Find the maximum efficiency of the machine and the input at which it occurs. (C. & G., El. Eng. Pract., Int.)

32. Enumerate the losses in a d.c. shunt motor and explain how each loss is affected by a change of load.

The current taken by a 460-V shunt motor when running light is 7 A. The resistance of the armature circuit is 0·15 Ω and that of the field circuit is 230 Ω. Calculate the output (in horsepower) and the efficiency when the current taken is 130 A. Calculate also the armature current at which the efficiency is a maximum.

(App. El., L.U.)

33. A d.c. shunt motor has a full-load rating of 10 h.p., 750 r.p.m., 400 V. The resistance of the armature circuit is 1·2 Ω and of the field 800 Ω. The efficiency on full load is 83 per cent. Determine (a) the no-load armature current, (b) the speed when the motor takes 12 A and (c) the armature current when the gross torque is 35 lb.ft. Assume the flux to remain constant.   (App. El., L.U.)

34. Draw a circuit diagram for the back-to-back method (Hopkinson) of testing two similar d.c. generators and discuss the utility of this method. In such a test on two 220-V, 100-kW generators, the circulating current is equal to the full-load current, and in addition 90 A are taken from the supply. Obtain the efficiency of each machine.

(U.E.I.)

35. Describe with the aid of a diagram the Hopkinson test for two similar 230-V shunt machines. The following figures were obtained during such a test on two similar machines: armature currents, 37 A and 30 A; field currents, 0·85 A and 0·8 A. Calculate the efficiencies of the machines and indicate the given currents on a circuit diagram. The armature resistances are each 0·33 Ω.   (E.M.E.U.)

36. A wave-wound, 4-pole armature winding has 738 conductors. The cross-sectional area of each conductor is 5 mm^2 and the mean length per conductor is 48 cm. Assuming the resistivity of copper to be 1·725 $\mu\Omega$-cm at 20°C and the temperature coefficient of resistance to be 1/234·5 at 0° C, calculate the resistance of the armature winding at 65° C.

37. A 6-pole machine has an armature lap-wound with 576 conductors. Each conductor has a cross-sectional area of 0·28 cm^2 and a mean length of 90 cm. Calculate the I^2R loss in the armature at a temperature of 50° C when the total armature current is 600 A. Assume the data for copper given in Q. 36.

CHAPTER V

SINGLE-PHASE CIRCUIT

80. Frequency. The waveform of the e.m.f. generated in an alternator undergoes one complete *cycle* of variation when the conductors move past a N and a S pole; and the shape of the wave over the negative half is exactly the same as that over the positive half. This symmetry of the positive and negative half-cycles does not necessarily hold for waveforms of voltages and currents in circuits incorporating rectifiers or thermionic valves.

The number of cycles occurring in 1 second is termed the *frequency*. If an alternator has *p pairs* of poles and if its speed is N r.p.m., then:

frequency $=f=$ no. of cycles/second

$\qquad$ $=$ no. of cycles/revolution $\times$ no. of revs/sec

$$=p \times \frac{N}{60} = \frac{Np}{60} \qquad \cdots \cdots \quad (138)$$

81. Average and R.M.S. Values of an Alternating Current. Let us first consider the general case of a current the waveform of which cannot be represented by a simple mathematical expression. For instance, the wave shown in Fig. 98 is typical of the current taken by a transformer on no load. If n equidistant mid-ordinates, i_1, i_2, etc., are taken over either the positive or the negative half-cycles, then:

$$\left.\begin{array}{c}\textit{average value of current} \\ \text{over half a cycle}\end{array}\right\} = I_{av} = \frac{i_1 + i_2 + \cdots + i_n}{n} \quad (139)$$

Or, alternatively, by simple geometry,

$$\left.\begin{array}{c}\text{average value} \\ \text{of current}\end{array}\right\} = \frac{\text{area enclosed over half-cycle}}{\text{length of base over half-cycle}} \quad (140)$$

This method of expressing the average value is the more convenient when we come to deal with sinusoidal waves.

In a.c. work, however, the average value is of comparatively little importance.   This is due to the fact that it is the power produced by the electric current that usually matters.   Thus, if the current represented in Fig. 98 (a) be passed through a resistance R ohms, the heating effect of i_1 is $i_1^2 R$, that of i_2 is $i_2^2 R$, etc., as shown

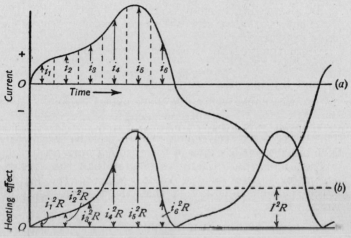

FIG. 98.—Average and r.m.s. values.

in Fig. 98 (b).   The variation of the heating effect during the second half-cycle is exactly the same as that during the first half-cycle,

$$\therefore \quad \text{average heating effect} = \frac{i_1^2 R + i_2^2 R + \ldots + i_n^2 R}{n}.$$

Suppose I to be the value of *direct* current through the same resistance R to produce a heating effect equal to the average heating effect of the alternating current, then:

$$I^2 R = \frac{i_1^2 R + i_2^2 R + \ldots + i_n^2 R}{n}$$

$$\therefore \qquad I = \sqrt{\left(\frac{i_1^2 + i_2^2 + \cdots + i_n^2}{n}\right)} \qquad \cdots \qquad (141)$$

=square *root* of the *mean* of the *squares* of the current

=root-mean-square (or r.m.s.) value of the current.

This quantity is also termed the *effective* value of the current. It will be seen that the r.m.s. or effective value of an alternating current is expressed in terms of the *direct* current that produces the same heating effect in the same resistance.*

Alternatively, the average heating effect may be expressed:

average heating effect over $\frac{1}{2}$-cycle

$$= \frac{\text{area enclosed by } i^2R \text{ curve over } \frac{1}{2}\text{-cycle}}{\text{length of base}} \qquad (142)$$

This is a more convenient expression to use when deriving the r.m.s. value of a sinusoidal current.

The r.m.s. value is always greater than the average except for a rectangular wave, in which case the heating effect remains constant so that the average and the r.m.s. values are the same.

$$\left.\begin{array}{c}\textit{Form factor} \text{ of a}\\ \text{wave}\end{array}\right\} = \frac{\text{r.m.s. value}}{\text{average value}} \qquad \cdots \qquad (143)$$

$$\left.\begin{array}{c}\textit{Peak} \text{ or } \textit{crest factor}\\ \text{of a wave}\end{array}\right\} = \frac{\text{peak or maximum value}}{\text{r.m.s. value}} \qquad (144)$$

---

* When power is being supplied to an a.c. motor, only a fraction of the electrical energy is being converted into heat, and it might appear that the above argument is not applicable. The difficulty of discussing the case of the electric motor at this stage is that the current taken by a motor is hardly ever in phase with the applied voltage. If the current is in phase with and has the same waveform as the applied voltage, then —as far as the electrical power is concerned—the motor can be replaced by a resistance equal to the ratio of voltage/current at any instant. The loss in such a resistance is exactly the same as the power taken by the motor and the definition of the r.m.s. value given in Art. 81 is applicable.

82. Average and R.M.S. Values of Sinusoidal Currents and Voltages.

If I_m* is the maximum value of a current which varies sinusoidally as shown in Fig. 99 (a), the instantaneous value i is represented by:

$$i = I_m \sin \theta$$

where θ = angle in radians from instant of zero current.

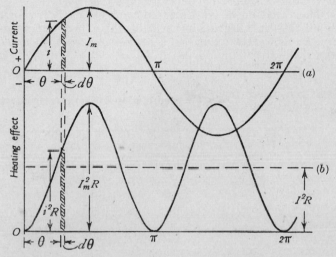

FIG. 99.—Average and r.m.s. values of sinusoidal current.

For a very small interval $d\theta$ radian, the area of the shaded strip is $i \cdot d\theta$ ampere-radians. The use of the unit "ampere-radian" avoids converting the scale on the horizontal axis from radians to seconds.

∴ total area enclosed by the current wave over $\frac{1}{2}$-cycle

$$= \int_0^\pi i \cdot d\theta = I_m \int_0^\pi \sin \theta \cdot d\theta = -I_m \left[\cos \theta \right]_0^\pi = -I_m \left[-1 - 1 \right]$$

$= 2I_m$ ampere-radians.

---

* Small letters are used to represent instantaneous values and capital letters represent definite values such as maximum, average or r.m.s. values. Capital I and V without any suffix epresent r.m.s. values.

From expression (140),

$$\left.\begin{array}{c}\text{average value of current}\\\text{over half a cycle}\end{array}\right\} = \frac{2I_m \text{ (ampere-radians)}}{\pi \text{ (radians)}}$$

i.e. $\qquad\qquad I_{av} = 0 \cdot 637\, I_m \text{ amperes} \qquad (145)$

If the current be passed through a resistance R ohms, instantaneous heating effect $= i^2 R$ watts.

The variation of $i^2 R$ during a complete cycle is shown in Fig. 99 (b). During interval $d\theta$ radian, heat generated is $i^2 R \, . \, d\theta$ watt-radians and is represented by the shaded strip.

Hence:

$$\left.\begin{array}{c}\text{heat generated during}\\\text{the first half-cycle}\end{array}\right\} = \text{area enclosed by the } i^2 R \text{ curve}$$

$$= \int_0^\pi i^2 R \, . \, d\theta = I_m^2 R \int_0^\pi \sin^2 \theta \, . \, d\theta$$

$$= \frac{I_m^2 R}{2} \int_0^\pi (1 - \cos 2\theta) \, . \, d\theta$$

$$= \frac{I_m^2 R}{2} \left[\theta - \tfrac{1}{2} \sin 2\theta \right]_0^\pi$$

$$= \frac{\pi}{2} I_m^2 R \text{ watt-radians.}$$

From expression (142),

$$\left.\begin{array}{c}\text{average heat-}\\\text{ing effect}\end{array}\right\} = \frac{(\pi/2) I_m^2 R \text{ (watt-radians)}}{\pi \text{ (radians)}}$$

$$= \tfrac{1}{2} I_m^2 R \text{ watts} \qquad . \quad . \quad (146)$$

If I be the value of direct current through the same resistance to produce the same heating effect,

$$I^2 R = \tfrac{1}{2} I_m^2 R$$

$$\therefore \qquad\qquad I = \frac{I_m}{\sqrt{2}} = 0 \cdot 707\, I_m \quad . \quad . \quad (147)$$

Since the voltage across the resistance is directly proportional to the current, it follows that the relationships derived for current also apply to voltage. Hence, in general:

average value of a sinusoidal current or voltage
$$=0 \cdot 637 \times \text{maximum value} \qquad (148)$$

r.m.s. value of a sinusoidal current or voltage
$$=0 \cdot 707 \times \text{maximum value} \qquad (149)$$

From expressions (143) and (144),

$$\left. \begin{array}{c} \text{form factor of a} \\ \text{sine wave} \end{array} \right\} = \frac{0 \cdot 707 \times \text{maximum value}}{0 \cdot 637 \times \text{maximum value}}$$
$$= 1 \cdot 11 \qquad \cdots \qquad (150)$$

$$\left. \begin{array}{c} \text{and peak or crest factor} \\ \text{of a sine wave} \end{array} \right\} = \frac{\text{maximum value}}{0 \cdot 707 \times \text{maximum value}}$$
$$= 1 \cdot 414 \qquad \cdots \qquad (151)$$

Example 29. *A moving-coil ammeter, a thermal* ammeter and a rectifier are connected in series across a 110-V a.c. supply. The rectifier has a resistance of 50 Ω in one direction and an infinite resistance in the reverse direction. Calculate: (a) the readings on the ammeters, and (b) the form and peak factors of the current wave. Assume the supply voltage to be sinusoidal and the resistance of the instruments to be very small.*

(a) Maximum value of the voltage $= \dfrac{110}{0 \cdot 707} = 155 \cdot 5$ V

∴ maximum value of the current $= \dfrac{155 \cdot 5}{50} = 3 \cdot 11$ A.

During the positive half-cycle the current is proportional to the voltage and is therefore sinusoidal, as shown in Fig 100 (a),

$$\left. \begin{array}{c} \therefore \quad \text{average value of current over} \\ \text{the positive half-cycle} \end{array} \right\} = 0 \cdot 637 \times 3 \cdot 11$$
$$= 1 \cdot 98 \text{ A.}$$

During the negative half-cycle the current is zero. Owing, however, to the inertia of the moving system, the

---

* A thermal ammeter is an instrument the operation of which depends upon the heating effect of a current.

moving-coil ammeter reads the average value of the current over the *whole* cycle,

$$\therefore \quad \text{reading on M.C. ammeter} = \frac{1 \cdot 98}{2} = 0 \cdot 99 \text{ A.}$$

The variation of the heating effect in the thermal ammeter is shown in Fig. 100 (b), the maximum power being $I_m^2 R$, where R is the resistance of the instrument.

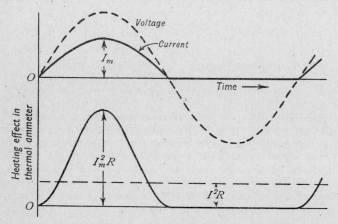

FIG. 100.—Waveforms of voltage, current and power.

From expression (146) it is seen that the average heating effect over the positive half-cycle is $\frac{1}{2} I_m^2 R$; and since no heat is generated during the second half-cycle, it follows that the average heating effect over a complete cycle is $\frac{1}{4} I_m^2 R$.

If I be the direct current to produce the same heating effect,

$$I^2 R = \tfrac{1}{4} I_m^2 R$$
$$\therefore \quad I = \tfrac{1}{2} I_m = 3 \cdot 11/2 = 1 \cdot 555 \text{ A,}$$

i.e. reading on thermal ammeter $= 1 \cdot 555$ A.

A mistake that may very easily be made is to calculate the r.m.s. value of the current over the positive half-cycle as $0 \cdot 707 \times 3 \cdot 11$, namely $2 \cdot 2$ A, and then say that the reading on thermal ammeter is half this value, namely

1·1 A. The importance of working such a problem from first principles will therefore be evident.

(b) From (143), form factor $= \dfrac{1 \cdot 555}{0 \cdot 99} = 1 \cdot 57$

and from (144), peak factor $= \dfrac{3 \cdot 11}{1 \cdot 555} = 2$.

83. Addition and Subtraction of Sinusoidal Alternating Quantities. In Art. 97 of *Principles of Electricity* it was shown that if the maximum value of a sinusoidal alternating quantity such as a voltage or current is represented to scale by the length of a vector rotating anti-clockwise at $2\pi f$ radians/sec and if the vector is in a horizontal position and pointing towards the right when the value of the alternating quantity is passing from negative to positive, then the projection of the vector on the vertical axis represents to scale the instantaneous value of that quantity. It was also shown that if OA and OB in Fig. 101 represent the maximum values of, say, two

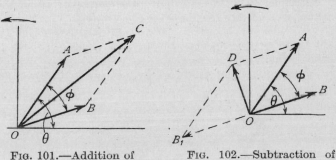

FIG. 101.—Addition of vectors.　　FIG. 102.—Subtraction of vectors.

alternating voltages differing in phase by an angle ϕ, then the maximum value of the *sum* of these voltages is represented by OC, the diagonal of the parallelogram drawn on OA and OB, i.e. OC is the *vectorial sum* of OA and OB.

If voltage OB is to be subtracted from OA, then OB is produced backwards so that OB_1 is equal and opposite to OB (Fig. 102). The diagonal OD of the parallelogram drawn on OA and OB_1 represents the *vectoral difference* of OA and OB.

If vector OA has rotated through an angle θ radians after the quantity has passed through zero value, then:

$$\text{its instantaneous value} = OA \sin \theta \quad . \quad (152)$$
$$= OA \sin \omega t \quad . \quad (153)$$
$$= OA \sin 2\pi f t \quad (154)$$

where $t =$ time in seconds to rotate through θ radians

$\omega =$ angular velocity in radians per second

$= 2\pi f$ radians/second

and $f =$ frequency in cycles per second.

If the quantity represented by OB lags by an angle ϕ behind OA,

$$\text{its instantaneous value} = OB \sin (\theta - \phi)$$
$$= OB \sin (\omega t - \phi)$$
$$= OB \sin (2\pi f t - \phi).$$

Example 30.   *The instantaneous values of two alternating voltages are represented respectively by $v_1 = 60 \sin \theta$ and $v_2 = 40 \sin (\theta - \pi/3)$. Derive an expression for the instantaneous value of (a) the sum and (b) the difference of these voltages.*

(a) It is convenient to draw the vectors in the position

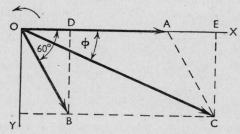

Fig. 103—Addition of vectors in Example 30.

corresponding to $\theta = 0$; i.e. OA in Fig. 103 is drawn to scale along the X axis to represent 60 volts, and OB is drawn $\pi/3$ radians or 60° behind OA to represent 40 volts.

The diagonal OC of the parallelogram drawn on OA and OB represents the vectorial sum of OA and OB. By measurement, $OC=87$ volts and angle ϕ between OC and the X axis is 23·5°, namely 0·41 radian; hence:

instantaneous sum of the two voltages $=87 \sin (\theta -0\cdot41)$.

Alternatively, this expression can be found thus:

Horizontal component of $OA=60$ V

horizontal component of $OB=OD=40 \cos 60°=20$ V.

$\therefore \quad$ resultant horizontal $\Big\}=OA+OD=60+20$
component

$=80$ V $=OE$ in Fig. 103.

Vertical component of $OA=0$

vertical component of $OB=BD=-40 \sin 60°$

$=-34\cdot64$ V.

$\therefore \quad$ resultant vertical $\Big\}=-34\cdot64$ V $=CE$.
component

The minus sign merely indicates that the resultant vertical component is *below* the horizontal axis and that the resultant voltage must therefore lag behind OA.

Hence maximum value of $\Big\}=OC=\sqrt{[(80)^2+(-34\cdot64)^2]}$
resultant voltage

$=87\cdot2$ V.

If ϕ be the angle of lag of OC behind OA,

$$\tan \phi=\frac{EC}{OE}=\frac{-34\cdot64}{80}=-0\cdot433$$

$\therefore \qquad \phi=23\cdot4°=0\cdot41$ radian

and instantaneous value of $\Big\}=87\cdot2 \sin (\theta -0\cdot41)$
resultant voltage

(b) The construction for subtracting OB from OA is obvious from Fig. 104. By measurement, $OC=53$ volts and $\phi=41°=0\cdot715$ radian.

$\therefore \quad$ instantaneous difference $\Big\}=53 \sin (\theta +0\cdot715)$.
of the two voltages

Alternatively, resultant horizontal component $\bigg\} = OA - OE = 60 - 20$

$$= 40 \text{ V} = OD \text{ in Fig. 104,}$$

and resultant vertical component $\bigg\} = B_1E = 34 \cdot 64 \text{ V}$

$$= DC \text{ in Fig. 104}$$

$\therefore$ maximum value of resultant voltages $\bigg\} = OC = \sqrt{[(40)^2 + (34 \cdot 36)^2]}$

$$= 52 \cdot 9 \text{ V}$$

and $\qquad\qquad \tan \phi = \dfrac{DC}{OD} = \dfrac{34 \cdot 64}{40} = 0 \cdot 866$

$\therefore \qquad\qquad\qquad \phi = 40 \cdot 9° = 0 \cdot 714 \text{ radian}$

and instantaneous value of resultant voltage $\bigg\} = 52 \cdot 9 \sin (\theta + 0 \cdot 714).$

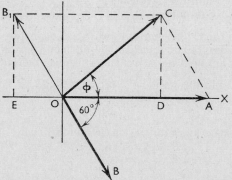

FIG. 104.—Subtraction of vectors in Example 30.

84. Vector Diagrams drawn with R.M.S. Values instead of Maximum Values.

It is important to note that when alternating voltages and currents are represented by vectors, it is assumed that their waveforms are sinusoidal. It has already been shown that for sine waves the r.m.s. or effective value is $0 \cdot 707$ times the maximum value. Furthermore, ammeters and voltmeters are

almost invariably calibrated to read the r.m.s. values.
Consequently it is much more convenient to make the
vectors represent r.m.s. rather than maximum values.
If the vectors of Fig. 103, for instance, were drawn to
represent to scale the r.m.s. instead of the maximum
values of the voltages, the shape of the diagram would
remain unaltered and the phase relationships between the
various quantities would remain unaffected. Hence in
all vector diagrams from now onwards, the vectors will,
for convenience, be drawn to represent r.m.s. values.

85. Alternating Current in a Circuit possessing Resistance only.

Suppose the instantaneous voltage applied
across a resistance R ohms to be represented by:

$$v = V_m \sin \theta,$$

then instantaneous value of the current is represented by:

$$i = \frac{v}{R} = \frac{V_m}{R} \sin \theta = I_m \sin \theta$$

and the current is obviously in phase with the voltage.
If V and I be the r.m.s. values of the voltage and
current,

$$V = 0 \cdot 707 V_m \quad \text{and} \quad I = 0 \cdot 707 I_m,$$

so that
$$I = \frac{V}{R} \quad \cdots \quad (155)$$

The voltage and current vectors are shown in Fig. 105.
The two vectors are actually
coincident, but are drawn
slightly apart so that the
identity of each may be clearly recognized.

FIG. 105.—Vector diagram for non-reactive circuit.

86. Alternating Current in a Circuit possessing Inductance only.

Suppose a coil having an inductance L
henrys and negligible resistance to be connected across
an a.c. supply and suppose the instantaneous value of the
current to be represented by

$$i = I_m \sin \theta = I_m \sin 2\pi ft \quad \cdots \quad (156)$$

where t = time, in seconds, after the current has passed through zero from negative to positive, as shown in Fig. 106.

Suppose the current to increase by di ampere in dt second, then

instantaneous value of e.m.f. induced in coil $\Big\} = e = -L \cdot di/dt$

$$= -LI_m \frac{d}{dt} (\sin 2\pi ft)$$
$$= -2\pi f LI_m \cos 2\pi ft$$
$$= 2\pi f LI_m \sin (2\pi ft - \pi/2) \quad (157)$$

Since f represents the number of cycles/second, the duration of 1 cycle = $1/f$ second. Consequently:

when $t = 0$, $\cos 2\pi ft = 1$

and $\qquad\qquad$ induced e.m.f. $= -2\pi f LI_m$.

When $t = 1/2f$, $\cos 2\pi ft = \cos \pi = -1$,

and $\qquad\qquad$ induced e.m.f. $= 2\pi f LI_m$.

Hence the wave of the induced e.m.f. is represented by

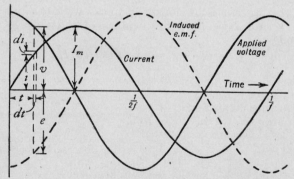

Fig. 106.—Voltage and current curves for purely inductive circuit.

the dotted curve in Fig. 106 lagging a quarter of a cycle behind the current.

Since the resistance of the coil is assumed negligible, the whole of the applied voltage is absorbed in neutralizing the induced e.m.f.

∴ instantaneous value of⎫
   the applied voltage ⎬ $= v$

$$= 2\pi f L I_m \cos 2\pi f t$$
$$= 2\pi f L I_m \sin (2\pi f t + \pi/2)$$
$$\text{(158)}$$

Comparison of expressions (156) and (158) shows that the applied voltage leads a quarter of a cycle in front of the current. Also, from (158), it follows that the maximum value V_m of the applied voltage is $2\pi f L I_m$,

i.e. $\quad V_m = 2\pi f L I_m,\quad$ so that $\quad \dfrac{V_m}{I_m} = 2\pi f L.$

If I and V be the r.m.s. values, then:

$$\frac{V}{I} = \frac{0 \cdot 707 \, V_m}{0 \cdot 707 \, I_m} = 2\pi f L$$
$$= \text{inductive reactance.}$$

The inductive reactance is expressed in ohms and is represented by the symbol X_L.

Hence $\qquad I = \dfrac{V}{2\pi f L} = \dfrac{V}{X_L}\qquad$ . . . (159)

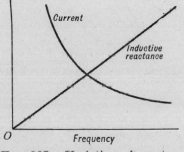

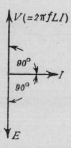

FIG. 107.—Variation of reactance and current with frequency in a purely inductive circuit.

FIG. 108.—Vector diagram for purely inductive circuit.

The inductive reactance is proportional to the frequency and the current produced by a given voltage is inversely proportional to the frequency, as shown in Fig. 107.

The vector diagram for a purely inductive circuit is given in Fig. 108, where E represents the r.m.s. value of the e.m.f. induced in the circuit; and V, equal and opposite to E, represents the r.m.s. value of the applied voltage.

87. Alternating Current in a Circuit possessing Capacitance only.

Suppose a capacitor having a capacitance of C farads to be connected across an a.c. supply and suppose the instantaneous value of the applied voltage* to be represented by:

$$v = V_m \sin \theta = V_m \sin 2\pi ft \quad . \quad . \quad (160)$$

If the applied voltage increases by dv volt in dt second (Fig. 109), then from (102),

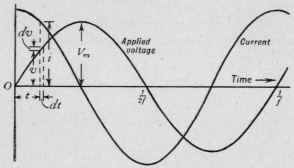

FIG. 109.—Voltage and current waves for purely capacitive circuit.

$$\left. \begin{array}{l} \text{instantaneous value} \\ \text{of current} \end{array} \right\} = i = C \cdot dv/dt$$

$$= C \frac{d}{dt}(V_m \sin 2\pi ft)$$

$$= 2\pi fC V_m \cos 2\pi ft$$

$$= 2\pi fC V_m \sin (2\pi ft + \pi/2) \quad (161)$$

* It will be noted that we start with the voltage wave in this case, whereas with inductance we started with the current wave. The reason for this is that in the case of inductance, we derive the induced e.m.f. by differentiating the current expression; whereas with capacitance, we derive the current by differentiating the voltage expression.

Comparison of (160) and (161) shows that the current leads in front of the applied voltage by a quarter of a cycle, and the current and voltage can be represented vectorially as in Fig. 110.

From expression (161) it follows that the maximum value I_m of the current is $2\pi f C V_m$,

$$\therefore \qquad \frac{V_m}{I_m} = \frac{1}{2\pi f C}.$$

Hence, if I and V be the r.m.s. values,

$$\frac{V}{I} = \frac{1}{2\pi f C} = \text{capacitive reactance of capacitor.}$$

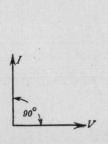

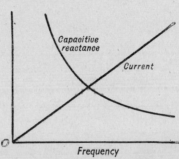

FIG. 110.—Vector diagram for purely capacitive circuit.

FIG. 111.—Variation of reactance and current with frequency in a purely capacitive circuit.

The capacitive reactance is expressed in ohms and is represented by the symbol X_c.

Hence, $\qquad I = 2\pi f C V = \dfrac{V}{X_c} \qquad . \quad . \quad . \quad (162)$

The capacitive reactance is inversely proportional to the frequency and the current produced by a given voltage is proportional to the frequency, as shown in Fig. 111.

88. Alternating Current in a Circuit consisting of Resistance, Inductance and Capacitance in Series. We have already considered resistive, inductive and capacitive

circuits separately.   An actual circuit, however, may
have resistance and inductance,* or resistance and
capacitance, or resistance, inductance and capacitance in
series.   Hence, if we first consider the general case of
R, L and C in series, we can adapt the results to the
other two cases by merely omitting the capacitive or
the inductive reactance from the expressions derived for
the general case.

Fig. 112 shows a resistance R ohms, an inductance L
henrys and a capacitance C farads connected in series
across an a.c. supply of V volts (r.m.s.).   Let I be the
r.m.s. value of the current in amperes.

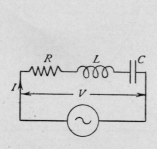

FIG. 112.—Circuit with R, L
and C in series.

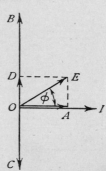

FIG. 113.—Vector diagram
for Fig. 112.

From Art. 85 the p.d. across R is RI volts in phase
with the current and is represented by OA in phase with
OI in Fig. 113.†   From Art. 86, the p.d. across L is

* A coil possesses resistance and inductance, and its
resistance can be considered as part of the total resistance of
the circuit.   If the coil has an iron core, the hysteresis and
eddy-current losses in the core are equivalent to an increase in
the effective resistance of the coil.   Thus, if the iron loss in the
core is 40 watts when the current in the coil is 5 A, the resistor
to give the same loss when connected in series with the circuit
has a resistance of $40/5^2$, namely $1 \cdot 6$ Ω.   Hence if the winding
has a resistance of, say, 4 Ω, the effective resistance of the coil
is $(4+1 \cdot 6)$, namely $5 \cdot 6$ Ω.

† When drawing a vector diagram of this type, one should
always start with the vector representing the quantity that is

$2\pi fLI$, leading $90°$ in front of the current and is represented by vector OB; and from Art. 87 the p.d. across C is $I/(2\pi fC)$, lagging $90°$ behind the current and is represented by vector OC.

Since OB and OC are in direct opposition, their resultant is $OD=OB-OC$, OB being assumed greater than OC in Fig. 113; and the supply voltage is the vectorial sum of OA and OD, namely OE.

From Fig. 113,

$$OE^2=OA^2+OD^2=OA^2+(OB-OC)^2$$

$$\therefore \qquad V^2=(RI)^2+\left(2\pi fLI-\frac{I}{2\pi fC}\right)^2$$

so that

$$I=\frac{V}{\sqrt{\left[R^2+\left(2\pi fL-\frac{1}{2\pi fC}\right)^2\right]}}=\frac{V}{Z} \qquad (163$$

where $Z=$impedance of circuit in ohms

$$=\sqrt{\left[R^2+\left(2\pi fL-\frac{1}{2\pi fC}\right)^2\right]} \qquad . \quad . \quad (164)$$

From this expression it is seen that:

$$\text{resultant reactance}=2\pi fL-\frac{1}{2\pi fC}$$
$$=\text{inductive reactance}-\text{capacitive reactance.}$$

If $\phi=$phase difference between the current and the supply voltage,

$$\tan \phi=\frac{AE}{OA}=\frac{OD}{OA}=\frac{OB-OC}{OA}=\frac{2\pi fLI-I/(2\pi fC)}{RI}$$

$$=\frac{\text{inductive reactance}-\text{capacitive reactance}}{\text{resistance}} \qquad (165)$$

If the inductive reactance is greater than the capacitive reactance, $\tan \phi$ is positive and the current lags behind

common to the various components of the circuit.   Thus with a series circuit it is the current that is the same in all the components, so that in Fig 113, OI is the first vector to be drawn.   For parallel circuits it is the voltage that is common to the various components, so that the voltage vector is then the first to be drawn.

the supply voltage; if less, tan ϕ is negative, signifying that the current leads in front of the supply voltage.

If a circuit consists of a coil having resistance R ohms and inductance L henrys, such a circuit can be considered as a resistance and an inductance in series; and from (164),

$$\text{impedance} = \sqrt{[R^2 + (2\pi f L)^2]}$$

and from (165) the phase difference ϕ between the current and the supply voltage is given by:

$\phi = \tan^{-1} (2\pi f L/R)$, the current lagging behind the voltage.

Example 31. *A resistance of 12 Ω, an inductance of 0·15 H and a capacitance of 100 μF are connected across a 100-V, 50-c/s supply. Calculate:* (a) *the impedance,* b) *the current,* (c) *the voltages across R, L and C and* (d) *the phase difference between the current and the supply voltage.*

The circuit diagram is the same as that of Fig. 112.

(a) From (164),

$$Z = \sqrt{\left[(12)^2 + \left(2 \times 3 \cdot 14 \times 50 \times 0 \cdot 15 - \frac{10^6}{2 \times 3 \cdot 14 \times 50 \times 100} \right)^2 \right]}$$
$$= \sqrt{[144 + (47 \cdot 1 - 31 \cdot 85)^2]} = 19 \cdot 4 \ \Omega.$$

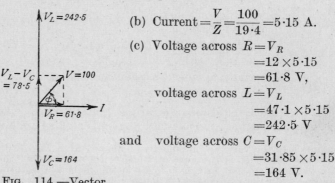

(b) Current $= \dfrac{V}{Z} = \dfrac{100}{19 \cdot 4} = 5 \cdot 15$ A.

(c) Voltage across $R = V_R$
$$= 12 \times 5 \cdot 15$$
$$= 61 \cdot 8 \ \text{V},$$
voltage across $L = V_L$
$$= 47 \cdot 1 \times 5 \cdot 15$$
$$= 242 \cdot 5 \ \text{V}$$
and voltage across $C = V_C$
$$= 31 \cdot 85 \times 5 \cdot 15$$
$$= 164 \ \text{V}.$$

Fig. 114.—Vector diagram for Example 31.

These voltages and current are represented vectorially in Fig. 114.

(d) Phase difference between current and supply voltage

$$=\phi=\cos^{-1}(V_R/V)=\cos^{-1} 61\cdot8/100=51° 50'.$$

Or alternatively, from (165),

$$\phi=\tan^{-1}\frac{47\cdot1-31\cdot85}{12}=\tan^{-1} 1\cdot271=51° 48'.$$

89. Circuit with R, L and C in Series; Effect of Frequency Variation. In Fig. 113, we assumed the capacitive reactance to be less than the inductive reactance, and in consequence the expressions for capacitive reactance in (163), (164) and (165) have a negative sign in front of them. This was a matter of chance in the above discussion, but it is, in general, found convenient to regard inductive reactance as positive and capacitive reactance as negative.*

Fig. 115 shows the effect of frequency upon the inductive and capacitive reactances and upon the resultant reactance and the impedance of a circuit having R, L and C in series; and Fig. 116 shows how the values of the current and of the voltages across R, L and C vary with the frequency, the applied voltage being assumed constant. The actual shapes and the relative magnitudes of these curves depend upon the values chosen for R, L and C; and the curves in Fig. 115 and 116 have been derived for the circuit of Ex. 31, where $R=12\ \Omega$, $L=0\cdot15$ H and $C=100\ \mu$F.

It will be seen from Fig. 115 that for frequency OA, the inductive reactance AB and the capacitive reactance AC are equal in value so that their resultant is zero. Consequently the impedance is then the same as the resistance AD of the circuit. Furthermore, as the frequency is reduced below OA or increased above OA, the impedance increases and therefore the current decreases.

* These positive and negative signs are merely conventions. A 100-Ω capacitive reactance has exactly the same effect as 100-Ω inductive reactance as far as the magnitude of the current for a given voltage is concerned. It is only the phase of the current that is affected.

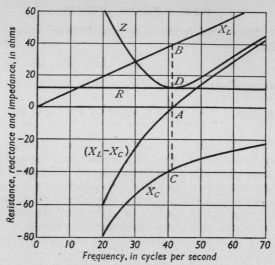

Fig. 115.—Variation of reactances and impedance with frequency.

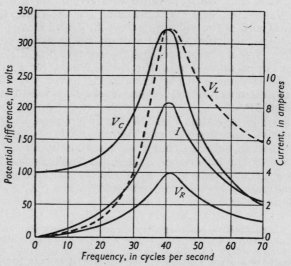

Fig. 116.—Effect of frequency variation upon voltages across R, L and C in series.

Also, it will be seen from Fig. 116 that when the frequency is OA, the voltages across L and C are equal and each is much greater than the supply voltage. Such a condition is referred to as *resonance*, an effect that is extremely important in radio work, partly because it provides a simple method of increasing the sensitivity of a radio receiver and partly because it gives selectivity, i.e. it enables a signal of given frequency to be considerably magnified so that it can be separated from signals of other frequencies.

90. Resonance in a Circuit having R, L and C in Series. From the preceding Article, it is evident that for a series circuit, resonance occurs when:

inductive reactance —capacitive reactance $=0$

i.e. when $\qquad 2\pi fL = \dfrac{1}{2\pi fC}$

or $\qquad\qquad f = \dfrac{1}{2\pi\sqrt{(LC)}}$ . . . (166)

At this resonant frequency, $Z = R$ and $I = V/R$. If the resistance is small compared with the inductive and capacitive reactances, the p.d.'s across the latter, namely $2\pi fLI$ and $I/(2\pi fC)$, are many times the supply voltage, as represented vectorially in Fig. 117.

$$\text{Voltage magnification obtained at resonance} \left.\right\} = \frac{\text{voltage across } L \text{ (or } C)}{\text{supply voltage}}$$

$$= \frac{2\pi fLI}{RI} = \frac{2\pi fL}{R} \qquad (167)$$

$= Q$-factor of the circuit.

Since $2\pi f = 1/\sqrt{(LC)}$ at resonance,

$\therefore \qquad Q\text{-factor} = \dfrac{2\pi fL}{R} = \dfrac{1}{R}\sqrt{\left(\dfrac{L}{C}\right)}$. (168)

In Art. 112 of *Principles of Electricity* it was explained that in a series resonant circuit the magnetic energy stored in L at the instant of maximum current is exactly

7

equal to the electrostatic energy stored in C at the instant of maximum p.d. across C, and that the power taken from the supply is merely that required to provide the I^2R loss involved in moving this energy backwards and forwards between L and C. It was also shown in Art. 111 of the above-mentioned book that when a capacitor is discharged through an inductor of low resistance, the frequency of the oscillations is given by $f = 1/[2\pi\sqrt{(LC)}]$ cycles per second, and this is termed the *natural frequency* of the circuit. Since the value of the resonant frequency

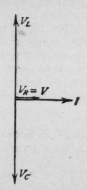

FIG. 117.—Vector diagram for resonant circuit.

is also given by the same expression, it follows that resonance occurs in a series circuit when the frequency of the applied voltage is the same as the natural frequency of oscillation of the circuit.

Example 32. *A circuit consists of a resistance of 4 Ω, an inductance of 0·5 H and a variable capacitance in series across a 100-V, 50-c/s supply. Calculate:* (a) *the capacitance to give resonance,* (b) *the voltages across the inductance and the capacitance and* (c) *the Q-factor of the circuit.*

(a) For resonance, $\quad 2\pi fL = \dfrac{1}{2\pi fC}$

$\therefore \qquad\qquad\qquad C = \dfrac{1}{(2 \times 3\cdot14 \times 50)^2 \times 0\cdot5}$

$\qquad\qquad\qquad\qquad = 20\cdot3 \times 10^{-6}$ F

$\qquad\qquad\qquad\qquad = 20\cdot3 \ \mu$F

(b) At resonance, $\quad I = \dfrac{V}{R} = \dfrac{100}{4} = 25$ A.

$\therefore$ p.d. across inductance $= V_L = 2 \times 3\cdot14 \times 50 \times 0\cdot5 \times 25$

$\qquad\qquad\qquad\qquad\qquad = 3925$ V

and p.d. across capacitor $= V_C = 3925$ V.

Or alternatively, from (162),
$$V_C = \frac{25 \times 10^6}{2 \times 3 \cdot 14 \times 50 \times 20 \cdot 3} = 3925 \text{ V}.$$

The voltages and current are represented vectorially, but not to scale, in Fig. 117.

(c) From (167),
$$Q\text{-factor} = \frac{2 \times 3 \cdot 14 \times 50 \times 0 \cdot 5}{4} = 39 \cdot 25.$$

A resonant circuit of this type is often termed an *acceptor* since the current is a maximum at resonant frequency.

91. Alternating Current in a Circuit consisting of Resistance, Inductance and Capacitance in Parallel. Suppose

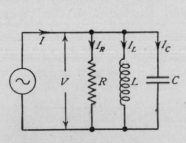

FIG. 118.—*R*, *L* and *C* in parallel.

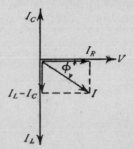

FIG. 119.—Vector diagram for Fig. 118.

a resistance R ohms, an inductance L henrys and a capacitance C farads to be connected in parallel, as in Fig. 118, across a supply voltage V of frequency f cycles per second.

Current through $R = I_R = \dfrac{V}{R}$, in phase with V,

current through $L = I_L = \dfrac{V}{2\pi fL}$, lagging 90° behind V

and current through $C = I_C = 2\pi fCV$, leading 90° in front of V.

These currents and the supply voltage are represented vectorially in Fig. 119, where it is assumed that I_L is greater than I_C.

Resultant of I_L and $I_C = I_L - I_C$,
and current from supply $= I =$ vectorial sum of I_R and $(I_L - I_C)$
$$= \sqrt{[I_R^2 + (I_L - I_C)^2]}.$$

If $\phi =$ phase difference between the supply voltage and the resultant current,

$$\tan \phi = \frac{I_L - I_C}{I_R}.$$

If $\tan \phi$ is positive, the resultant current lags behind the supply voltage; if negative, the resultant current leads.

92. Resonance in Parallel Circuits. If the values of L and C in Fig. 118 were such that $I_L = I_C$, $(I_L - I_C)$ would be zero and the resultant current $I = I_R$; so that,

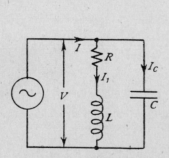

FIG. 120.—Coil and capacitor in parallel.

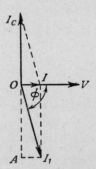

FIG. 121.—Vector diagram for Fig. 120.

theoretically, current could be flowing backwards and forwards round L and C without any current having to be supplied from the mains. In practice, the inductive circuit would have some resistance, however small, so that the parallel inductive and capacitive circuits would actually be as represented in Fig. 120.

Current through inductive circuit $\left.\right\} = I_1 = \dfrac{V}{\sqrt{[R^2 + (2\pi f L)^2]}}$

and   phase angle between$\left.\begin{array}{c} \\ I_1 \text{ and } V \end{array}\right\} = \phi = \tan^{-1} \dfrac{2\pi fL}{R}.$

Since R is assumed to be very small compared with $2\pi fL$, ϕ is nearly 90°.

Current taken by capacitor $= I_C = 2\pi fCV$, leading 90° in front of V.

If I_1 and I_C be such that the resultant current I is in phase with the supply voltage as shown in Fig. 121, the circuit is said to be in resonance.

From Fig. 121, $I_C = OA = I_1 \sin \phi$ . . .   (169)

But $\sin \phi = \dfrac{\text{reactance of coil}}{\text{impedance of coil}} = \dfrac{2\pi fL}{\sqrt{[R^2 + (2\pi fL)^2]}}.$

Substituting for I_C, I_1 and $\sin \phi$ in (169), we have:

$$2\pi fCV = \frac{2\pi fLV}{R^2 + (2\pi fL)^2}.$$

If R is very small compared with $2\pi fL$, as in radio circuits (see Ex. 33),

$$C = \frac{1}{(2\pi f)^2 L}$$

so that $$f = \frac{1}{2\pi\sqrt{(LC)}}$$ . . . .   (170)

which is the same as the resonant frequency of a series circuit.

From Fig. 121, it is seen that when resonance occurs in a parallel circuit, the current circulating in L and C may be many times greater than the resultant current; in other words, by means of a parallel resonant circuit, the current taken from the supply can be greatly magnified, thus:

$$\frac{I_C}{I} = \frac{I_1 \sin \phi}{I} = \frac{\sin \phi}{\cos \phi} = \tan \phi = \frac{2\pi fL}{R}$$
$$= Q\text{-factor of circuit.}$$

It will be noted that the Q-factor is a measure of voltage magnification in a series circuit and of current magnification in a parallel circuit.

The resultant current in a resonant parallel circuit is in phase with the supply voltage,

$$\left.\begin{array}{c}\text{and impedance of such}\\ \text{a circuit}\end{array}\right\} = \frac{V}{I} = \frac{V}{OA \cot \phi}$$

$$= \frac{V}{I_C} \tan \phi = \frac{1}{2\pi fC} \cdot \frac{2\pi fL}{R}$$

$$= \frac{L}{CR} \quad \cdots \quad \cdots \quad (171)$$

This means that a resonant parallel circuit is equivalent to a non-inductive resistance of $L/(CR)$ ohms. This quantity is often termed the *dynamic impedance* of the circuit; and it is obvious that the lower the resistance of the coil, the higher is the dynamic impedance of the parallel circuit. This type of circuit when used in radio work is referred to as a *rejector* since its impedance is a maximum and the current a minimum at resonance.

Example 33. *A tuned circuit consisting of a coil having an inductance of 200 μH and a resistance of 20 Ω in parallel with a variable capacitance is connected in series with a resistance of 8000 Ω across a 60-V supply having a frequency of 1 megacycle/second. Calculate: (a) the value of C to give resonance, (b) the dynamic impedance and the Q-factor of the tuned circuit and (c) the current in each branch.*

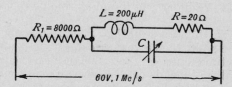

Fig. 122.—Circuit diagram for Example 33.

(This arrangement is the equivalent circuit of a thermionic valve used with a tuned-output circuit referred to in Art. 175.)

(a) 1 megacycle/sec $= 10^6$ c/s,

∴   reactance of $L = 2 \times 3{\cdot}14 \times 10^6 \times 200 \times 10^{-6}$
                 $= 1256 \ \Omega,$

so that the resistance of the coil is very small compared with its reactance.

Substituting in expression (170), we have:

$$10^6 = \frac{1}{2 \times 3 \cdot 14 \sqrt{(200 \times 10^{-6} \times C)}}$$

$$\therefore \qquad C = 126 \cdot 7 \times 10^{-12} \text{ farad}$$
$$= 126 \cdot 7 \text{ picofarads.}$$

(b) $\left.\begin{array}{c}\text{Dynamic} \\ \text{impedance}\end{array}\right\} = \dfrac{L}{CR} = \dfrac{200 \times 10^{-6}}{126 \cdot 7 \times 10^{-12} \times 20} = 79{,}000 \ \Omega$

and $\quad Q\text{-factor} = \dfrac{2\pi f L}{R} = \dfrac{2 \times 3 \cdot 14 \times 10^6 \times 200 \times 10^{-6}}{20}$

$$= 62 \cdot 8.$$

(c) Total equivalent resistance of circuit

$$= 79{,}000 + 8000$$
$$= 87{,}000 \ \Omega.$$

$$\therefore \qquad \text{current} = \frac{60}{87{,}000} \text{ A}$$
$$= 0 \cdot 69 \text{ mA.}$$

$\left.\begin{array}{c}\text{P.d.} \quad \text{across} \\ \text{tuned circuit}\end{array}\right\} = 0 \cdot 69 \times 10^{-3} \times 79{,}000 = 54 \cdot 5 \text{ V}$

$\therefore$ current through inductive branch of tuned circuit

$$= \frac{54 \cdot 5}{\sqrt{[(20)^2 + (1256)^2]}} = \frac{54 \cdot 5}{1256} \text{ A}$$
$$= 43 \cdot 4 \text{ mA,}$$

and $\left.\begin{array}{c}\text{current} \\ \text{through} \quad C\end{array}\right\} = 2 \times 3 \cdot 14 \times 10^6 \times 126 \cdot 7 \times 10^{-12} \times 54 \cdot 5 \text{ A}$

$$= 43 \cdot 4 \text{ mA.}$$

Actually there must be a very slight difference between the currents in the two parallel branches but it is so small as to be negligible. The results show that the current in each of the parallel circuits is about $62 \cdot 8$ times the resultant current taken from the supply.

93. Current Locus for a Circuit having Constant Inductance and Variable Resistance. Suppose a circuit having a constant inductive reactance of X ohms and a variable resistance to be connected across a constant voltage V at a frequency of f cycles/second, as in Fig. 123.

When $R=0$, current $=V/X$ and is represented by

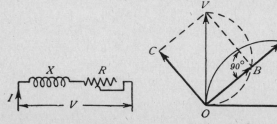

FIG. 123.—Constant inductance and variable resistance in series.

FIG. 124.—Vector diagram for Fig. 123.

OA in Fig. 124, lagging 90° behind the supply voltage OV.

For the general case of R equal to some finite value,

$$I = \frac{V}{\sqrt{(R^2+X^2)}},$$

and is represented by OI in Fig. 124.

Draw VB perpendicular to OI and complete the rectangle $OBVC$; then, $OB=IR$, and $BV=OC=XI$.

Also, since VB and OB are at right angles to each other, the locus of B must be a semicircle on OV.

Join IA, as shown dotted in Fig. 124.

For triangles IOA and VOB, $I\hat{O}A = 90° - V\hat{O}B = O\hat{V}B$

Also, $\dfrac{OV}{BV} = \dfrac{V}{XI} = \dfrac{V}{X} \cdot \dfrac{1}{I} = \dfrac{OA}{OI}.$

Hence the two triangles are similar,

so that $\qquad\qquad O\hat{I}A = O\hat{B}V = 90°,$

and the locus of the extremity of the current vector must therefore be a semicircle on OA.

94. Current Locus for a Circuit having Constant Resistance and Variable Inductance. The circuit and vector diagrams are given in Fig. 125 and 126 respectively.

When $X = 0$, current $= V/R$ and is represented by OA in phase with OV.

If OI represents the current for the general case of X having some finite value, then OB and OC represent the corresponding voltages across R and X respectively.

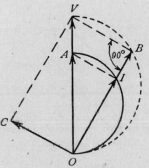

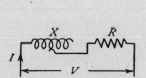

FIG. 125.—Constant resistance and variable inductance in series.

FIG. 126.—Vector diagram for Fig. 125.

Since $O\hat{B}V$ is a right angle, the locus of B is a semicircle on OV; and since OI is proportional to and in phase with OB, the locus of the extremity of the current vector must be a semicircle on OA.

When dealing with locus diagrams, it is helpful to remember that the value of the current is proportional to the p.d. across the constant part of the circuit, for example, across X in Fig. 123 and across R in Fig. 125.

95. Power in an A.C. Circuit. Let us consider the general case of the current differing in phase from the applied voltage; thus in Fig. 127 (a), the current is shown lagging by an angle ϕ behind the voltage.

Let   instantaneous value of voltage $= v = V_m \sin \theta$
then   instantaneous value of current $= i = I_m \sin (\theta - \phi)$.

7*

At any instant, the value of the power is given by the product of the voltage and the current at that instant, i.e. instantaneous value of power $=vi$ watts.

By multiplying the corresponding instantaneous values of voltage and current, the curve representing the variation of power in Fig. 127 (b) can be derived:

i.e. instantaneous $\left.\vphantom{\rule{0pt}{2em}}\right\}$ power

$=vi = V_m \sin\theta \,.\, I_m \sin(\theta - \phi)$

$= \frac{1}{2} V_m I_m [\cos\phi - \cos(2\theta - \phi)]$

$= \frac{1}{2} V_m I_m \cos\phi - \frac{1}{2} V_m I_m \cos(2\theta - \phi).$

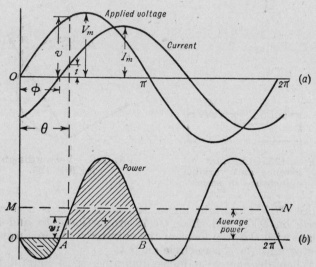

FIG. 127.—Voltage, current and power curves.

From this expression, it is seen that the instantaneous value of the power consists of two components:

(1) $\frac{1}{2} V_m I_m \cos\phi$, which contains no reference to θ and therefore remains constant in value.

(2) $\frac{1}{2} V_m I_m \cos(2\theta - \phi)$, the term 2θ indicating that it varies at twice the supply frequency; thus in Fig. 127 (b), it is seen that the power undergoes two cycles of variation for one cycle of the voltage wave. Furthermore, since

the average value of a cosine curve over a *complete* cycle is zero, it follows that this component does not contribute anything towards the *average* value of the power absorbed by the circuit.

Hence, $\left.\begin{array}{l}\text{average power}\\ \text{over one cycle}\end{array}\right\} = \frac{1}{2}V_m I_m \cos\phi$

$$= \frac{V_m}{\sqrt{2}} \cdot \frac{I_m}{\sqrt{2}} \cdot \cos\phi$$

$$= VI \cos\phi \quad . \quad . \quad . \quad (172)$$

where V and I are the r.m.s. values of the voltage and current respectively. In Fig. 127 (b), the average power is represented by the height above the horizontal axis of the dotted line MN drawn midway between the positive and negative peaks of the power curve.

It will be noticed that during interval OA in Fig. 127 (b), the power is negative, and the shaded negative area represents energy returned from the circuit to the alternator. The shaded positive area during interval AB represents energy supplied from the alternator to the circuit; and the difference between the two areas represents the net energy absorbed by the circuit during interval OB. (The physical interpretation of the negative and positive energies is fully discussed in Art. 102 of *Principles of Electricity*.) The larger the phase difference between the voltage and current, the smaller is the difference between the positive and negative areas and the smaller, therefore, is the average power over the complete cycle.

96. Power Factor. In a.c. work the product of the r.m.s. values of the applied voltage and current is VI *voltamperes*,[*] the latter term being used to distinguish this quantity from the power, expressed in watts. In general, the number of watts is less than the number of voltamperes and the latter has to be multiplied by a quantity termed *power factor* to give the power in watts:

i.e. power in watts $=$ no. of voltamperes $\times$ power factor

$$= VI \times \text{power factor} \quad . \quad . \quad (173)$$

---

[*] The term "apparent power" is obsolete.

or   power factor $= \left\{ \dfrac{\overline{\text{power in watts}}}{\substack{\text{product of r.m.s. values} \\ \text{of voltage and current}}} \right.$ (174)

Comparison of expressions (172) and (173) shows that for *sinusoidal* voltage and current:

$$\text{power factor} = \cos \phi \quad . \quad . \quad (175)$$

From the general vector diagram of Fig. 113 for a *series* circuit, it follows that:

$$\cos \phi = \frac{IR}{V} = \frac{IR}{IZ} = \frac{\text{resistance}}{\text{impedance}} \quad . \quad (176)$$

97. Active and Reactive Currents. If a current I lags behind the applied voltage V by an angle ϕ, as in

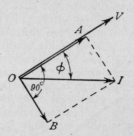

Fig. 128.—Active and reactive components of current.

Fig. 128, it can be resolved into two components, OA in phase with the voltage and OB lagging by 90°.

Since power $= IV \cos \phi = V \times OI \cos \phi = V \times OA$ watts, therefore OA is termed the *active* or *power* component of the current:

i.e.   active component of current $= I \cos \phi$. (177)

Power due to component $OB = V \times OB \cos 90° = 0$, so that OB is termed the *reactive* or *wattless* component of the current:

i.e   reactive component of current $= I \sin \phi$. (178)

Example 34. *A single-phase motor operating off a 400-V, 50-c/s supply is developing 10 b.h.p. with an*

*efficiency of 84 per cent and a power factor of 0·7 lagging.
Calculate:* (a) *the input kilovoltamperes and* (b) *the active
and reactive components of the current.*

(a) $\qquad$ Efficiency $= \dfrac{\text{output power in watts}}{\text{input power in watts}}$

$$= \frac{\text{b.h.p.} \times 746}{IV \times \text{p.f.}}$$

∴ $\qquad\qquad 0 \cdot 84 = \dfrac{10 \times 746}{IV \times 0 \cdot 7}$

so that $\qquad\qquad IV = 12{,}690$ voltamperes.

∴ input kilovoltamperes $= 12 \cdot 69$ kVA.

(b) Current taken by motor $= \dfrac{\text{input voltamperes}}{\text{voltage}}$.

$$= \frac{12{,}690}{400} = 31 \cdot 7 \text{ A}$$

∴ $\qquad \left.\begin{array}{l} \text{active component} \\ \text{of current} \end{array}\right\} = 31 \cdot 7 \times 0 \cdot 7 = 22 \cdot 19 \text{ A}$

Since $\sin \phi = \sqrt{(1 - \cos^2 \phi)} = \sqrt{[1 - (0 \cdot 7)^2]} = 0 \cdot 714$,

∴ $\qquad \left.\begin{array}{l} \text{reactive component} \\ \text{of current} \end{array}\right\} = 31 \cdot 7 \times 0 \cdot 714 = 22 \cdot 6 \text{ A}.$

Example 35. *Calculate the capacitance required in
parallel with the motor of Example 34 to raise the power
factor to* 0·9 *lagging.*

The circuit and vector diagrams are given in Fig. 129
and 130 respectively, M being the motor taking a current
I_M of 31·7 A.

Current I_C taken by the capacitor must be such that
when combined with I_M, the resultant current I lags
behind the voltage by an angle ϕ, where $\cos \phi = 0 \cdot 9$.
From Fig. 130,

$$\text{active component of } I_M = I_M \cos \phi_M = 31 \cdot 7 \times 0 \cdot 7$$
$$= 22 \cdot 19 \text{ A}$$

and active component of $I = I \cos \phi = I \times 0 \cdot 9$.

Since these active components are equal,

$$\therefore \qquad I = \frac{22 \cdot 19}{0 \cdot 9} = 24 \cdot 65 \text{ A.}$$

Reactive component of $I_M = I_M \sin \phi_M$
$$= 22 \cdot 6 \text{ A (from Example 34)}$$

and reactive component of $I = I \sin \phi = 24 \cdot 65 \sqrt{[1 - (0 \cdot 9)^2]}$
$$= 24 \cdot 65 \times 0 \cdot 436 = 10 \cdot 75 \text{ A.}$$

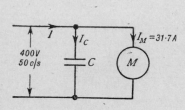

FIG. 129.—Circuit diagram for Example 35.

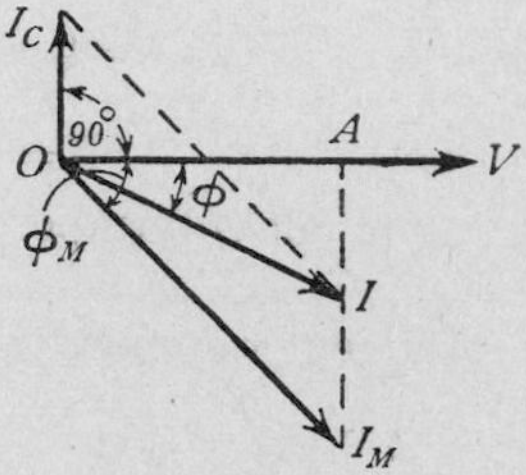

FIG. 130.—Vector diagram for Fig. 129.

From Fig. 130 it will be seen that:

I_C =reactive component of I_M —reactive component of I
$$= 22 \cdot 6 - 10 \cdot 75 = 11 \cdot 85 \text{ A.}$$

But $I_C = 2\pi f C V$

$\therefore 11 \cdot 85 = 2 \times 3 \cdot 14 \times 50 \times C \times 400$

and $C = 94 \cdot 3 \times 10^{-6}$ farad
$$= 94 \cdot 3 \ \mu\text{F.}$$

From the above example it will be seen that the effect of connecting $94 \cdot 3 \ \mu$F in parallel with the motor has been to reduce the current taken from the supply from $31 \cdot 7$ to $24 \cdot 65$ A, without altering either the current or the power taken by the motor. This enables an economy to be effected in the size of the generating plant and in the cross-sectional area of copper in the cable.

98. Measurement of Power in a Single-phase Circuit. Since the product of the voltage and current in an a.c. circuit must be multiplied by the power factor to give the power in watts, the most convenient method of measuring the power is to use a wattmeter, the simplest form of which is the dynamometer type shown diagrammatically in Fig. 153. The fixed coil is connected in series with the load, and the moving coil is connected in series with a high non-inductive resistance across the supply so that the current through the moving coil is proportional to and practically in phase with the supply voltage.

The principle of action of the dynamometer wattmeter has been described in Art. 145 of *Principles of Electricity*.

Summary of Important Formulae in Chapter V

$$\text{Frequency} = f = \frac{Np}{60} \quad . \quad . \quad . \quad (138)$$

For n equidistant mid-ordinates over half a cycle,

$$\text{average value} = \frac{i_1 + i_2 + \cdots + i_n}{n} \quad . \quad . \quad (139)$$

$$\text{and r.m.s. or effective value} \Big\} = \sqrt{\left(\frac{i_1^2 + i_2^2 + \cdots + i_n^2}{n} \right)} \quad . \quad (141)$$

For sinusoidal waves,

$$\text{average value} = 0 \cdot 637 \times \text{maximum value} \quad (145)$$

$$\text{and r.m.s. or effective value} \Big\} = 0 \cdot 707 \times \text{maximum value} \quad (147)$$

$$\text{Form factor} = \frac{\text{r.m.s. value}}{\text{average value}} \quad . \quad . \quad (143)$$

$$= 1 \cdot 11 \text{ for a sine wave} \quad . \quad (150)$$

$$\text{Peak or crest factor} \Big\} = \frac{\text{peak or maximum value}}{\text{r.m.s. value}} \quad (144)$$

$$= 1 \cdot 414 \text{ for a sine wave} \quad . \quad (151)$$

For a circuit with R, L and C in series,

$$\text{Impedance} = Z = \sqrt{\left[R^2 + \left(2\pi f L - \frac{1}{2\pi f C} \right)^2 \right]} \quad (164)$$

where $\qquad 2\pi f L = $ inductive reactance in ohms

and $\qquad \dfrac{1}{2\pi f C} = $ capacitive reactance in ohms

If $\phi=$phase difference between current and supply voltage,

$$\tan \phi = \frac{2\pi fL - 1/(2\pi fC)}{R} \quad . \quad . \quad (165)$$

$$\cos \phi = R/Z \quad . \quad . \quad . \quad . \quad . \quad (176)$$

$$\sin \phi = \frac{2\pi fL - 1/(2\pi fC)}{Z}$$

For purely resistive circuit,

$$I = \frac{V}{R} \quad \text{and} \quad \phi = 0.$$

For purely inductive circuit,

$$I = \frac{V}{2\pi fL}$$

and $\quad\quad\quad\quad \phi = 90°$, current lagging.

For purely capacitive circuit,

$$I = 2\pi fCV$$

and $\quad\quad\quad\quad \phi = 90°$, current leading.

For resonance in a series circuit,

$$f = \frac{1}{2\pi\sqrt{(LC)}} \quad . \quad . \quad . \quad (166)$$

and $\quad\quad$ Q-factor $= \dfrac{2\pi fL}{R} = \dfrac{1}{R}\sqrt{\left(\dfrac{L}{C}\right)} \quad . \quad (168)$

For resonance in a parallel circuit,

$$C = \frac{L}{R^2 + (2\pi fL)^2}$$

and $\quad\quad$ $f = \dfrac{1}{2\pi\sqrt{(LC)}}$ when $R \ll 2\pi fL \quad . \quad (170)$

Dynamic impedance of reson-$\Big\}$ $= \dfrac{L}{CR} \quad . \quad (171)$
ant parallel circuit

In an a.c. circuit, $\Big\}$ $= VI \times$ power factor $\quad (173)$
power in watts

or $\quad$ power factor $= \dfrac{\text{power in watts}}{\text{r.m.s. volts} \times \text{r.m.s. amperes}}$

$$= \frac{\text{kilowatts}}{\text{kilovoltamperes}} = \frac{\text{kW}}{\text{kVA}} \quad . \quad (174)$$

For sinusoidal waves of voltage and current having phase difference ϕ,

$$\text{power factor} = \cos \phi \qquad . \quad . \quad (175)$$

$$\text{and power (in watts)} = VI \cos \phi \qquad . \quad (172)$$

$$\left.\begin{array}{l}\text{Active or power com-}\\ \text{ponent of current}\end{array}\right\} = I \cos \phi \quad . \quad . \quad (177)$$

$$\left.\begin{array}{l}\text{Reactive or wattless com-}\\ \text{ponent of current}\end{array}\right\} = I \sin \phi \quad . \quad . \quad (178)$$

EXAMPLES V

1. Describe, and explain the action of, an ammeter suitable for measuring the r.m.s. value of a current.

An alternating current has a periodic time $2T$. The current for a time one-third of T is 50 A; for a time one-sixth of T it is 20 A; and zero for a time equal to one-half of T. Calculate the r.m.s. and average values of this current. (E.M.E.U.)

2. Define form-factor.

Determine (a) the mean value; (b) the r.m.s. value; (c) the form-factor of the alternating e.m.f. 'wave, of which the instantaneous values measured at equal intervals of time over half a cycle are as follows: 0, 42, 120, 210, 320, 450, 480, 360, 180, 62, 0. (U.E.I.)

3. An alternating voltage has a trapezoidal wave-form with the following values over one complete cycle:

Time (sec) .	.	0	0·02	0·04	0·06	0·08	0·10	0·12	0·14	0·16
Voltage (V)	.	0	40	80	80	0	−40	−80	−80	0

Plot to scale, on the same axes, (a) this voltage, (b) the current which would flow when the voltage is applied to a 100-μF capacitor. The points are connected by straight lines.

Calculate the r.m.s. value and the form factor of the current.

(U.L.C.I.)

4. Define the root-mean-square value of an alternating current. Explain carefully why this value is more generally employed in a.c. measurements than either the average or the peak value.

Under what circumstances would it be necessary to know (a) the average and (b) the peak value of an alternating current or voltage?

Calculate the ratio of the peak values of two alternating currents which have the same r.m.s. values, when the wave-form of one is sinusoidal and that of the other triangular. What effect would lack of symmetry of the triangular wave about its peak value have upon this ratio? (App. El., L.U.)

5. Explain why an alternating quantity is normally expressed in terms of its root-mean-square value.

The positive half of a symmetrical a.c. voltage waveform varies in the following manner:

From 0 to 0·005 sec—a uniform rise from 0 to 50 V.

From 0·005 to 0·015 sec—remains constant at 50 V.

From 0·015 to 0·02 sec—a uniform fall from 50 V to 0 V.

Determine, graphically or by calculation, the r.m.s. value of the waveform and calculate its form factor. (U.E.I.)

6. Explain the meaning of the term "root-mean-square" and discuss its applicability to the measurement of alternating currents and voltages.

A voltage $100 \sin 314t$ is applied to a half-wave rectifier in series with a resistance of 50 Ω. The rectifier may be assumed to have a negligible resistance in the forward direction and an infinite resistance in the reverse direction. Determine the r.m.s. value of the current taken from the source. (Joint Section A)

7. Explain why the r.m.s. value of an alternating current or voltage is used to denote its magnitude.

A circuit has a resistance to current in one direction of 10 Ω and a resistance of 50 Ω to current in the opposite direction. A sinusoidal voltage of maximum value 100 V is applied to the above circuit in series with (a) a moving-iron ammeter, (b) a moving-coil ammeter and (c) a moving-coil ammeter with a full-wave rectifier. Calculate the readings. (E.M.E.U.)

8. (a) What is the peak value of a sinusoidal alternating current of 4·78 r.m.s. amperes?

(b) What is the r.m.s. value of a rectangular voltage wave with an amplitude of 9·87 V?

(c) What is the average value of a sinusoidal alternating current of 31 A maximum value?

(e) An alternating current is represented by $i = 70 \cdot 7 \sin 520t$. Determine (i) the frequency; (ii) the current 0·0015 second after passing through zero, increasing positively. (U.E.I.)

9. Define clearly the following terms: *period, frequency* and *phase*.

An alternating current is represented by the equation $i_1 = 10 \sin 50t$, where t is in seconds. What is the frequency? A second current of the same frequency but half the amplitude lags behind the first current by 30 electrical degrees. Find the value of the second current when the first current is at a positive peak value and also the values of both currents 0·02 second later. Sketch the waveforms of the two currents in their correct relationships. (U.E.I.)

10. Define r.m.s. and mean values for an alternating voltage, and give an example of the use of each value.

A circuit having a power factor of 0·866 lagging takes a current of 10 A from a 240-V, 50-c/s supply. Write down an expression for the instantaneous values of voltage and current, and find the value of the current when the voltage is (a) passing through its maximum value, (b) 0·005 second later and (c) after a further 0·005 second.

What is the significance of a negative current? (Joint Section A)

11. Find vectorially or otherwise the resultant of the following four voltages:

$$e_1 = 25 \sin \omega t, \qquad e_2 = 30 \sin (\omega t + \pi/6),$$
$$e_3 = 30 \cos \omega t, \qquad e_4 = 20 \sin (\omega t - \pi/4).$$

Express the answer in a similar form. (U.L.C.I.)

12. Four e.m.f.'s, $e_1 = 100 \sin \omega t$, $e_2 = 80 \sin (\omega t - \pi/6)$, $e_3 = 120 \sin (\omega t + \pi/4)$ and $e_4 = 100 \sin (\omega t - 2\pi/3)$, are induced in four coils connected in series so that the vector sum of the four e.m.f.'s is obtained. Find graphically *or* by calculation the resultant e.m.f. and its phase difference with (a) e_1 and (b) e_2.

If the connections to the coil in which the e.m.f. e_2 is induced are reversed, find the new resultant e.m.f. (E.M.E.U.)

13. Two sinusoidal alternating voltages v_1 and v_2 have peak values of 25 V and 20 V respectively and the same frequency. If v_1 leads v_2 by 40°, plot to scale one half-cycle of each voltage on the same axes.

From these curves derive and plot, on the same axes as before, one half-cycle of (a) the sum, $v_1 + v_2$, (b) the difference, $v_1 - v_2$, of the two voltages. State the peak values of these resultants and their phase angles relative to v_1.   (U.L.C.I.)

14. An e.m.f. given by 326 sin 418t is applied to a certain circuit and the current is 2 sin (418t − 1·3736). Find the frequency, the resistance and inductance of the circuit. What readings would be obtained on a moving-iron ammeter and a wattmeter connected to measure the current and the power taken by the above circuit?

Sketch the waveforms of the instantaneous e.m.f., current and power. Some values of the instantaneous power are negative. Why is this possible with the above circuit?   (E.M.E.U.)

15. A circuit consists of two parallel branches supplied from a source of voltage given by $v = 50\sqrt{2}$ sin ωt, at 50 c/s. One circuit takes a current $i_1 = 40$ sin $(\omega t - \pi/6)$, and the other circuit a current $i_2 = 20$ sin $(\omega t - \pi/4)$. Obtain (a) the value of ω, (b) the phase angle between the two currents, (c) the total current and its phase angle to the voltage, (d) the total power. Draw a vector diagram to scale.   (U.E.I.)

16. A coil uniformly wound with 1000 turns of wire has an effective resistance of 10 Ω and takes a current of 7·07 A when connected to 100-V, 50-c/s mains. Calculate the flux produced when carrying a steady current of 1 A.   (C. & G., El. Eng. Pract., Int.)

17. An inductive coil and a non-inductive resistance R ohms are connected in series across an a.c. supply. Derive expressions for the power taken by the coil and its power factor in terms of the voltages across the coil, the resistance and the supply respectively.

If $R = 12$ Ω and the three voltages are, in order, 110 V, 180 V and 240 V, calculate the power and power factor of the coil.

Sketch a vector diagram to show the method of calculation.   (U.L.C.I.)

18. A non-inductive resistance is connected in series with a coil across a 230-V, 50-c/s supply. The current is 1·8 A and the potential differences across the resistance and the coil are 80 and 170 V respectively. Calculate the resistance and the inductance of the coil, and the phase difference between the current and the supply voltage. Also draw the vector diagram representing the current and the voltages.   (App. El., L.U.)

19. An inductive circuit, in parallel with a non-inductive resistance of 20 Ω is connected across a 50-c/s supply. The currents through the inductive circuit and the non-inductive resistance are 4·3 and 2·7 A respectively, and the current taken from the supply is 5·8 A. Find:

(a) the power absorbed by the inductive circuit,
(b) its inductance and
(c) the power factor of the combined circuits.

(App. El., L.U.)

20. Give an account of the phenomena of self and mutual induction. Define the practical unit in which self and mutual inductance are measured.

Two identical coils, each of 25 Ω resistance, are mounted coaxially a short distance apart. When one coil is supplied at 100 V, 50 c/s, the current taken is 2·1 A and the e.m.f. induced in the other coil on open-circuit is 54 V. Calculate the self-inductance of each coil and the mutual inductance between them.

What current will be taken if a p.d. of 100 V, 50 c/s, is supplied across the two coils in series?   (App. El., L.U.)

21. An iron-cored electromagnet has a d.c. resistance of 7·5 Ω and, when connected to a 400-V, 50-c/s supply, takes 10 A and consumes 2 kW. Calculate for this value of current (a) the power loss in the iron core; (b) the inductance of the coil; (c) the power factor; (d) the value of the series resistance which is equivalent to the effect of the iron core. Draw the vector diagram. (U.E.I.)

22. Sketch a diagram of connections showing a voltmeter, ammeter and wattmeter connected to read the input from an a.c. supply to an iron-cored reactor.

In such a test the readings on the instruments were 50 V, 1·4 A and 40 W respectively. Find the inductance and the effective resistance of the reactor, if the supply frequency was 50 c/s.

In a further test on the reactor, 50 V d.c. were applied and the current was 10 A. Explain (a) why the current was greater with d.c. than with a.c., (b) why the d.c. resistance was lower than the effective resistance using a.c. (U.L.C.I.)

23. Two coils are connected in series. With 2 A d.c. through the circuit, the p.d.'s across the coils are 20 and 30 V respectively. With 2 A a.c. at 40 c/s, the p.d.'s across the coils are 140 and 100 V respectively. If the two coils in series are connected to a 230-V, 50-c/s supply, calculate (a) the current; (b) the power; (c) the power factor. Draw the complete vector diagram for the circuit. (N.C.T.E.C.)

24. Two coils A and B are connected in series across a 240-V, 50-c/s supply. The resistance of A is 5 Ω and the inductance of B is 0·015 H. If the input from the supply is 3 kW and 2 kVAr, find the inductance of A and the resistance of B. Calculate the voltage across each coil. (U.L.C.I.)

25. When a coil is connected to a 200-V, 50-c/s supply, it takes a current of 1·5 A and the power consumption is 70 W. Calculate the resistance and inductance of the coil.

If the coil is wound with 4400 turns, calculate the instantaneous maximum flux which links with the coil. Prove any formula used in the calculation of the maximum flux. (E.M.E.U.)

26. A relay coil has an inductance of 8 millihenrys and resistance of 30 Ω. An alternating voltage $v = 5 \sin 5000t$ is applied to the coil. Determine the frequency, the r.m.s. value of the current and express the current in the form $i = I_m \sin(\omega t - \phi)$.

Find also the maximum rate of change of current and the value of the applied voltage when the rate of change of current is a maximum. (E.M.E.U.)

27. A coil takes a current of 4 A when 24 V d.c. are applied, and for the same power on a 50-c/s a.c. supply the applied voltage is 40. Explain the reason for the difference in the applied voltage.

Determine (a) the reactance, (b) the inductance, (c) the angle between the applied p.d. and current, (d) the power in watts. Draw a vector diagram to illustrate your results. (U.E.I.)

28. Draw the voltage and current curves in relative position for an a.c. circuit containing inductance and derive the expression for the current.

An arc lamp requires 10 A at a voltage of 60. If the supply is 200 V, 50 c/s, calculate the reactance and inductance of an inductor, with a resistance of 1·5 Ω, to be connected in series with the lamp. Draw a vector diagram and obtain the p.d. across the choke. (U.E.I.)

29. A solenoid with an iron core has a wire resistance of 50 Ω and takes a current of 1 A from 250-V, 50-c mains. With the iron core

withdrawn the current is 2·5 A. Calculate the maximum value of the flux-linkages in the coil with and without the iron core.

(C. & G., El. Eng. Pract., Int.)

30. Explain the principle of operation of *one* type of moving-iron instrument, showing how it is suitable for use on d.c. or a.c.

The total resistance of a moving-iron voltmeter is 1000 Ω and the coil has an inductance of 0·765 H. The instrument is calibrated with a full-scale deflection on 50 V d.c. Calculate the percentage error when the instrument is used on (a) 25-c/s supply, (b) 250-c/s supply, the applied p.d. being 50 V in each case. (U.E.I.)

31. An alternating voltage follows a triangular waveform, one cycle of which is given by:

Time (sec)	.	0	0·005	0·01	0·015	0·02
Voltage .	.	0	150	0	−150	0

Plot to scale the voltage waveform and on the same time axis plot the waveform of current which will flow in a 50-μF condenser when connected to the above voltage. Plot also the waveform of the power taken by the condenser. (N.C.T.E.C.)

32. Explain what is meant by *permittivity* or *dielectric constant*. How does it occur in underground cables?

A pair of cables, 8 miles long, have a capacitance between them of 0·3 μF per mile. If the supply voltage is 11 kV at a frequency of 60 c/s, calculate the charging current taken by the cables and the energy stored in the dielectric. (U.E.I.)

33. Deduce expressions for (a) the capacitance of a parallel-plate condenser, (b) the charging current taken by a condenser when connected to a sinusoidal supply. Two condensers of 20 and 60 μF capacitance are connected in series to a 230-V, 50-c/s supply. Calculate (i) the current taken from supply; (ii) the p.d. across each condenser; (iii) the energy stored in each condenser at the instant at which the charging current is zero. (N.C.T.E.C.)

34. A condenser and a resistor are connected in series to an a.c. supply of 50 V at 50 c/s. The current is 2 A and the power dissipated in the circuit is 80 watts. Calculate the resistance of the resistor and the capacitance of the condenser, and draw a vector diagram for the circuit. (U.L.C.I.)

35. The active and reactive components of the current taken by a circuit having a resistor and a capacitor in parallel are 10 A and 12 A respectively when the supply is 230 V, 50 c/s. Draw to scale a vector diagram showing the voltage and these current components and measure the total current and its phase angle.

Calculate the resistance and capacitance of the resistor and capacitor respectively, and find the resistance and capacitance which, when connected in series across the same 230-V supply, would take the same current components as the parallel circuit. (U.L.C.I.)

36. A resistor and a capacitor are connected in series across a 150-V a.c. supply. When the frequency is 40 c/s the current is 5 A, and when the frequency is 50 c/s the current is 6 A. Find the resistance and capacitance of the resistor and capacitor respectively.

If they are now connected in parallel across the 150-V supply, find the total current and its power factor when the frequency is 50 c/s.

(U.L.C.I.)

37. In order to use three 110-V, 60-watt lamps on a 230-V, 50-c/s supply, they are connected in parallel and a condenser put in series with the group. Find (a) the capacitance of the condenser required to give the correct voltage across the lamps, (b) the power factor of the circuit.

If one of the lamps is removed, to what value will the voltage across the remaining two rise, assuming that their resistances remain unchanged? (U.L.C.I.)

38. A series circuit consists of a non-inductive resistance of 10 Ω, an inductive reactance of 50 Ω and a capacitive reactance of 30 Ω. It is connected to a 230-V a.c. supply. Calculate (a) the current, (b) the power, (c) the power factor, (d) the voltage across each component circuit. Draw to scale a vector diagram showing the supply voltage and current and the voltage across each component. (N.C.T.E.C.)

39. Find the active and reactive components of the current taken by a series circuit consisting of a coil of inductance 0·1 H and resistance 8 Ω and a capacitor of 120 μF connected to a 240-V, 50-c/s supply.

Draw to scale a vector diagram showing the voltages across the coil and capacitor, the supply voltage and current, and the components of the current. (U.L.C.I.)

40. A series circuit has the following characteristics: $R = 10$ Ω; $L = 100/\pi$ millihenrys; $C = 500/\pi$ microfarads. Find the current flowing when the applied voltage is 100 V at 50 c/s. Draw the vector diagram and find also the power factor of the circuit.

What value of the supply frequency would produce series resonance? (U.L.C.I.)

41. A coil took 0·7 kW and 1·8 kVAr when connected to a 240-V, 50-c/s supply. If it is now connected in series with an 80-μF capacitor across the same supply, find the current, power and power factor. Draw to scale a vector diagram showing the current, the supply voltage and the voltages across the coil and the condenser respectively. State the values of these two voltages. (U.L.C.I.)

42. A series circuit consists of a resistance of 10 Ω, an inductance of 0·5 H and a capacitance of 50 μF. This circuit is connected in series with another series circuit having a resistance of 5 Ω and an inductance of 0·2 H. The combined circuit is connected across a voltage of 250 V, 50 c/s. Calculate the current flowing and the p.d. across each of the series circuits. Draw the complete vector diagram for the whole circuit. (U.E.I.)

43. Two circuits, A and B, are connected in parallel to a 200-V supply. Circuit A consists of a resistance of 10 Ω in series with an inductive reactance of 10 Ω, and circuit B consists of a resistance of 20 Ω in series with a capacitive reactance of 10 Ω. Find the current taken by each circuit and the total current. Find, also, the power factor of the circuit. (U.L.C.I.)

44. A coil whose resistance is not negligible takes a current of 1 A when connected to a voltage of 184 V at a frequency of 50 c/s. When a 14-μF capacitor (condenser) is connected in series with the coil, a p.d. of 70 V at the same frequency applied across the complete circuit also produces a current of 1 A in the circuit. The power factor in the second case is leading. Draw a vector diagram for the two circuits and hence find the resistance and inductance of the coil.

(E.M.E.U.)

45. A choking coil of inductive reactance 20 Ω has an ohmic resistance of 1 Ω and an iron loss of 100 watts when carrying 10 A. If it is shunted with a capacitance of 100 μF and connected to a 200-V, 50-c/s supply, find the total current taken from the supply and the power factor. Draw a vector diagram. (U.L.C.I.)

46. A parallel circuit consists of a non-inductive resistance of 50 Ω, a pure inductance of 0·15 H, and a pure capacitance of 100 μF, all in parallel. Find the impedance and phase angle of the circuit at a

frequency of 50 c/s. What values of resistance and reactance in series will have the same impedance and phase angle at this frequency?

(U.E.I.)

47. Explain, with the aid of a vector diagram, the circumstances in which voltages greatly in excess of the supply voltage may occur in a series circuit containing a coil and a capacitor.

A coil having a ratio $L/R = 0.01$ is connected in series with a capacitor. When an alternating voltage having a constant magnitude and variable frequency is applied, the reading on an ammeter in the circuit is seen to pass through a maximum of 2 A when the frequency is 120 c/s. If the voltage across the capacitor is then 40 V, calculate the supply voltage and the inductance of the coil. Also calculate the p.d. across the coil.

(U.L.C.I.)

48. A parallel combination of circuits is made up as follows:
Branch A—resistance 5 Ω, inductance 38·2 mH.
Branch B—resistance 6 Ω, capacitance 318·2 μF.
Branch C—resistance only 10 Ω.

Calculate the current in each branch if the combination is connected across a 200-V, 50-c/s supply. Draw a vector diagram to scale. Determine graphically or by calculation the total current and its phase angle.

(E.M.E.U.)

49. A parallel circuit has two branches. Branch (i) consists of a coil of inductance 0·2 H and a resistance 15 Ω; branch (ii) consists of a 30-μF condenser in series with a 10-Ω resistance. The circuit so formed is connected to a 230-V, 50-c/s supply. Calculate (a) the current in each branch, (b) the line current and its power factor, (c) the constants of the simplest series circuit which will take the same current at the same power factor as taken by the two branches in parallel.

(N.C.T.E.C.)

50. A series circuit, consisting of a coil ($R = 30$ Ω, $L = 0.5$ H) and a condenser, resonates at a frequency of 48 c/s. Calculate the capacitance of the condenser which, when connected in parallel with this circuit, will increase the resonant frequency to 60 c/s. Calculate, in the latter case, the total current and the current in each branch of the circuit if the line voltage is 100 V.

(App. El., L.U.)

51. A series circuit consists of a resistance of 20 Ω, an inductance of 0·3 H and a condenser. When supplied at constant voltage of 230 but at varying frequency, the current is a maximum at 50 c/s. Calculate (a) the capacitance of the condenser, (b) the p.d. across each component, (c) the power taken. Draw the vector diagram for the circuit. Sketch the curve showing the variation of current as the frequency is varied from below to above 50 c/s. What is understood by the Q value for a tuned circuit? Calculate its value for the above circuit.

(N.C.T.E.C.)

52. Explain what is meant by resonance in an electrical circuit and derive an expression for the frequency to give resonance in a circuit consisting of a condenser and an inductor in series.

An inductor having an inductance of 0·3 H and a resistance of 5 Ω is connected in series with a condenser across a 50-c/s supply. Calculate the capacitance required to give the circuit a power factor of 0·5 lagging, assuming the supply voltage to be sinusoidal.

(App. El., L.U.)

53. A coil of resistance 12 Ω and inductance 0·12 H is connected in parallel with a capacitor of 60-μF capacitance to a 100-V variable frequency supply. Calculate the frequency at which the circuit will act as a non-inductive resistance.

Draw for this condition the complete vector diagram. What is meant by the dynamic resistance of the circuit?   Calculate its value for this circuit.   (N.C.T.E.C.)

54. A mercury-vapour lamp unit consists of an inductor of negligible resistance in series with the lamp, this combination being shunted by a condenser of 23 μF.   The complete unit takes 500 W at unity power factor from a 250-V, 50-c/s supply.   Find the voltage across the lamp and the inductance of the inductor.

Draw the vector diagram for the circuit.

(C. & G., El. Eng. Pract., Int.)

55. A circuit having a constant resistance of 60 Ω and a variable inductance of 0 to 0·4 H is connected across a 100-V, 50-c/s supply. Derive from first principles the locus of the extremity of the current vector.   Find (a) the power and (b) the inductance of the circuit when the power factor is 0·8.   (App. El., L.U.)

56. An a.c. circuit consists of a variable resistance in series with a coil for which $R = 20$ Ω and $L = 0·1$ H.   Show that when this circuit is supplied at constant voltage and frequency, and the resistance is varied between zero and infinity, the locus of the current vector is a circular arc.   Calculate, when the supply voltage is 100 V and the frequency 50 c/s, (a) the radius (in amperes) of this arc, (b) the value of the variable resistance in order that the power taken from the mains may be a maximum.   (App. El., L.U.)

57. A variable capacitance and a resistance of 200 Ω are connected in series across a 200-V, 50-c/s supply.   Draw a vector locus diagram showing the variation of the current as the capacitance of the condenser is changed from 10 μF to 100 μF.   Find (a) the capacitance for a current of 0·8 A, (b) the current when the capacitance is 50 μF.

58. A group of fluorescent lamps takes a load of 800 W at a power factor of 0·9 (lagging).   The other loads on the same supply consist of 0·5 kW of filament lighting, 1 kW of heating and 5 kVA supplied to a motor operating at a power factor of 0·7 (lagging).   Calculate the total load in kW, the total kVA and the power factor.

Indicate a simple method of reducing the kVA and improving the power factor of the total demand on the supply without changing the existing individual loads.   (Joint Section A)

59. The load taken from a supply consists of (a) lamp load of 10 kW at unity power factor, (b) motor load of 80 kVA at 0·8 power factor lagging, (c) motor load of 40 kVA at 0·7 power factor leading.   Calculate the total load taken from supply in kW and in kVA and the power factor of the combined load.   (N.C.T.E.C.)

60. A 400-V, 50-c/s, 25-h.p., single-phase induction motor has a full-load efficiency of 85 per cent and a full-load power factor of 0·87 lagging.   Find the capacitance and kVA rating of a condenser connected in parallel with the motor to improve the power factor to 0·95 lagging.   (U.L.C.I.)

61. Define power factor and explain why it should be kept as high as possible in power-supply systems.

A single-phase motor takes 50 A at a power factor of 0·6 (lagging) from a 250-V, 50-c/s supply.   What value must a shunting condenser have to raise the overall power factor to 0·9 (lagging)?   How does the installation of the condenser affect the line and motor currents?

(Joint Section A)

62. A small factory has a lighting load of 2 kW and single-phase motors totalling 15 h.p. which operate at a mean power factor of 0·7 lagging and efficiency of 80 per cent.   What is the total kVA and power factor if the supply is 200 V, 50 c/s?

Determine the capacitance to be installed so that the total current does not exceed 100 A, and find its cost at £3 10s. per kVA. (U.E.I.)

CHAPTER VI

THREE-PHASE CIRCUITS

99. Disadvantages of the Single-phase System. The earliest application of alternating current was for heating the filaments of electric lamps. For this purpose the single-phase system was perfectly satisfactory. Some years later, a.c. motors were developed and it was found that for this application the single-phase system was not very satisfactory. For instance, the single-phase induction motor—the type most commonly employed—was not self-starting unless it was fitted with an auxiliary winding. By using two separate windings with currents differing in phase by a quarter of a cycle or three windings with currents differing in phase by a third of a cycle, it was found that the induction motor was self-starting and had better efficiency and power factor than the corresponding single-phase machine. Four-wire and three-wire two-phase systems were developed, but have since been discarded except for a few special applications; the four-wire system is cumbersome, and with the three-wire system there is difficulty in keeping the voltages balanced, i.e. equal and in quadrature, at the end of a transmission line. The three-phase system is superior to the two-phase system both in convenience and in performance, and has therefore been universally adopted for the generation and transmission of electrical energy.

100. Generation of Three-phase E.M.F.'s. In Fig. 131, RR_1, YY_1 and BB_1* represent three similar loops fixed

* The letters R, Y and B are abbreviations of "red," "yellow" and "blue," namely the colours used to identify the three phases. Also, "red—yellow—blue" is the sequence that is universally adopted to denote that the e.m.f. in the yellow phase lags a third of a cycle behind that in the red phase and the e.m.f. in the blue phase lags another third of a cycle behind that in the yellow phase.

to one another at angles of 120°, each loop terminating in
a pair of slip-rings carried on the shaft as indicated in
Fig. 132. We shall refer to the slip-rings connected to

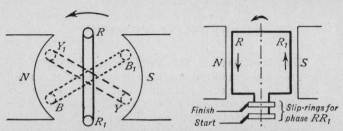

FIG. 131.—Generation of   FIG. 132.—Loop RR_1 at instant
three-phase e.m.f.'s.   of maximum e.m.f.

sides R, Y and B as the "finishes" of the respective
phases and those connected to R_1, Y_1 and B_1 as the
"starts."

Suppose the three coils to be rotated anti-clockwise at
a uniform speed in the magnetic field due to poles NS.

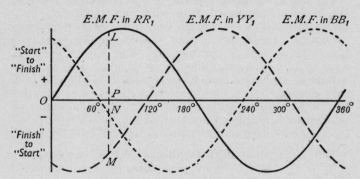

FIG. 133.—Waveforms of e.m.f.'s.

The e.m.f. generated in loop RR_1 is zero for the position
shown in Fig. 131. When the loop has moved through
90° to the position shown in Fig. 132, the generated e.m.f.
is at its maximum value, its direction round the loop

being from the "start" slip-ring towards the "finish" slip-ring. Let us regard this direction as positive; consequently the e.m.f. induced in loop RR_1 can be represented by the full-line curve of Fig. 133.

Since the loops are being rotated anti-clockwise, it is evident from Fig. 131 that the e.m.f. generated in side Y of loop YY_1 has exactly the same amplitude as that generated in side R, but lags by 120° (or 1/3 cycle). Similarly the e.m.f. generated in side B of loop BB_1 is equal to but lags 120° behind that in side Y. Hence the e.m.f.'s generated in loops RR_1, YY_1 and BB_1 are represented by the three equally spaced curves of Fig. 133, the e.m.f.'s being assumed positive when their directions round the loops are from "start" to "finish" of their respective loops.

If the instantaneous value of the e.m.f. generated in phase RR_1 is represented by $e_R = E_m \sin \theta$,

then instantaneous e.m.f. in $YY_1 = e_Y = E_m \sin (\theta - 120°)$

and instantaneous e.m.f. in $BB_1 = e_B = E_m \sin (\theta - 240°)$.

101. Mesh or Delta Connection of Three-phase Windings. The three phases of Fig. 131 can, for convenience, be represented as in Fig. 134, where the phases are shown isolated from one another. L_1, L_2 and L_3 represent loads connected across the respective phases. Since we have assumed the e.m.f.'s to be positive when acting from "start" to "finish," they can be represented by the arrows e_R, e_Y and e_B in Fig. 134. This arrangement necessitates six line conductors and is there-

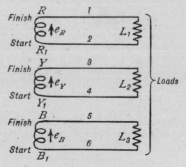

FIG. 134.—Three-phase windings with six line conductors.

fore cumbersome and expensive, so let us consider how it may be simplified. For instance, let us join R_1 and Y

together as in Fig. 135, thereby enabling conductors 2 and 3 of Fig. 134 to be replaced by a single conductor. Similarly, let us join Y_1 and B together so that conductors 4 and 5 may be replaced by another single conductor. Before we can proceed to join "start" B_1 to "finish" R, we have to prove that the resultant e.m.f. between these two points is zero at every instant, so that no circulating current is set up when they are joined together.

Instantaneous value of total e.m.f. acting from B_1 to R

$$=e_R+e_Y+e_B=E_m[\sin \theta+\sin (\theta-120°)+\sin (\theta-240°)]$$
$$=E_m(\sin \theta+\sin \theta . \cos 120°-\cos \theta . \sin 120°+$$
$$\sin \theta . \cos 240°-\cos \theta . \sin 240°)$$
$$=E_m(\sin \theta-0·5 \sin \theta-0·866 \cos \theta-0·5 \sin \theta+0·866 \cos \theta)$$
$$=0.$$

Since this condition holds for every instant, it follows

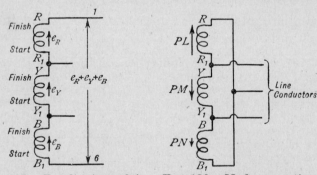

FIG. 135.—Resultant e.m.f. in a mesh-connected winding.

FIG. 136.—Mesh connection of three-phase winding.

that R and B_1 can be joined together, as in Fig. 136, without any circulating current being set up around the circuit. The three line conductors are joined to the junctions thus formed.

It may be helpful at this stage to consider the actual values and directions of the e.m.f.'s at a particular instant. For instance, at instant P in Fig. 133, the e.m.f. generated in phase R is positive and is represented by PL acting from R_1 to R in Fig. 136. The e.m.f. in phase

Y is negative and is represented by PM acting from Y to Y_1, and that in phase B is also negative and is represented by PN acting from B to B_1.   But the sum of PM and PN is exactly equal numerically to PL; consequently the algebraic sum of the e.m.f.'s round the closed circuit formed by the three windings is zero.

It should be noted that the directions of the arrows in Fig. 136 represent the directions of the e.m.f.'s at a *particular instant*, whereas arrows placed alongside symbol e, as in Fig. 135, represent the *positive* directions of the e.m.f.'s.

The circuit derived in Fig. 136 is usually drawn as in Fig. 137, and the arrangement is referred to as *mesh* (i.e. a closed circuit) or *delta* (from the Greek capital letter Δ) connection.

It will be noticed that in Fig. 137, R is connected to Y_1 instead of B_1 as in Fig. 136. Actually, it is immaterial which method is used. What is of importance is that the "start" of one

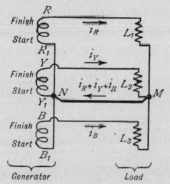

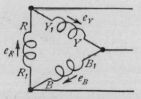

Fig. 137. — Conventional representation of a mesh-connected winding.

Fig. 138.—Star connection of three-phase winding.

phase should be connected to the "finish" of another phase, so that the arrows representing the positive directions of the e.m.f.'s point in the same direction round the mesh formed by the three windings.

102. Star Connection of Three-phase Windings. Let us go back to Fig. 134 and join together the three "starts," R_1, Y_1 and B_1 at N, as in Fig. 138, so that the three

conductors 2, 4 and 6 of Fig. 134 can be replaced by the
single conductor NM of Fig. 138.

Since the generated e.m.f. has been assumed positive
when acting from "start" to "finish," the current in
each phase must also be regarded as positive when flowing
in that direction, as represented by the arrows in Fig. 138.
If i_R, i_Y and i_B be the instantaneous values of the
currents in the three phases, the instantaneous value of
the current in the common wire MN is $(i_R+i_Y+i_B)$,
having its positive direction from M to N.

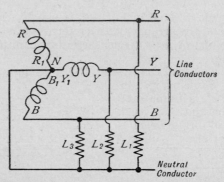

FIG. 139.—Four-wire star-connected system.

This arrangement is referred to as a *four-wire star-
connected* system and is more conveniently represented as
in Fig. 139; and junction N is referred to as the *star* or
neutral point. Three-phase motors are connected to the
line conductors R, Y and B, whereas lamps, heaters, etc.,
are usually connected between the line and neutral conductors, as indicated by L_1, L_2 and L_3, the total load
being distributed as equally as possible between the three
lines. If these three loads are exactly alike, the phase
currents will have the same peak value, I_m, and differ in
phase by 120°. Hence if the instantaneous value of the
current in load L_1 be represented by:

$$i_1 = I_m \sin \theta$$

instantaneous current in $L_2 = i_2 = I_m \sin (\theta - 120°)$
and instantaneous current in $L_3 = i_3 = I_m \sin (\theta - 240°)$.

Hence instantaneous value of resultant current in neutral conductor MN (Fig. 138)

$$=i_1+i_2+i_3$$
$$=I_m[\sin\,\theta+\sin\,(\theta-120°)+\sin\,(\theta-240°)]$$
$$=I_m\times0=0,$$

i.e. with a balanced load the resultant current in the neutral conductor is zero at *every* instant; hence this conductor can be dispensed with, thereby giving us the *three-wire star-connected* system shown in Fig. 140.

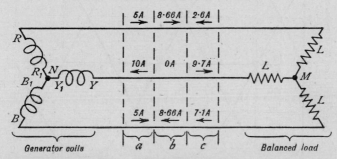

FIG. 140.—Three-wire star-connected system with balanced load.

When considering the distribution of current in a three-wire three-phase system, it is helpful to bear in mind: (a) that arrows such as those of Fig. 138, placed alongside *symbols*, indicate the direction of the current when it is assumed to be *positive* and not the direction at a particular instant; and (b) that the current flowing outwards in one or two conductors is equal to that flowing back in the remaining conductor or conductors.

Let us consider the second statement in greater detail. Suppose the curves in Fig. 141 to represent the three currents differing in phase by 120° and having a peak value of 10 A. At instant a, the currents in phases R and B are each 5 A, whereas the current in phase Y is −10 A. These values are indicated above a in Fig. 140, i.e. 5 A are flowing outwards in phases R and B and 10 A are returning in phase Y.

At instant b, the current in Y is zero, that in R is 8·66 A and that in B is —8·66 A, i.e. 8·66 A are flowing outwards in phase R and returning in phase B. At instant c, the currents in R, Y and B are —2·6, 9·7 and —7·1 A respectively; i.e. 9·7 A flow outwards in phase Y and return via phases R (2·6 A) and B (7·1 A).

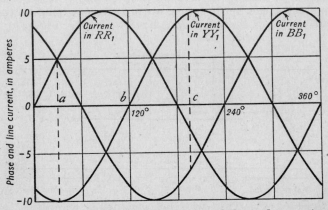

FIG. 141.—Curves of current in a balanced three-phase system.

It will be seen that the distribution of currents between the three lines is continually changing; but at every instant the algebraic sum of the currents is zero.

103. Relationships between Line and Phase Voltages and Currents in a Star-connected System.

Let us again assume the e.m.f. in each phase to be positive when acting from the neutral point outwards, so that the r.m.s. values of the e.m.f.'s generated in the three phases can be represented by E_{NR}, E_{NY} and E_{NB} in Fig. 142 and 143. The value of the e.m.f. acting from Y via N to R is the vectorial *difference* of E_{NR} and E_{NY}. Hence E_{YN} is drawn equal and opposite to E_{NY} and added vectorially to E_{NR} giving E_{YNR} as the e.m.f. acting from Y to R via N. Note that the *three* suffix letters YNR are necessary to indicate unambiguously the *positive* direction of this e.m.f. —

Having decided on YNR as the positive direction of the line e.m.f. between Y and R, we must adhere to the same sequence for the e.m.f.'s between the other lines, i.e. the sequence must be YNR, RNB and BNY. E_{RNB} is obtained by subtracting E_{NR} vectorially from E_{NB} and E_{BNY} is obtained by subtracting E_{NB} vectorially from E_{NY} as shown in Fig. 143. From the symmetry of this diagram it is evident that the line voltages are equal and are spaced 120° apart. Further, since the sides of

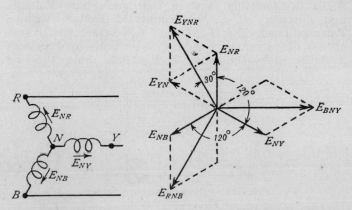

FIG. 142.—Star-connected system.

FIG. 143.—Vector diagram for Fig. 142.

all the parallelograms are of equal length, the diagonals bisect one another at right angles. Also, they bisect the angles of their respective parallelograms; and since the angle between E_{NR} and E_{YN} is 60°,

$$\therefore \qquad E_{YNR} = 2E_{NR} \cos 30° = \sqrt{3}E_{NR}$$

i.e.   line voltage $= 1.73 \times$ phase or star voltage.

From Fig. 142 it is obvious that in a star-connected system the current in a line conductor is the same as that in the phase to which that line conductor is connected.

8

Hence, in general:

if V_l=p.d.* between any two line conductors
       =line voltage

and V_p=p.d. between a line conductor and the neutral
       point
       =phase or star voltage (or voltage to neutral)

and if I_l and I_p=line and phase currents respectively,
then for a star-connected system,

$$V_l = 1\cdot73 V_p \qquad \cdot \quad \cdot \quad \cdot \quad (179)$$
and
$$I_l = I_p \cdot \quad \cdot \quad \cdot \quad \cdot \quad \cdot \quad (180)$$

104. Relationship between Line and Phase Voltages and Currents in a Mesh-connected System with a Balanced Load. Let I_R, I_Y and I_B be the r.m.s. values of the phase currents having their positive directions as indicated by the arrows in Fig. 144. Since the load

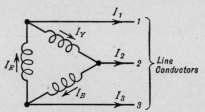

FIG. 144.—Mesh-connected system
with balanced load.

is assumed to be balanced, these currents are equal in magnitude and differ in phase by 120°, as shown in Fig. 145.

From Fig. 144 it will be seen that I_R, when positive, flows towards line conductor 1, whereas I_Y, when positive, flows away from it. Consequently, I_1 is obtained by subtracting I_Y vectorially from I_R, as in

* In practice, it is the voltage between two line conductors or between a line conductor and the neutral point that is measured. Owing to the impedance drop in the windings, this p.d. is different from the corresponding e.m.f. generated in the winding, except when the alternator is on open circuit; hence, in general, it is preferable to work with the potential difference, V, rather than with the e.m.f., E.

Fig. 145. Similarly, I_2 is the vectorial difference of I_Y and I_B, and I_3 is the vectorial difference of I_B and I_R. From Fig. 145 it is evident that the line currents are equal in magnitude and differ in phase by 120°. Also,

$$I_1 = 2I_R \cos 30° = \sqrt{3} I_R.$$

Hence for a mesh-connected system with a balanced load,

line current $= 1 \cdot 73 \times$ phase current

i.e. $I_l = 1 \cdot 73 I_p$. (181)

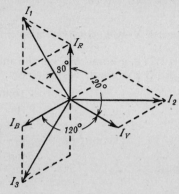

Fig 145.—Vector diagram for Fig. 144.

From Fig. 144 it is obvious that in a mesh-connected system, the line and the phase voltages are the same, i.e.

$$V_l = V_p \quad . \quad . \quad . \quad (182)$$

Example 36. *In a three-phase four-wire system the*

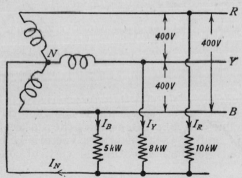

Fig. 146.—Circuit diagram for Example 36.

line voltage is 400 V and non-inductive loads of 10, 8 and 5 kW are connected between the three line conductors and the neutral as in Fig. 146. Calculate : (a) the current in each line and (b) the current in the neutral conductor.

(a) Voltage to neutral $=\dfrac{\text{line voltage}}{1\cdot73}=\dfrac{400}{1\cdot73}=231$ V.

If I_R, I_Y and I_B be the currents taken by the 10, 8 and 5 kW loads respectively,

$$I_R=\frac{10\times1000}{231}=43\cdot3\ \text{A},$$

$$I_Y=\frac{8\times1000}{231}=34\cdot6\ \text{A}$$

and $$I_B=\frac{5\times1000}{231}=21\cdot65\ \text{A}.$$

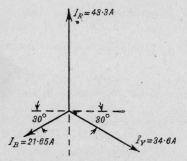

FIG. 147. Vector   diagram for
Fig. 146.

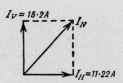

FIG. 148.—Vertical
and   horizontal
components of I_N.

These currents are represented vectorially in Fig. 147.

(b) The current in the neutral is the vectorial sum of the three line currents.   In general, the most convenient method of adding such quantities vectorially is to calculate the resultant horizontal and vertical components thus:

Horizontal component $=I_H=I_Y \cos 30^\circ -I_B \cos 30^\circ$
$$=0\cdot866(34\cdot6-21\cdot65)$$
$$=11\cdot22\ \text{A}.$$

and vertical component $=I_V=I_R-I_Y\cos 60^\circ-I_B\cos 60^\circ$
$$=43\cdot 3-0\cdot 5(34\cdot 6+21\cdot 65)$$
$$=15\cdot 2\text{ A.}$$

These components are represented in Fig. 148.

$\therefore$ current in neutral $=I_N=\sqrt{[(11\cdot 22)^2+(15\cdot 2)^2]}=18\cdot 9$ A.

Example 37. *A delta-connected load is arranged as in Fig. 149. Calculate:* (a) *the phase currents and* (b) *the line currents. The supply voltage* is 400 V at 50 c/s.*

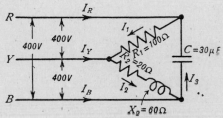

FIG. 149.—Circuit diagram for Example 37.

(a) Since the phase sequence is R, Y, B, the voltage having its positive direction from R to Y leads 120° in front of that having its positive direction from Y to B, i.e. V_{RY} is 120° in front of V_{YB}. Similarly, V_{YB} is 120° in front of V_{BR}. Hence the line (and phase) voltages are as represented vectorially in Fig. 150.

If I_1, I_2 and I_3 be the phase currents in loads RY, YB and BR respectively,

$$I_1=\frac{400}{100}=4\text{ A, in phase with }V_{RY}.$$

$$I_2=\frac{400}{\sqrt{(20^2+60^2)}}=\frac{400}{63\cdot 25}=6\cdot 325\text{ A.}$$

I_2 lags behind V_{YB} by an angle ϕ_2 such that

$$\phi_2=\tan^{-1}60/20=71^\circ 34'.$$

Also $I_3=2\times 3\cdot 14\times 50\times 30\times 10^{-6}\times 400$
$$=3\cdot 77\text{ A, leading }90^\circ\text{ in front of }V_{BR}.$$

* The voltage given for a three-phase system is always the line voltage unless it is stated otherwise.

(b) If the current I_R in line conductor R be assumed to be positive when flowing towards the load, the vector representing this current is obtained by subtracting I_3 from I_1, as in Fig. 150.

$$\therefore \qquad I_R^2 = 4^2 + (3 \cdot 77)^2 + 2 \times 4 \times 3 \cdot 77 \cos 30° = 56 \cdot 3$$
$$\therefore \qquad I_R = 7 \cdot 5 \text{ A.}$$

Current in line conductor Y is obtained by subtracting I_1 from I_2, as shown separately in Fig. 151.

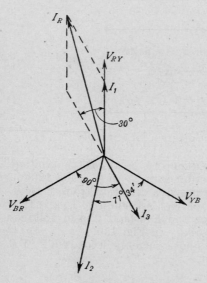

FIG. 150.—Vector diagram for Fig. 149.

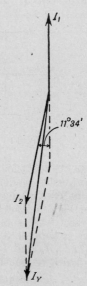

FIG. 151.—Vector diagram for deriving I_Y.

But angle between I_2 and I_1 reversed $= \phi_2 - 60°$
$$= 71° \ 34' - 60°$$
$$= 11° \ 34'.$$

$$\therefore \qquad I_Y^2 = 4^2 + (6 \cdot 325)^2 + 2 \times 4 \times 6 \cdot 325 \times \cos 11° \ 34'$$
$$= 105 \cdot 5$$
$$\therefore \qquad I_Y = 10 \cdot 27 \text{ A.}$$

Similarly the current in line conductor B is obtained by subtracting I_2 from I_3, as shown in Fig. 152.

Angle between I_3 and I_2 reversed $=180°-30°-11°$ 34′
$$=138°\ 26'.$$

$$\therefore\ \ I_B^2=(3·77)^2+(6·325)^2+2\times3·77\times6·325\times\cos138°\ 26'$$
$$=18·52.$$

$$\therefore\ \ I_B=4·3\ \text{A}.$$

This problem could be solved graphically, but in that case it would be necessary to draw the vectors to a large scale to ensure reasonable accuracy.

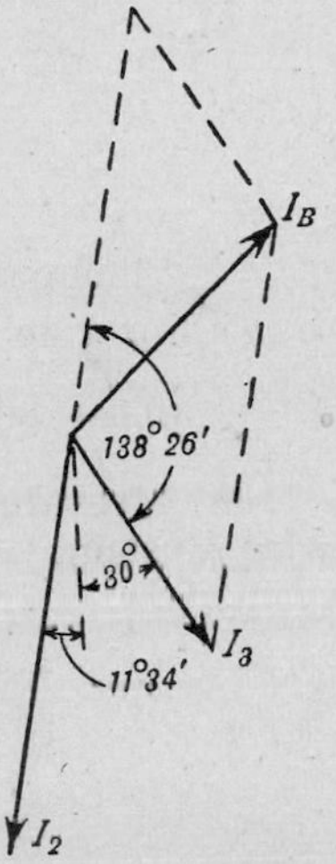

105. Power in a Three-phase System with a Balanced Load.

If I_p =r.m.s. value of the current in each phase

and V_p =r.m.s. value of the p.d. across each phase,

power per phase $=I_pV_p\times$power factor

and total power $=3I_pV_p\times$power factor   (183)

If I_l and V_l be the r.m.s. values of the line current and voltage respectively, then for a *star-connected system*,

$$V_p=V_l/1·73\quad\text{and}\quad I_p=I_l.$$

Fig. 152.—Vector diagram for deriving I_B.

Substituting for I_p and V_p in (183), we have:

total power in watts $=1·73I_lV_l\times$power factor.

For a *mesh-connected system*,

$$V_p=V_l\quad\text{and}\quad I_p=I_l/1·73.$$

Again, substituting for I_p and V_p in (183), we have:

total power in watts $=1·73I_lV_l\times$power factor.

Hence it follows that for any balanced load, total power (in watts)

$$=1·73\ \text{line current}\times\text{line voltage}\times\text{power factor}$$
$$=1·73I_lV_l\times\text{power factor}\quad.\quad.\quad.\quad.\quad(184)$$

Example 38. *A three-phase motor operating off a 400-V system is developing 25 b.h.p. at an efficiency of 0·87 p.u. and a power factor of 0·82. Calculate: (a) the line current and (b) the phase current if the windings are delta-connected.*

(a) Since efficiency $= \dfrac{\text{output power in watts}}{\text{input power in watts}}$

$$= \frac{\text{b.h.p.} \times 746}{1 \cdot 73 I_l V_l \times \text{p.f.}}$$

∴ $$0 \cdot 87 = \frac{25 \times 746}{1 \cdot 73 \times I_l \times 400 \times 0 \cdot 82}$$

∴ line current $= I_l = 37 \cdot 8$ A.

(b) For a delta-connected winding,

$$\text{phase current} = \frac{\text{line current}}{1 \cdot 73} = \frac{37 \cdot 8}{1 \cdot 73} = 21 \cdot 8 \text{ A.}$$

106. Measurement of Power in a Three-phase Three-wire System. *Case* (a). *Star-connected balanced load*

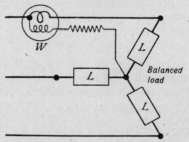

FIG. 153.—Measurement of power in a star-connected balanced load.

with neutral point accessible. If a wattmeter W be connected with its current coil in one line and the voltage circuit between that line and the neutral point, as shown in Fig. 153, the reading on the wattmeter gives the power per phase:

∴ total power $= 3 \times$ wattmeter reading.

Case (b). *Balanced or unbalanced load, star- or delta-connected. The two-wattmeter method.* Suppose the three loads L_1, L_2 and L_3 to be connected in star, as in Fig. 154. The current coils of the two wattmeters are connected in any two lines, say the "red" and "blue" lines, and the voltage circuits are connected between these lines and the third line.

Suppose v_{RN}, v_{YN} and v_{BN} to be the instantaneous values of the p.d.'s across the loads, these p.d.'s being

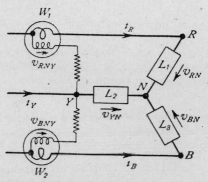

FIG. 154.—Measurement of power by two wattmeters.

assumed positive when the respective line conductors are positive in relation to the neutral point. Also, suppose i_R, i_Y and i_B to be the corresponding instantaneous values of the line (and phase) currents.

∴   instantaneous power in load $L_1 = i_R v_{RN}$
            instantaneous power in load $L_2 = i_Y v_{YN}$
and   instantaneous power in load $L_3 = i_B v_{BN}$

∴   total instantaneous power $= i_R v_{RN} + i_Y v_{YN} + i_B v_{BN}$.

From Fig. 154 it is seen that:

instantaneous current through current coil of W_1 $\Big\} = i_R$

and instantaneous p.d. across voltage circuit of W_1 $\Big\} = v_{RN} - v_{YN}$

∴   instantaneous power measured by W_1 $\Big\} = i_R(v_{RN} - v_{YN})$

8*

Similarly,

$$\left.\begin{array}{l}\text{instantaneous current through}\\ \text{current coil of } W_2\end{array}\right\} = i_B$$

$$\left.\begin{array}{l}\text{and instantaneous p.d.* across}\\ \text{voltage circuit of } W_2\end{array}\right\} = v_{BN} - v_{YN}$$

$$\therefore \left.\begin{array}{l}\text{instantaneous power measured}\\ \text{by } W_2\end{array}\right\} = i_B(v_{BN} - v_{YN}).$$

$$\left.\begin{array}{l}\text{Hence the sum of the}\\ \text{instantaneous powers}\\ \text{of } W_1 \text{ and } W_2\end{array}\right\} = i_R(v_{RN} - v_{YN}) + i_B(v_{BN} - v_{YN})$$

$$= i_R v_{RN} + i_B v_{BN} - (i_R + i_B)v_{YN}.$$

From Kirchhoff's First Law (Art. 9), the algebraic sum of the instantaneous currents at N is zero,

i.e. $$i_R + i_Y + i_B = 0$$

$$\therefore \qquad i_R + i_B = -i_Y$$

$$\left.\begin{array}{l}\text{so that sum of instantan-}\\ \text{eous powers measured}\\ \text{by } W_1 \text{ and } W_2\end{array}\right\} = i_R v_{RN} + i_B v_{BN} + i_Y v_{YN}$$

$$= \text{total instantaneous power.}$$

Actually, the power measured by each wattmeter varies from instant to instant, but the inertia of the moving system causes the pointer to read the average value of the power. Hence the sum of the wattmeter readings gives the average value of the total power absorbed by the three phases.

Since the above proof does not assume a balanced load or sinusoidal waveforms, it follows that the sum of the two wattmeter readings gives the total power under all conditions. The above proof was derived for a star-connected load and it is a useful exercise to prove that the same conclusion holds for a delta-connected load.

* It is important to note that this p.d. is not $v_{YN} - v_{BN}$. This is due to the fact that a wattmeter reads positively when the currents in the current and voltage coils are *both* flowing from the junction of these coils or *both* towards that junction; and since the positive direction of the current in the current coil of W_2 has already been taken as that of the arrowhead alongside i_B in Fig. 154, it follows that the current in the voltage circuit of W_2 is positive when flowing from the "blue" to the "yellow" line.

107. Measurement of the Power Factor of a Three-phase System by means of Two Wattmeters, assuming Balanced Load and Sinusoidal Voltages and Currents. Suppose L in Fig. 155 to represent three similar loads connected in star, and suppose V_{RN}, V_{YN} and V_{BN} to be the r.m.s. values of the phase voltages and I_R, I_Y and I_B to be the r.m.s. values of the currents. Since these

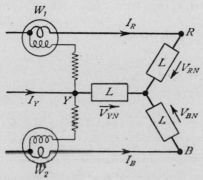

FIG. 155.—Measurement of power and power factor by two wattmeters.

voltages and currents are assumed sinusoidal, they can be represented by vectors, as in Fig. 156, the currents being assumed to lag by an angle ϕ behind the corresponding phase voltages.

Current through current coil of $W_1 = I_R$.

P.d. across voltage circuit of $W_1 = V_{RN} - V_{YN}$
$$\text{(vectorially)}$$
$$= V_{RNY}.$$

Phase difference between I_R and $V_{RNY} = 30° + \phi$

$\therefore$ reading on $W_1 = P_1 = I_R V_{RNY} \cos(30° + \phi)$.

Current through current coil of $W_2 = I_B$.

P.d. across voltage circuit of $W_2 = V_{BN} - V_{YN}$
$$\text{(vectorially)}$$
$$= V_{BNY}.$$

Phase difference between I_B and $V_{BNY} = 30° - \phi$

$\therefore$ reading on $W_2 = P_2 = I_B V_{BNY} \cos(30° - \phi)$.

Since the load is balanced,

$$I_R = I_Y = I_B = (\text{say}) \ I_l, \text{ numerically}$$

and $\qquad V_{RNY} = V_{BNY} = (\text{say}) \ V_l, \text{ numerically,}$

Hence $\quad P_1 = I_l V_l \cos (30° + \phi)$ . . . . (185)

and $\quad P_2 = I_l V_l \cos (30° - \phi)$ . . . . (186)

$\therefore \ P_1 + P_2 = I_l V_l [\cos (30° + \phi) + \cos (30° - \phi)]$

$\qquad = I_l V_l \ (\cos 30° . \cos \phi - \sin 30° . \sin \phi +$
$\qquad\qquad\qquad \cos 30° . \cos \phi + \sin 30° . \sin \phi)$

$\qquad = 1 \cdot 73 I_l V_l \cos \phi$ . . . . . . (187)

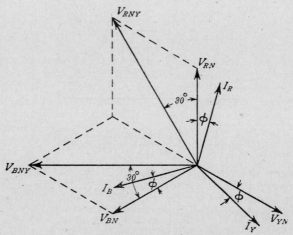

FIG. 156.—Vector diagram for Fig. 155.

namely the expression deduced in Art. 105 for the total power in a balanced three-phase system. This is an alternative method of proving that the sum of the two wattmeter readings gives the total power, but it should be noted that this proof assumes a balanced load and sinusoidal voltages and currents.

Dividing (185) by (186), we have:

$$\frac{P_1}{P_2} = \frac{\cos \ (30° + \phi)}{\cos \ (30° - \phi)} = (\text{say}) \ y$$

$$\therefore \qquad y = \frac{(\sqrt{3}/2) \cos \phi - (1/2) \sin \phi}{(\sqrt{3}/2) \cos \phi + (1/2) \sin \phi}$$

so that $\sqrt{3}y \cos \phi + y \sin \phi = \sqrt{3} \cos \phi - \sin \phi$

from which $\sqrt{3}(1-y) \cos \phi = (1+y) \sin \phi$

$$\therefore \qquad 3 \left(\frac{1-y}{1+y}\right)^2 \cos^2 \phi = \sin^2 \phi = 1 - \cos^2 \phi$$

$$\left[1 + 3 \left(\frac{1-y}{1+y}\right)^2\right] \cos^2 \phi = 1$$

$$\therefore \qquad \text{power factor} = \cos \phi = \frac{1}{\sqrt{\left[1 + 3\left(\frac{1-y}{1+y}\right)^2\right]}} \qquad (188)$$

Since y is the ratio of the wattmeter readings, the corresponding power factor can be calculated from expression (188), but this procedure is very laborious. A more convenient method is to draw a graph of the power factor for various ratios of P_1/P_2; and in order that these ratios may lie between $+1$ and -1, as in Fig. 156A, it is always the practice to take P_1 as the smaller of the two readings. By adopting this practice, it is possible to derive reasonably accurate values of power factor from the graph.

When the power factor of the load is 0·5 lagging, ϕ is 60°; and from (185), the reading on $W_1 = I_l V_l \cos 90°$ $= 0$. When the power factor is less than 0·5 lagging, ϕ is greater than 60° and $(30° + \phi)$ is therefore greater than 90°. Hence the reading on W_1 is negative. To measure this power it is necessary to reverse the connections to either the current or the voltage coil, but the reading thus obtained must be taken as negative when calculating the total power and the ratio of the wattmeter readings.

An alternative method of deriving the power factor is as follows:

From (185), (186) and (187), $P_2 - P_1 = I_l V_l \sin \phi$

and $\qquad \tan \phi = \dfrac{\sin \phi}{\cos \phi} = 1·73 \left(\dfrac{P_2 - P_1}{P_2 + P_1}\right)$. (189)

Hence, ϕ and $\cos \phi$ can be determined with the aid of trigonometrical tables.

Example 39. *The input power to a three-phase motor was measured by the two-wattmeter method. The readings were 5·2 kW and −1·7 kW, and the line voltage was 400 V. Calculate:* (a) *the total power,* (b) *the power factor and* (c) *the line current.*

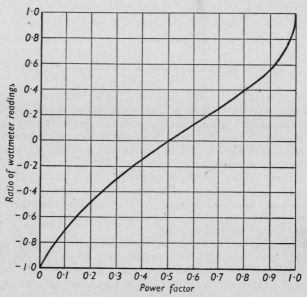

FIG. 156A.—Relationship between power factor and ratio of wattmeter readings.

(a) Total power $= 5·2 - 1·7 = 3·5$ kW.

(b) Ratio of wattmeter readings $= \dfrac{-1·7}{5·2} = -0·327$.

From Fig. 156A, power factor $= 0·28$.

Or alternatively, from (189),

$$\tan \phi = 1·73 \left[\frac{5·2 - (-1·7)}{5·2 + (-1·7)} \right] = 3·41$$

$$\therefore \qquad \phi = 73° 39'$$

and power factor $= \cos \phi = 0·281$.

From the data it is impossible to state whether the power factor is lagging or leading.

(c) From (184), $3500 = 1 \cdot 73 \times I_l \times 400 \times 0 \cdot 281$

∴ $I_l = 18$ A.

Summary of Important Formulae in Chapter VI

For a star-connected system,

$$V_l = 1 \cdot 73 V_p \quad . \quad . \quad . \quad . \quad (179)$$

and $$I_l = I_p \quad . \quad . \quad . \quad . \quad . \quad (180)$$

For mesh-connected system with balanced load,

$$V_l = V_p \quad . \quad . \quad . \quad . \quad . \quad (182)$$

and $$I_l = 1 \cdot 73 I_p \quad . \quad . \quad . \quad (181)$$

For star- or mesh-connected system with balanced load,

total power $= 1 \cdot 73 \times$ line current $\times$ line voltage $\times$
power factor

$$= 1 \cdot 73 I_l V_l \times \text{power factor} \quad . \quad . \quad (184)$$

If P_1 and P_2 be the readings obtained with the two-wattmeter method on a three-wire, three-phase system,

total power $= P_1 + P_2$ under all conditions,

and for a balanced load,

$$\text{power factor} = \frac{1}{\sqrt{\left[1 + 3\left(\dfrac{P_2 - P_1}{P_2 + P_1}\right)^2\right]}} \quad (188)$$

and $$\tan \phi = 1 \cdot 73 \left(\frac{P_2 - P_1}{P_2 + P_1}\right) \quad . \quad . \quad (189)$$

EXAMPLES VI

1. Deduce the relationship between the phase and the line voltages of a three-phase star-connected alternator.

If the phase voltage of a three-phase star-connected alternator be 200 V, what will be the line voltages (a) when the phases are correctly connected, (b) when the connections to one of the phases are reversed?
(App. El., L.U.)

2. Three impedance coils, each having a resistance of 20 Ω and a reactance of 15 Ω, are connected in star to a 400-V, three-phase, 50-c/s supply. Calculate (i) the line current, (ii) the power supplied, (iii) the power factor.

If three condensers, each of the same capacitance, are connected in delta to the same supply so as to form a parallel circuit with the above impedance coils, calculate (i) the capacitance of each condenser to obtain a resultant power factor of $0 \cdot 95$ (lagging), (ii) the line current taken by the combined circuits. Draw to scale a vector diagram showing (a) the line voltage, (b) the voltage across each of the impedances, (c) the line current taken by the combined circuits, (d) current in each condenser, (e) the current in each of the impedance coils. (App. El., L.U.)

3. Deduce the relationship between the line and phase currents in a delta-connected circuit. A three-phase star-connected alternator supplies a delta-connected load, each phase of which has a resistance of 20 Ω and a reactance of 10 Ω. Calculate (a) the current supplied by the alternator; (b) the output of the alternator in kW and in kVA, neglecting the losses in the line between the alternator and the load. The line voltage is 400 V. (N.C.T.E.C.)

4. Derive the numerical relationship between the line and phase currents for a balanced three-phase delta-connected load.

Three coils are connected in delta to a three-phase, three-wire, 415-V, 50-c/s supply and take a line current of 5 A at $0 \cdot 8$ power factor lagging. Calculate the resistance and inductance of the coils.

If the coils are star-connected to the same supply, calculate the line current and the total power.

Calculate the line currents if one coil becomes open-circuited when the coils are connected in star. (E.M.E.U.)

5. Three similar coils, connected in star, take a total power of $1 \cdot 5$ kW at a power factor of $0 \cdot 2$ from a three-phase, 400-V, 50-c/s supply. Calculate (a) the resistance and inductance of each coil and (b) the line currents if one of the coils is short-circuited.

6. Three inductors, each of reactance 36 Ω and resistance 15 Ω, are connected in star. Calculate the current and power taken from a 220-V, three-phase supply. Draw a vector diagram to scale to show the *phase* voltages and currents. Calculate the impedance of each of three other chokes which when connected in delta will take the same current from the supply. (U.E.I.)

7. The load connected to a three-phase supply comprises three similar coils connected in star. The line currents are 25 A and the kVA and kW inputs are 20 and 11 respectively. Find the line and phase voltages, the kVAr input and the resistance and reactance of each coil.

If the coils are now connected in delta to the same three-phase supply, calculate the line currents and the power taken.
(U.L.C.I.)

8. Each phase of a delta-connected load comprises a resistor of 50 Ω and a capacitor of 50 μF in series. Calculate the line and phase currents, the total power and the kVA when this load is connected to a 440-V, three-phase, 50-c/s supply.

Draw to scale a vector diagram showing the voltage and current in each phase and the three line currents. (U.L.C.I.)

9. The load on a three-phase generator giving 100 V between lines consists of 150 60-watt, 100-V lamps connected in three groups of 50 in each group; also a three-phase delta-connected induction motor having a phase current of 40 A at a power factor of $0 \cdot 8$.

Draw to scale vector diagrams representing the phase and line currents of the lamps and of the motor. With the aid of these diagrams, determine the value of the total current taken from the generator and the power factor of the total load. (U.E.I.)

10. Non-inductive loads of 10, 6 and 4 kW are connected between the neutral and the red, yellow and blue phases respectively of a three-phase, four-wire system. The line voltage is 400 V. Find the current in each line conductor and in the neutral. (App. El., L.U.)

11. Explain the advantage of connecting the low-voltage winding of distribution transformers in star.

A factory has the following load with power factor of 0·9 lagging in each phase. Red phase 40 A, white phase 50 A and blue phase 60 A. If the supply is 400-V, three-phase, four-wire, calculate the current in the neutral and the total power. Give a vector diagram for phase and line quantities. Assume that, relative to the current in the red phase, the current in the white phase lags by 120° and that in the blue phase leads by 120°. (U.E.I.)

12. (a) Three 20-μF capacitors are star-connected across a 420-V, 50-c/s, three-phase three-wire supply. Calculate the current in each line.

(b) If one of the capacitors is short-circuited, calculate the line currents.

(c) If one of the capacitors is open-circuited, calculate (i) the line currents and (ii) the p.d. across each of the other two capacitors.

13. A three-phase, 400-V system has the following load connected in mesh:—Between the red and yellow lines: a resistance of 100 Ω. Between the yellow and blue lines: a coil having a reactance of 60 Ω and negligible resistance. Between the blue and red lines: a capacitor having a reactance of 130 Ω. Calculate (a) the phase currents, (b) the line currents. Assume the phase sequence to be R–Y, Y–B and B–R. Also, draw the complete vector diagram.

14. The phase currents in a mesh-connected three-phase load are as follows:—Between the red and yellow lines, 30 A at p.f. 0·707 leading. Between the yellow and blue lines, 20 A at unity p.f. Between the blue and red lines, 25 A at p.f. 0·866 lagging. Calculate the line currents and draw the complete vector diagram.

15. A 400-V, three-phase, star-connected motor has an output of 45 b.h.p., with an efficiency of 90 per cent and a power factor of 0·91. Calculate the line current. Sketch a vector diagram showing the voltages and currents in the motor.

If the motor were reconnected in mesh, what would be the correct voltage of a three-phase supply suitable for the motor?

(Joint Section A)

16. A three-phase, 20-h.p., 400-V, 50-c/s motor has a full-load efficiency of 86 per cent and a full-load power factor of 0·8 lagging. Calculate the input kW, kVA and kVAr. If the motor phases are connected in delta, calculate the current in each phase when the motor is operating at full load. (N.C.T.E.C.)

17. Find an expression for determining the power in a balanced three-phase load in terms of the line current, the line voltage and the power factor.

A three-phase motor operating off a 400-V supply has an output of 40 b.h.p., the efficiency and the power factor being 88 per cent and 0·84 respectively. Calculate the phase current if the stator winding is mesh-connected. (App. El., L.U.)

18. Two wattmeters connected to measure the input to a balanced three-phase circuit indicate 2500 W and 500 W respectively. Find the

power factor of the circuit (a) when both readings are positive, and (b) when the latter reading is obtained after reversing the connections to the current-coil of one instrument. Give vector and connection diagrams in explanation and deduce any formula used.
(C. & G., El. Eng. Pract., Final Part I)

19. Give the circuit arrangement and the theory of the two-wattmeter method of measuring power in a three-phase, three-wire system.

A balanced star-connected load, each phase having a resistance of 10 Ω and an inductive reactance of 30 Ω, is connected to a 400-V, 50-c/s supply. The phase rotation is red, yellow, blue. Wattmeters connected to read the total power have their current coils in the red and blue lines respectively. Calculate the reading of each watt-meter.
(App. El., L.U.)

20. A balanced star-connected load, each phase having a resistance of 10 Ω in series with a capacitive reactance of 20 Ω, is connected to a 400-V, 3-phase supply. The phase rotation is red, yellow, blue, and wattmeters connected to read the total power have their current coils in the red and blue lines respectively. Calculate the reading on each wattmeter and draw a vector diagram in explanation.

21. Two wattmeters are used to measure the total power in a balanced 440-V, three-phase circuit. The current coil of W_1 is in the red line and its voltage-coil circuit is connected across the red and blue lines. The current coil of W_2 is in the yellow line and its voltage-coil circuit is connected across the yellow and blue lines. The indications of W_1 and W_2 are 42·6 kW and 31·2 kW respectively. Calculate the current and the power factor of the load and draw the vector diagram.

Find also the reading on W_1 when its current coil is inserted in the yellow line, the connections to the voltage-coil circuit remaining unaltered.
(C & G., El. Eng. Pract., Final Part I)

22. A wattmeter has its current coil connected in the yellow line and its voltage circuit is connected between the red and blue lines. The line voltage is 400 V and the balanced load takes a line current of 30 A at a power factor of 0·7 lagging. Derive an expression for the reading on the wattmeter in terms of the line voltage and current and of the phase difference between the phase voltage and current, and calculate the value of the wattmeter reading in the above case.

23. A 440-V, three-phase induction-motor load takes 900 kVA at a power factor of 0·707. Calculate the kVA rating of the condenser bank required to raise the resultant power factor of the installation to 0·866 lagging.

Find also the resultant power factor when the condensers are in circuit and the motor load has fallen to 300 kVA at 0·5 power factor.
(C. & G., El. Eng. Pract., Int.)

24. A short three-phase transmission line delivers 5000 kW at 33 kV, the load power factor being 0·8 lagging. The reactance (line to neutral) is 9 Ω and the resistance per conductor is 11 Ω. Calculate the sending-end voltage and give a vector diagram to show how the calculation is made.
(C. & G., El. Eng. Pract., Int.)

25. A factory requires a three-phase supply of 500 kW at a line voltage of 3000 V, the power factor being 0·75 (lagging). If the current density in the supply cables is not to exceed 1·5 A/mm², determine the minimum cross-sectional area of each line conductor and the power wasted in the cables if the supply station is three miles away. Assume that 1 metre of the conductor 1 mm² in cross section has a resistance of 0·02 Ω.

What will be the line voltage at the supply station if each line conductor has an effective inductive reactance of 0·4 Ω per mile?

(App. El., L.U.)

26. Show that the neutral current in a three-phase, balanced, four-wire system supplying a three-phase balanced load is zero.

Compare the amounts of copper required to transmit power to a 20-h.p. motor having an efficiency of 88 per cent and a power factor of 0·8 lagging, with (a) a 400-V, three-phase, three-wire system and (b) a 400-V, single-phase supply. Assume the same efficiency, power factor and current density of 1000 A/in.² in each case. The transmission distance in each case is 1000 yards.

If the three-phase motor is delta-connected, find the phase currents.

(E.M.E.U.)

CHAPTER VII

TRANSFORMERS

108. Introductory. One of the main advantages of a.c. transmission and distribution is the ease with which an alternating voltage can be increased or reduced. For instance, the general practice in this country is to generate at 11,000 V, then step up by means of transformers to 33,000 V or even to 132,000 V for the transmission lines. At suitable points other transformers are installed to step the voltage down to values suitable for motors, lamps, heaters, etc. A medium-size transformer has a full-load efficiency of about 97 to 98 per cent, so that the loss at each point of transformation is very small. Also, since there are no moving parts, the amount of supervision required is practically negligible.

109. Principle of Action of a Transformer. Fig. 157 shows the general arrangement of a transformer. The

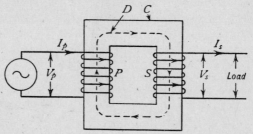

FIG. 157.—A transformer.

vertical portions of the laminated iron core C are referred to as the "limbs," and the top and bottom portions are the "yokes." Coils P and S are wound on the limbs. P, being connected to the supply, is therefore termed the "primary"; coil S is connected to the load and is termed the "secondary."

244

The alternating voltage applied to P circulates an alternating current through P and this current produces an alternating flux in the iron core, the mean path of this flux being represented by the dotted line D. If the whole of the flux produced by P passes through S, the e.m.f. induced in each turn is the same for P and S. Hence if N_p and N_s be the number of turns on P and S respectively,

$$\frac{\text{total e.m.f. induced in } S}{\text{total e.m.f. induced in } P} = \frac{N_s \times \text{e.m.f. per turn}}{N_p \times \text{e.m.f. per turn}}$$

$$= \frac{N_s}{N_p}$$

When the secondary is on open circuit, its terminal voltage is the same as the induced e.m.f. The primary current is then very small, so that the applied voltage V_p is practically equal and opposite to the e.m.f. induced in P. Hence:

$$\frac{V_s}{V_p} \simeq \frac{N_s}{N_p} \quad \cdot \quad \cdot \quad \cdot \quad \cdot \quad (190)$$

Since the full-load efficiency of a transformer is nearly 1·0 per unit,

$I_p V_p \times \text{primary power factor}$

$\simeq I_s V_s \times \text{secondary power factor.}$

But the primary and secondary power factors are nearly the same,

$$\therefore \qquad \frac{I_p}{I_s} \simeq \frac{V_s}{V_p} \quad \cdot \quad \cdot \quad \cdot \quad \cdot \quad (191)$$

An alternative and more illuminating method of deriving the relationship between the primary and secondary currents is based upon a comparison of the primary and secondary ampere-turns. When the secondary is on open circuit, the primary current is such that the primary ampere-turns are just sufficient to produce the flux necessary to induce an e.m.f. that is practically equal and opposite to the applied voltage. This magnetizing current is usually about 3 to 5 per cent of the full-load primary current.

When load is switched on the secondary, the secondary current—by Lenz's Law—produces a demagnetizing effect. Consequently the flux and the e.m.f. induced in the primary are reduced slightly. But this small change may increase the difference between the applied voltage and the e.m.f. induced in the primary from, say, 0·05 per cent to, say, 1 per cent, in which case the new primary current would be 20 times the no-load current. The demagnetizing ampere-turns of the secondary are thus *nearly* neutralized by the increase in the primary ampere-turns; and since the primary ampere-turns on no load are very small compared with the full-load ampere-turns:

∴ full-load primary ampere-turns

$\simeq$full-load secondary ampere-turns,

i.e. $I_p N_p \simeq I_s N_s$

so that $\dfrac{I_p}{I_s} \simeq \dfrac{N_s}{N_p} \simeq \dfrac{V_s}{V_p}$ . . . . (192)

It will be seen that the magnetic flux forms the connecting link between the primary and secondary circuits and that any variation of the secondary current is accompanied by a small variation of the flux and therefore of the e.m.f. induced in the primary, thereby enabling the primary current to vary approximately proportionally to the secondary current.

110. E.M.F. Equation of a Transformer. Suppose the

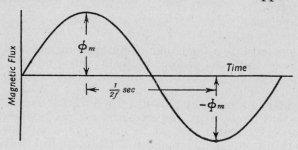

Fig. 158.—Curve of flux variation.

maximum value of the flux to be Φ_m webers and the frequency to be f cycles/second. From Fig. 158 it is seen that the flux has to change from $+\Phi_m$ to $-\Phi_m$ in half a cycle, namely in $1/2f$ second.

$\therefore$ average rate of change of flux $= 2\Phi_m \div \dfrac{1}{2f}$

$\qquad\qquad\qquad\qquad = 4f\Phi_m$ webers/second

$\therefore$ average e.m.f. induced/turn $= 4f\Phi_m$ volts.

But for a sinusoidal wave the r.m.s. or effective value is 1·11 times the average value,

$\therefore$ r.m.s. value of e.m.f. induced/turn $= 1\cdot11 \times 4f\Phi_m$.

Hence, r.m.s. value of e.m.f. induced in primary

$$= E_p = 4\cdot44 N_p f \Phi_m \qquad . \quad . \quad (193)$$

and r.m.s. value of e.m.f. induced in secondary

$$= E_s = 4\cdot44 N_s f \Phi_m \qquad . \quad . \quad (194)$$

An alternative method of deriving these formulae is as follows:

If $\quad \Phi =$ instantaneous value of flux in webers

$\qquad = \Phi_m \sin 2\pi ft$

$\therefore$ instantaneous value of induced e.m.f. per turn

$$= -\frac{d\Phi}{dt} \text{ volts}$$

$$= -2\pi f \Phi_m \times \cos 2\pi ft \text{ volts}$$

$$= 2\pi f \Phi_m \times \sin (2\pi ft - \pi/2) \qquad . \quad . \quad (195)$$

$\therefore$ maximum value of induced e.m.f./turn

$$= 2\pi f \Phi_m$$

and r.m.s. value of induced e.m.f./turn

$$= 0\cdot707 \times 2\pi f \Phi_m$$

$$= 4\cdot44 f \Phi_m \text{ volts}.$$

Hence r.m.s. value of primary e.m.f. $= E_p$

$$= 4\cdot44 N_p f \Phi_m$$

and r.m.s. value of secondary e.m.f. $= E_s$

$$= 4\cdot44 N_s f \Phi_m$$

Example 40. *A 200-kVA, 6600/400-V, 50-c/s single-phase transformer has 80 turns on the secondary. Calculate: (a) the approximate values of the primary and* *secondary currents,* (b) *the number of primary turns and* (c) *the maximum value of the flux.*

If the transformer is to be used on a 25-c/s system, calculate : (d) *the primary voltage, assuming that the flux can be increased by 10 per cent, and* (e) *the kVA rating of the transformer, assuming the current density in the windings to be unaltered.*

(a) Full-load primary current$\simeq \dfrac{200 \times 1000}{6600} = 30 \cdot 3$ A,

and full-load secondary current$\simeq \dfrac{200 \times 1000}{400} = 500$ A.

(b)   No. of primary turns $= \dfrac{80 \times 6600}{400} = 1320$.

(c) From the expression (194),
$$400 = 4 \cdot 44 \times 80 \times 50 \times \Phi_m$$
$$\therefore \qquad \Phi_m = 0 \cdot 0225 \text{ weber.}$$

(d)   Flux at 25 c/s $= 0 \cdot 0225 \times 1 \cdot 1$
$$= 0 \cdot 02475 \text{ weber,}$$
$$\therefore \qquad \text{primary voltage} = 4 \cdot 44 \times 1320 \times 25 \times 0 \cdot 02475$$
$$= 3630 \text{ V.}$$

(e) For the same current density, the full-load primary and secondary currents remain unaltered,

$$\therefore \text{ kVA rating of transformer} = \dfrac{30 \cdot 3 \times 3630}{1000} = 110 \text{ kVA.}$$

111. Vector Diagram for a Transformer on No Load.

It is most convenient to commence the vector diagram with the vector representing the quantity that is common to the two windings, namely the flux Φ. This vector can be made any convenient length and may be regarded merely as a vector of reference relative to which other vectors have to be drawn.

In the preceding Article, expression (195) shows that the e.m.f. induced by a sinusoidal flux lags a quarter of a cycle behind the flux. Consequently the e.m.f.'s, E_s and E_p, induced in the secondary and primary windings respectively, are represented by vectors drawn 90°

behind Φ, as in Fig. 159. The values of E_s and E_p are proportional to the number of turns on the secondary and primary windings, since practically the whole of the flux set up by the primary is linked with the secondary when the latter is on open circuit. For convenience in drawing the vector diagrams for transformers, it will be assumed that N_s and N_p are equal, so that $E_s = E_p$, as shown in Fig. 159.

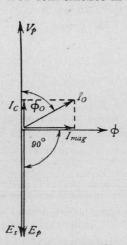

Since the difference between the applied voltage V_p and the induced e.m.f. E_p is only about 0·05 per cent when the transformer is on no load, the vector representing V_p can be drawn equal and opposite to that representing E_p.

The no-load current, I_o, taken by the primary consists of two components: (a) a reactive or magnetizing component, I_{mag}, producing the flux and therefore in phase with the latter, and (b) an active or power component, I_c, supplying the hysteresis and eddy-current losses in the iron core and the negligible I^2R loss in the

FIG. 159.—Vector diagram for transformer on no load.

primary winding. Component I_c is in phase with the applied voltage: i.e. $I_c V_p =$ core loss. This component is usually very small compared with I_{mag}, so that the no-load power factor is very low.

From Fig. 159, it will be seen that:

$$\text{no-load current} = I_o = \sqrt{(I_c^2 + I_{mag}^2)} \quad . \quad (196)$$

and power factor on no load $= \cos \phi_o = I_c/I_o$. (197)

Example 41. *A single-phase transformer has 480 turns on the primary and 90 turns on the secondary. The mean length of the flux path in the iron core is 180 cm and the joints are equivalent to an air-gap of 0·1 mm. If the maximum value of the flux density is to be 1·1 Wb/m^2*

when 2200 volts at 50 c/s are applied to the primary, calculate : (a) *the cross-sectional area of the core,* (b) *the secondary voltage on no load,* (c) *the primary current and power factor on no load. Assume the ampere-turns/m for 1·1 Wb/m² to be 400, the corresponding iron loss to be 0·8 watt per lb at 50 c/s and the density of the iron to be 7·8.*

(a) From (193),　　$2200 = 4·44 \times 480 \times 50 \times \Phi_m$

$\therefore$　　　　　　　　　$\Phi_m = 0·0206$ weber

and　　　$\left.\begin{array}{l}\text{cross-sectional}\\\text{area of core}\end{array}\right\} = \dfrac{0·0206}{1·1} = 0·0187$ m²

$$= 187 \text{ cm}^2.$$

This is the net area of the iron; the gross area will be about 10 per cent greater than this value to allow for the insulation between the laminations.

(b) $\left.\begin{array}{l}\text{Secondary voltage on}\\\text{no load}\end{array}\right\} = 2200 \times \dfrac{90}{480} = 412·5$ volts.

(c) $\left.\begin{array}{l}\text{Total ampere-turns}\\\text{for the iron core}\end{array}\right\} = 400 \times 1·8 = 720$

and $\left.\begin{array}{l}\text{ampere-turns for the}\\\text{equivalent air-gap}\end{array}\right\} = \dfrac{1·1}{4\pi \times 10^{-7}} \times 0·0001 = 87·5$

$\therefore$ $\left.\begin{array}{l}\text{total ampere-turns to}\\\text{produce the maxi-}\\\text{mum flux density}\end{array}\right\} = 720 + 87·5 = 807·5$

$\therefore$ $\left.\begin{array}{l}\text{maximum value of}\\\text{magnetizing current}\end{array}\right\} = \dfrac{807·5}{480} = 1·682$ A.

Assuming the current to be sinusoidal,

$\left.\begin{array}{l}\text{r.m.s. value of magne-}\\\text{tizing current}\end{array}\right\} = I_{mag} = 0·707 \times 1·682$

$$= 1·19 \text{ A.}$$

Volume of iron $= 180 \times 187 = 33,700$ cm³

$\therefore$　　　weight of iron $= 33,700 \times 7·8$ g

$$= \dfrac{33,700 \times 7·8}{453·6} = 580 \text{ lb}$$

and　　　　　iron loss $= 580 \times 0·8 = 464$ W

$\therefore$ $\left.\begin{array}{l}\text{core-loss component}\\\text{of current}\end{array}\right\} = I_c = \dfrac{464}{2200} = 0·21$ A

From (196),   no-load current $= I_o = \sqrt{[(1 \cdot 19)^2 + (0 \cdot 21)^2]}$
$$= 1 \cdot 21 \text{ A,}$$

and from (197), power factor $\Big\}$ on no load $= \dfrac{0 \cdot 21}{1 \cdot 21} = 0 \cdot 174.$

112. Useful and Leakage Fluxes in a Transformer.
When the secondary winding of a transformer is on open-circuit, the current taken by the primary winding is responsible for setting up the magnetic flux and providing a very small power component to supply the iron loss in the core. To simplify matters in the present discussion, let us assume:

(a) the iron loss in the core and the I^2R loss in the primary winding to be negligible;

(b) the permeability of the iron to remain constant, so that the magnetizing current is proportional to the flux; and

(c) the primary and secondary windings to have the same number of turns, i.e. $N_p = N_s$.

Fig. 160 shows all the flux set up by the primary winding passing through the secondary winding. There is a very small amount of flux returning through the air space around the primary winding, but since the relative permeability of transformer iron is of the order of 1000 or more, the reluctance of the air path may be 1000 times that of the parallel path through the iron limb carrying the secondary winding. Consequently

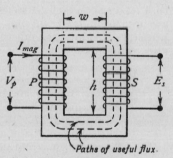

Fig. 160.—Transformer on no load.

the flux passing through the air space is negligible compared with that through the secondary. It follows that the e.m.f.'s induced in the primary and secondary windings are equal and that the primary applied voltage, V_p, is equal and opposite to the e.m.f., E_p, induced in the primary, as shown in Fig. 161 and 162.

Next, let us assume a load having a power factor such

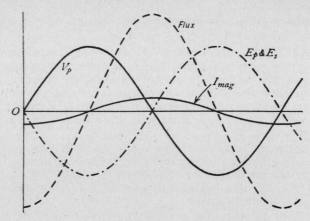

FIG. 161.—Curves for voltages, current and flux of a transformer on no load.

that the secondary current is in phase with E_s. As already explained in Art. 109, the primary current, I_p, must now have two components:

(a) I_{mag} to maintain the useful flux which remains constant within about 2 per cent between no load and full load; and

(b) a component, I_p', to neutralize the demagnetizing effect of the secondary current, as shown in Fig. 163 (a) and 164.

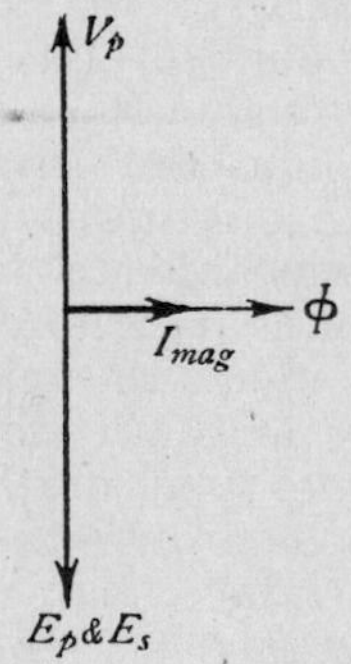

At instant A in Fig. 163 (a), the magnetizing current is *zero*, but I_s and I_p' are at their *maximum* values; and if the direction of the current in primary winding P is such as to

FIG. 162.—Vector diagram for Fig. 161.

produce flux upwards in the left-hand limb, the secondary current must be in such a direction as to produce flux upwards in the right-hand limb, and the flux of each limb has to return across the air space, as shown in Fig. 165. Since the flux of each limb is linked only with the winding by which it is produced, it is referred to as *leakage* flux and is responsible for inducing

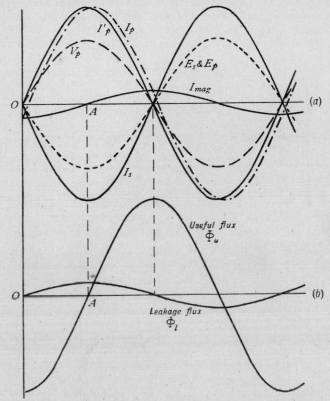

Fig. 163.—Curves for induced e.m.f.'s, currents and fluxes in a transformer on load.

an e.m.f. of self-inductance in each winding. The reluctance of the paths of the leakage flux, Φ_l, is almost entirely due to the long air paths and is therefore practically constant; consequently the value of the leakage flux is proportional to the load current, whereas the value of the useful flux remains almost independent of the load. On the other hand, the reluctance of the paths of the leakage flux is very high, so that the value of this flux is relatively small even on full load when the values of I_p' and I_s are about 20 to 30 times the magnetizing current I_{mag}.

From the above discussion it follows that the actual

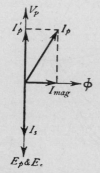

FIG. 164.—Vector diagram for Fig. 163.

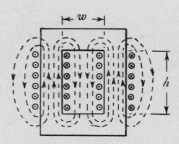

FIG. 165.—Paths of leakage flux.

flux in a transformer can be regarded as being due to the two components shown in Fig. 163 (b), namely:

(a) the useful flux, Φ_u, linked with both windings and remaining practically constant in value at all loads; and

(b) the leakage flux, Φ_l, half of which is linked with the primary winding and half with the secondary, and its value is proportional to the load.

The case of the secondary current in phase with the secondary induced e.m.f. has been considered because it is easier to see that the useful and the leakage fluxes can be considered independently of each other for this condition than it is for loads of other power factor.

113. Leakage Flux responsible for the Inductive Reactance of a Transformer. When a transformer is on no load there is no secondary current, and the secondary winding has not the slightest effect upon the primary current. The primary winding is then behaving as a choke having a very high inductance and a very low resistance. When the transformer is supplying a load, however, this conception of the inductance of the windings is of little use and it is rather difficult at first to understand why the useful flux is not responsible for any inductive drop in the transformer. So let us first of all assume an ideal transformer, namely a transformer the

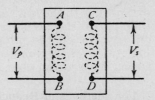

FIG. 166.—Ideal transformer enclosed in a box.

windings of which have negligible resistance and in which there is no iron loss and no magnetic leakage. Also for convenience let us assume unity transformation ratio, i.e. $N_p = N_s$. If such a transformer were enclosed in a box and the ends of the windings brought to terminals A, B, C and D on the lid, as shown in Fig. 166, then the p.d. between C and D would be exactly equal to that between A and B; and as far as the effect upon the output voltage is concerned, the transformer behaves as if A were connected to C and B to D. In other words, the useful flux is not responsible for any voltage drop in a transformer.

In the preceding Article it was explained that the leakage flux is proportional to the primary and secondary currents and that its effect is to induce e.m.f.'s of self-induction in the windings. Consequently the effect of leakage flux can be considered as equivalent to inductive reactances X_p and X_s connected in series with a transformer having no leakage flux, as shown in Fig. 167, these reactances being such that

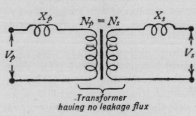

FIG. 167.—Transformer with leakage reactances.

the flux-linkages produced by the primary current through X_p are equal to those due to the leakage flux linked with the primary winding, and the flux-linkages produced by the secondary current through X_s are equal to those due to the leakage flux linked with the secondary winding of the actual transformer. The straight line drawn between the primary and secondary windings in Fig. 167 is the symbol used to indicate that the transformer has an iron core.

114. Methods of Reducing Leakage Flux.

The leakage flux can be practically eliminated by winding the primary and secondary, one over the other, uniformly around a laminated iron ring of uniform cross-section. But such an arrangement is not commercially practicable except in very small sizes, owing to the cost of threading a large number of turns through the ring.

The principal methods used in practice are:

(a) *Making the transformer "window" long and narrow.* The area of the window, $h \times w$ in Fig. 165, is determined by the cross-sectional area of the primary and secondary windings. For a given area the reluctance of the paths of the leakage flux is increased by increasing the height h and reducing the width w of the window. But if the window is made very narrow, an excessive proportion of the width is occupied by insulation. Hence, in practice the ratio of h/w is limited to about 4.

(b) *Arranging the primary and secondary windings concentrically.* Each winding is equally divided between the two limbs, the general practice being to place the low-voltage winding LVW next to the core and the high-voltage winding HVW on the outside, as shown in Fig. 168. At the instant when the currents are in the direction represented by the dots and crosses and their ampere-turns are exactly equal in value, the useful flux is zero and the paths where the leakage flux has its maximum density are represented by the dotted lines. With concentric windings, the leakage flux is approximately a half of that with the coils on separate limbs. Furthermore, this leakage flux is linked with only a part of the primary or secondary winding, so that the leakage reactance has been considerably reduced.

(c) *By sandwiching the primary and secondary windings.* Fig. 169 shows the primary winding P in two sections, one on each limb, each section being sandwiched between sections of the secondary windings S. From the dots and crosses representing the directions of the primary

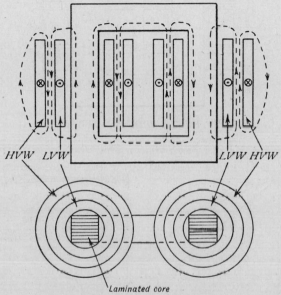

HVW LVW LVW HVW

Laminated core

Fig. 168.—Concentric windings.

and secondary currents at the instant when their ampere-turns are equal, it follows that most of the leakage flux passes horizontally across the window. The dotted lines in Fig. 169 represent the leakage flux in the regions where its density is highest.

The leakage flux can be reduced still further by using more sandwiched sections; but this arrangement has the disadvantage that adjacent sections must be well insulated from each other, so that with a large number of

9

sections an excessive amount of space is taken up by insulation.

Fig. 170 (a) shows the results obtained with a certain

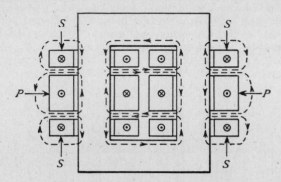

FIG. 169.—Sandwiched windings.

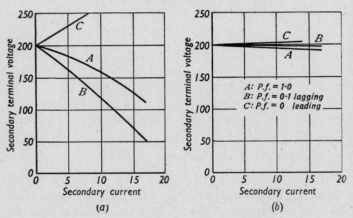

A: P.f. = 1·0
B: P.f. = 0·1 lagging
C: P.f. = 0 leading

(a)

(b)

FIG. 170.—Load characteristics of a transformer (a) with windings on separate limbs, (b) with windings sandwiched.

transformer for loads of different power factors when the primary and secondary windings were on separate limbs, as in Fig. 160. Fig. 170 (b) shows the results obtained with the same transformer when each limb had 10 sections of primary winding sandwiched with 10 sections of secondary winding. A comparison of these figures shows that the leakage flux can be reduced to a very small value by effective sandwiching of the primary and secondary windings.

(d) *By using shell-type construction.* In the construction shown in the above diagrams the iron core forming the limbs is surrounded by the windings, and this arrangement is referred to as the "core" type. With

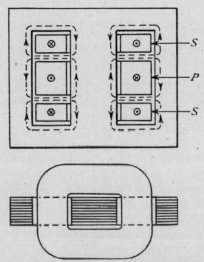

Fig. 171.—Shell-type construction.

the "shell-type" construction the windings are more completely surrounded by iron, as will be seen from Fig. 171, where the primary and secondary windings are shown sandwiched. The width of the centre limb is about twice that of each of the outer limbs. The dotted lines are again shown in regions where the density of the leakage flux is highest.

115. Equivalent Circuit of a Transformer. The behaviour of a transformer may be conveniently considered by assuming it to be equivalent to an ideal transformer, i.e. a transformer having no losses and no magnetic leakage and an iron core of infinite permeability requiring no magnetizing current, and then allowing for the imperfections of the actual transformer by means of additional circuits or impedances inserted between the supply and the primary winding and between the secondary and the load. Thus, in Fig. 172, P and S represent the primary and secondary windings of the ideal transformer. R_p and R_s are resistances equal to the resistances of the primary and secondary windings of the actual transformer. Similarly, inductive reactances

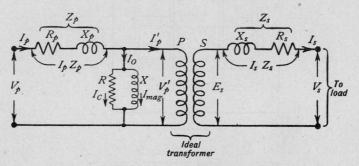

FIG. 172.—Equivalent circuit of a transformer.

X_p and X_s represent the reactances of the windings due to leakage flux in the actual transformer, as already explained in Art. 113.

The inductive reactance X is such that it takes a purely reactive current equal to the magnetizing current I_{mag} of the actual transformer. The core losses due to hysteresis and eddy currents are allowed for by a resistance R of such value that it takes a current I_c equal to the core-loss component of the primary current, i.e. $I_c^2 R$ is equal to the core loss of the actual transformer. The resultant of I_{mag} and I_c is I_o, namely the current which the transformer takes on no load. The vector diagram for the equivalent circuit on no load is exactly the same as that given in Fig. 159.

116. Vector Diagram for a Transformer on Load. For convenience let us assume equal number of turns on the primary and secondary windings, so that $E_p = E_s$. Both E_p and E_s lag 90° behind the flux Φ, as shown in Fig. 173, and V_p' represents the voltage applied to the primary of the ideal transformer to neutralise the induced e.m.f. E_p, and is therefore equal and opposite to the latter. Let us also assume the general case of a load having a lagging power factor; consequently, in Fig. 173, I_s has been drawn lagging about 45° behind E_s. Then:

$I_s R_s$ = voltage drop due to secondary resistance,
$I_s X_s$ = voltage drop due to secondary reactance
and $I_s Z_s$ = voltage drop due to secondary impedance.

The secondary terminal voltage V_s is the vectorial difference of E_s and $I_s Z_s$; in other words, V_s must be such that the vectorial sum of V_s and $I_s Z_s$ is E_s, and the derivation of the vector representing V_s is evident from Fig. 173. The power factor of the load is cos ϕ_s, where ϕ_s is the phase difference between V_s and I_s. I_p' represents the component of the primary current to neutralize the demagnetizing effect of the secondary current and is drawn equal and opposite to I_s. I_o is the no-load current of the transformer, as already explained in Art. 111. The vectorial sum of I_p' and I_o gives the total current I_p taken from the supply.

$I_p R_p$ = voltage drop due to primary resistance,
$I_p X_p$ = voltage drop due to primary reactance,
$I_p Z_p$ = voltage drop due to primary impedance
and V_p = vectorial sum of V_p' and $I_p Z_p$
= supply voltage.

If ϕ_p is the phase difference between V_p and I_p, then cos ϕ_p is the power factor on the primary side of the transformer. In Fig. 173 the vectors representing the no-load current and the primary and secondary voltage drops are, for clearness, shown far larger relative to the other vectors than they are in an actual transformer.

117. Approximate Equivalent Circuit of a Transformer. Since the no-load current of a transformer is only about 3 to 5 per cent of the full-load primary current, we can

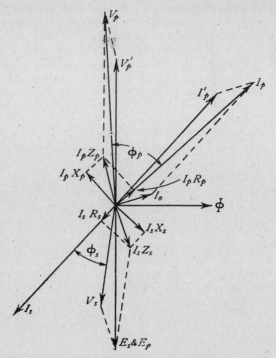

Fig. 173.—Vector diagram for a transformer on load.

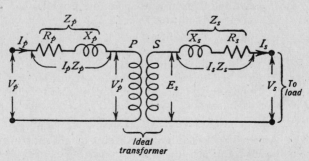

Fig. 174.—Approximate equivalent circuit of a transformer.

omit the parallel circuits R and X in Fig. 172 without introducing an appreciable error when we are considering the behaviour of the transformer on full load. Thus we have the simpler equivalent circuit of Fig. 174.

118. Simplification of the Approximate Equivalent Circuit of a Transformer. We can replace the resistance R_s of the secondary of Fig. 174 by inserting additional resistance R_s' in the primary circuit such that the power absorbed in R_s' when carrying the primary current is equal to that in R_s due to the secondary current.

i.e. $\qquad I_p^2 R_s' = I_s^2 R_s$

$\therefore \qquad R_s' = R_s(I_s/I_p)^2 \simeq R_s(V_p/V_s)^2.$

Hence if R_e be a single resistance in the primary circuit equivalent to the primary and secondary resistances of the actual transformer, then:

$$R_e = R_p + R_s' = R_p + R_s(V_p/V_s)^2 \qquad (198)$$

Similarly, since the inductance of a coil is proportional to the square of the number of turns, the secondary reactance X_s can be replaced by an equivalent reactance X_s' in the primary circuit, such that:

$$X_s' = X_s(N_p/N_s)^2 \simeq X_s(V_p/V_s)^2.$$

If X_e be the single reactance in the primary circuit equivalent to X_p and X_s of the actual transformer,

$$X_e = X_p + X_s' = X_p + X_s(V_p/V_s)^2 \quad . \quad (199)$$

If Z_e be the equivalent impedance of the primary and secondary windings referred to the primary circuit,

$$Z_e = \sqrt{(R_e^2 + X_e^2)} \qquad . \quad . \quad (200)$$

If ϕ_e be the phase difference between I_p and $I_p Z_e$, then

$$R_e = Z_e \cos \phi_e \text{ and } X_e = Z_e \sin \phi_e.$$

The simplified equivalent circuit of the transformer is given in Fig. 175, and Fig. 176 (a) is the corresponding vector diagram.

119. Voltage Regulation of a Transformer. The voltage regulation of a transformer is defined as the variation of the secondary voltage between no load and full load expressed as either a per-unit value or a percentage of the

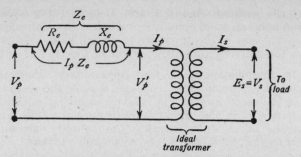

FIG. 175.—Simplified equivalent circuit of a transformer.

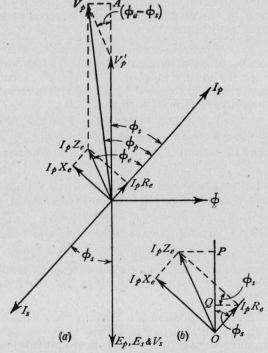

FIG. 176.—Vector diagram for Fig. 175.

no-load voltage, the primary voltage being assumed constant, i.e.

$$\left.\begin{array}{c}\text{voltage}\\ \text{regulation}\end{array}\right\} = \frac{\text{no-load voltage} - \text{full-load voltage}}{\text{no-load voltage}} \quad (201)$$

If V_p = primary applied voltage,

secondary voltage on no load = $V_p \times N_s/N_p$

If V_s = secondary terminal voltage on full load,

$$\text{voltage regulation} = \frac{V_p(N_s/N_p) - V_s}{V_p(N_s/N_p)}$$

$$= \frac{V_p - V_s(N_p/N_s)}{V_p} \text{ per unit}$$

$$= \frac{V_p - V_s(N_p/N_s)}{V_p} \times 100 \text{ per cent}$$

In the vector diagram of Fig. 176, N_p and N_s were assumed equal so that $V'_p = V_s$. In general,

$$V'_p = V_s(N_p/N_s),$$

$$\therefore \qquad \left.\begin{array}{c}\text{per-unit voltage}\\ \text{regulation}\end{array}\right\} = \frac{V_p - V'_p}{V_p} \quad . \quad . \quad (202)$$

In Fig. 176 (a), let us draw a perpendicular from V_p to meet the extension of V'_p at A; then:

$$V_p^2 = (V'_p + V'_p A)^2 + (V_p A)^2$$

$$= [V'_p + I_p Z_e \cos (\phi_e - \phi_s)]^2 + [I_p Z_e \sin (\phi_e - \phi_s)]^2$$

In actual practice, $I_p Z_e \sin (\phi_e - \phi_s)$ is very small compared with V'_p, so that:

$$V_p \simeq V'_p + I_p Z_e \cos (\phi_e - \phi_s).$$

Hence,

$$\left.\begin{array}{c}\text{per-unit voltage}\\ \text{regulation}\end{array}\right\} = \frac{V_p - V'_p}{V_p}$$

$$= \frac{I_p Z_e \cos (\phi_e - \phi_s)}{V_p} \quad . \quad (203)$$

Since $Z_e \cos (\phi_e - \phi_s) = Z_e (\cos \phi_e . \cos \phi_s + \sin \phi_e . \sin \phi_s)$

$$= R_e \cos \phi_s + X_e \sin \phi_s$$

$$\therefore \left.\begin{array}{c}\text{per-unit voltage}\\ \text{regulation}\end{array}\right\} = \frac{I_p(R_e \cos \phi_s + X_e \sin \phi_s)}{V_p} \quad (204)$$

9*

This expression can also be derived by projecting I_pR_e and I_pZ_e on to OA, as shown enlarged in Fig. 176 (b), from which it follows that:

$V_p'A$ in Fig. 176 (a) $= OP$ in Fig. 176 (b)

$$= OQ + QP = I_pR_e \cos \phi_s + I_pX_e \sin \phi_s$$

$$\therefore \quad \left. \begin{array}{c} \text{per-unit voltage} \\ \text{regulation} \end{array} \right\} = \frac{V_p - V_p'}{V_p} \simeq \frac{V_p'A}{V_p}$$

$$= \frac{OP}{V_p}$$

$$= \frac{I_p(R_e \cos \phi_s + X_e \sin \phi_s)}{V_p}.$$

The above expressions have been derived on the assumption that the power factor is lagging. Should the power factor be leading, the angle in expression (203) would be $(\phi_e + \phi_s)$ and the term in brackets in expression (204) would be $(R_e \cos \phi_s - X_e \sin \phi_s)$.

Example 42. *A 100-kVA transformer has 400 turns on the primary and 80 turns on the secondary. The primary and secondary resistances are 0·3 and 0·01 Ω respectively, and the corresponding leakage reactances are 1·1 and 0·035 Ω respectively. The supply voltage is 2200 V. Calculate: (a) the equivalent impedance referred to the primary circuit and (b) the voltage regulation and the secondary terminal voltage for full load having a power factor of (i) 0·8 lagging and (ii) 0·8 leading.*

(a) From (198),

$$\left. \begin{array}{c} \text{equivalent resistance} \\ \text{referred to primary} \end{array} \right\} = R_e = 0·3 + 0·01(400/80)^2$$

$$= 0·55 \ \Omega.$$

From (199),

$$\left. \begin{array}{c} \text{equivalent reactance} \\ \text{referred to primary} \end{array} \right\} = X_e = 1·1 + 0·035(400/80)^2$$

$$= 1·975 \ \Omega.$$

From (200),

$$\left. \begin{array}{c} \text{equivalent impedance} \\ \text{referred to primary} \end{array} \right\} = Z_e = \sqrt{[(0·55)^2 + (1·975)^2]}$$

$$= 2·05 \ \Omega.$$

(b) (i) Since $\cos \phi_s = 0 \cdot 8$, $\therefore$ $\sin \phi_s = 0 \cdot 6$.

$$\left.\begin{array}{r}\text{Full-load primary} \\ \text{current}\end{array}\right\} = \frac{100 \times 1000}{2200} = 45 \cdot 45 \text{ A.}$$

Substituting in (204), we have:

$$\left.\begin{array}{r}\text{Voltage regulation} \\ \text{for power factor} \\ 0 \cdot 8 \text{ lagging}\end{array}\right\} = \frac{45 \cdot 45(0 \cdot 55 \times 0 \cdot 8 + 1 \cdot 975 \times 0 \cdot 6)}{2200}$$

$$= 0 \cdot 0336 \text{ per unit}$$
$$= 3 \cdot 36 \text{ per cent.}$$

$$\left.\begin{array}{r}\text{Secondary terminal volt-} \\ \text{age on no load}\end{array}\right\} = 2200 \times 80/400 = 440 \text{ V}$$

$\therefore$ decrease of secondary terminal voltage between no load and full load

$$= 440 \times 0 \cdot 0336 = 14 \cdot 8 \text{ V}$$

$\therefore$ secondary terminal voltage on full load

$$= 440 - 14 \cdot 8 = 425 \cdot 2 \text{ V.}$$

(ii) Voltage regulation for power factor $0 \cdot 8$ leading

$$= \frac{45 \cdot 45(0 \cdot 55 \times 0 \cdot 8 - 1 \cdot 975 \times 0 \cdot 6)}{2200} = -0 \cdot 0154 \text{ per unit}$$

$$= -1 \cdot 54 \text{ per cent.}$$

Increase of secondary terminal voltage between no load and full load

$$= 440 \times 0 \cdot 0154$$
$$= 6 \cdot 78 \text{ V}$$

$\therefore$ secondary terminal voltage on full load

$$= 440 + 6 \cdot 78 = 446 \cdot 8 \text{ V.}$$

Example 43. *Calculate the per-unit and the percentage resistance and reactance drops of the transformer referred to in Example 42.*

Per-unit resistance drop of a transformer

$$= \frac{\left(\begin{array}{c}\text{full-load primary} \\ \text{current}\end{array}\right) \times \left(\begin{array}{c}\text{equivalent resistance re-} \\ \text{ferred to primary circuit}\end{array}\right)}{\text{primary voltage}}$$

$$= \frac{\left(\begin{array}{c}\text{full-load secondary} \\ \text{current}\end{array}\right) \times \left(\begin{array}{c}\text{equivalent resistance re-} \\ \text{ferred to secondary circuit}\end{array}\right)}{\text{secondary voltage on no load}}$$

Thus, for Example 42,

full-load primary current $=45\cdot45$ A,

and equivalent resistance referred to primary circuit $\Big\}=0\cdot55\ \Omega$

$\therefore$ resistance drop $=\dfrac{45\cdot45\times0\cdot55}{2200}=0\cdot0114$ per unit

$=1\cdot14$ per cent.

Alternatively, full-load secondary current $\Big\}\simeq45\cdot45\times400/80$

$=227\cdot2$ A,

and equivalent resistance referred to secondary circuit $\Big\}=0\cdot01+0\cdot3\left(\dfrac{80}{400}\right)^2=0\cdot022\ \Omega.$

Secondary voltage on no load $\Big\}=440$ V,

$\therefore$ resistance drop $=\dfrac{227\cdot2\times0\cdot022}{440}=0\cdot0114$ per unit

$=1\cdot14$ per cent.

Similarly, reactance drop of a transformer

$$=\frac{\binom{\text{full-load primary}}{\text{current}}\times\binom{\text{equivalent reactance referred to primary circuit}}{}}{\text{primary voltage}}$$

$$=\frac{45\cdot45\times1\cdot975}{2200}=0\cdot0408 \text{ per unit}=4\cdot08 \text{ per cent.}$$

It is usual to refer to the per-unit or the percentage resistance and reactance drops on full load as merely the per-unit or the percentage resistance and reactance of the transformer; thus, the above transformer has a per-unit resistance and reactance of $0\cdot0114$ and $0\cdot0408$ respectively or a percentage resistance and reactance of $1\cdot14$ and $4\cdot08$ respectively.

120. Efficiency of a Transformer. The losses which occur in a transformer on load can be divided into two groups:

(a) Copper losses in primary and secondary windings, namely $I_p^2R_p+I_s^2R_s$.

(b) Iron losses in the core due to hysteresis and eddy currents. The factors determining these losses have already been discussed in Articles 27 and 76.

Since the flux in a normal transformer does not vary by more than about 2 per cent between no load and full load, it is usual to assume the iron loss to remain constant at all loads.

Hence, if P_i =total iron loss in core,

$$\text{total losses in transformer} = P_i + I_p^2 R_p + I_s^2 R_s$$

$$\text{and efficiency} = \frac{\text{output power}}{\text{input power}} = \frac{\text{output power}}{\text{output power} + \text{losses}}$$

$$= \frac{I_s V_s \times \text{power factor}}{I_s V_s \times \text{p.f.} + P_i + I_p^2 R_p + I_s^2 R_s} \quad . \quad (205)$$

Greater accuracy is possible by expressing the efficiency thus:

$$\text{efficiency} = \frac{\text{output power}}{\text{input power}} = \frac{\text{input power} - \text{losses}}{\text{input power}}$$

$$= 1 - \frac{\text{losses}}{\text{input power}} \quad . \quad . \quad . \quad (206)$$

Example 44. *The primary and secondary windings of a 500-kVA transformer have resistances of 0·42 and 0·0011 Ω respectively. The primary and secondary voltages are 6600 and 400 V respectively and the iron loss is 2·9 kW. Calculate the efficiency on (a) full load and (b) half load, assuming the power factor of the load to be 0·8.*

(a) Full-load secondary current $= \dfrac{500 \times 1000}{400} = 1250$ A

and full-load primary current $\simeq \dfrac{500 \times 1000}{6600} = 75\cdot8$ A

∴ secondary copper loss on full load $= (1250)^2 \times 0\cdot0011 = 1720$ W

and primary copper loss on full load $= (75\cdot8)^2 \times 0\cdot42 = 2415$ W

$\therefore$ $\quad$ total copper loss on full load $\Big\}$ $=4135$ W $=4\cdot135$ kW

and $\quad$ total loss on full load $\Big\}$ $=4\cdot135+2\cdot9=7\cdot035$ kW.

$\quad$ Output power on full load $\Big\}$ $=500\times0\cdot8=400$ kW

$\therefore$ $\quad$ input power on full load $\Big\}$ $=400+7\cdot035=407\cdot035$ kW.

From (206), efficiency on full load $\Big\}$ $=\Big(1-\dfrac{7\cdot035}{407\cdot0}\Big)=0\cdot9827$ per unit

$\qquad\qquad =98\cdot27$ per cent.

(b) Since the copper loss varies as the square of the current,

$\therefore$ $\quad$ total copper loss on half load $\Big\}$ $=4\cdot135\times(0\cdot5)^2=1\cdot034$ kW

and $\quad$ total loss on half load $\Big\}$ $=1\cdot034+2\cdot9=3\cdot934$ kW

$\therefore$ $\quad$ efficiency on half load $\Big\}$ $=\Big(1-\dfrac{3\cdot934}{203\cdot9}\Big)=0\cdot9807$ per unit

$\qquad\qquad =98\cdot07$ per cent.

121. Condition for Maximum Efficiency of a Transformer. If R_{es} be the equivalent resistance of the primary and secondary windings referred to the *secondary* circuit,

$$R_{es}=R_p(N_s/N_p)^2+R_s$$
$$=\text{a constant for a given transformer.}$$

Hence for any load current I_s,

$\quad$ total copper loss $=I_s^2R_{es}$

and $\qquad$ efficiency $=\dfrac{I_sV_s\times\text{p.f.}}{I_sV_s\times\text{p.f.}+P_i+I_s^2R_{es}}$

$$=\dfrac{V_s\times\text{p.f.}}{V_s\times\text{p.f.}+P_i/I_s+I_sR_{es}} \qquad (207)$$

For a normal transformer, V_s is approximately constant; hence for a load of given power factor, the efficiency is a maximum when the denominator of (207) is a minimum,

i.e. when $\dfrac{d}{dI_s}(V_s \times \text{p.f.} + P_i/I_s + I_s R_{es}) = 0$

$\therefore$ $\qquad\qquad\qquad -P_i/I_s^2 + R_{es} = 0$

or $\qquad\qquad\qquad\qquad I_s^2 R_{es} = P_i$ . . (208)

Hence the efficiency is a maximum when the variable copper loss is equal to the constant iron loss.

Example 45. *Find the output at which the efficiency of the transformer of Example 44 is a maximum and calculate its value, assuming the power factor of the load to be 0·8.*

With the full-load output of 500 kVA, the total copper loss is 4·135 kW.

Let $n = \begin{cases}\text{fraction of full-load kVA at which the} \\ \text{efficiency is a maximum.}\end{cases}$

Corresponding total copper loss $= n^2 \times 4\cdot135$ kW

Hence, from (208), $\qquad n^2 \times 4\cdot135 = 2\cdot9$

$\therefore$ $\qquad\qquad\qquad\qquad n = 0\cdot837,$

and output at maximum efficiency $= 0\cdot837 \times 500$

$\qquad\qquad\qquad\qquad\qquad\qquad = 418\cdot5$ kVA.

It will be noted that the value of the kVA at which the efficiency is a maximum is independent of the power factor of the load.

Since the copper and iron losses are equal when the efficiency is a maximum,

$\therefore$ $\qquad$ total loss $= 2 \times 2\cdot9 = 5\cdot8$ kW

Output power $= 418\cdot5 \times 0\cdot8 = 334\cdot8$ kW

$\therefore$ $\begin{matrix}\text{maximum} \\ \text{efficiency}\end{matrix}\Big\} = \Big(1 - \dfrac{5\cdot8}{334\cdot8 + 5\cdot8}\Big) = 0\cdot983$ per unit

$\qquad\qquad = 98\cdot3$ per cent.

122. Open-circuit and Short-circuit Tests on a Transformer. These two tests enable the efficiency and the voltage regulation to be calculated without actually loading the transformer and with an accuracy far higher than is possible by direct measurement of input and output powers and voltages. Also, the power required to carry out these tests is very small compared with the full-load output of the transformer.

Open-circuit test. The transformer is connected as in Fig. 177 to a supply at the rated voltage and frequency,

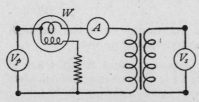

FIG. 177.—Open-circuit test on a transformer.

namely the voltage and frequency given on the name-plate. The ratio of the voltmeter readings, V_p/V_s, gives the ratio of the number of turns. Ammeter A gives the no-load current, and its reading is a check on the magnetic quality of the iron core and joints. The primary current on no load is usually less than 5 per cent of the full-load current so that the I^2R loss on no load is less than 1/400 of the primary I^2R loss on full load and is therefore negligible compared with the core loss. Hence the wattmeter reading can be taken as the core loss of the transformer.

Short-circuit test. The secondary is short-circuited through a suitable ammeter A_s, as shown in Fig. 178, and a *low* voltage is applied to the primary circuit. This voltage should, if possible, be adjusted to circulate full-load currents in the primary and secondary circuits. Assuming this to be the case, the copper loss in the wind-

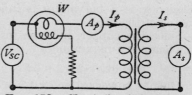

FIG. 178.—Short-circuit test on a transformer.

ings is the same as that on full load. On the other hand, the iron loss is negligibly small, since the applied voltage and therefore the flux are only about one-twentieth to one-thirtieth of the rated voltage and flux, and the iron loss is approximately proportional to the square of the flux. Hence the power registered on wattmeter W can be taken as the copper loss in the windings.

123. Calculation of Efficiency from the Open-circuit and Short-circuit Tests.

If P_{oc} = input power in watts on the open-circuit test,
= core loss,

and P_{sc} = input power in watts on the short-circuit test with full-load currents,

= total copper loss on full load,

then total loss on full load $\Big\} = P_{oc} + P_{sc}$

and efficiency on full load $\Big\} = \dfrac{\text{full-load VA} \times \text{p.f.}}{(\text{full-load VA} \times \text{p.f.}) + P_{oc} + P_{sc}}$ (209)

Also, for any load equal to $n \times$ full load,

corresponding total loss $\Big\} = P_{oc} + n^2 P_{sc}$

and corresponding efficiency

$$= \dfrac{n \times \text{full-load VA} \times \text{p.f.}}{n \times \text{full-load VA} \times \text{p.f.} + P_{oc} + n^2 P_{sc}} \quad (210)$$

124. Calculation of the Voltage Regulation from the S.C. Test.

Since the secondary voltage is zero, the whole of the applied voltage on the short-circuit test is absorbed in sending currents through the impedances of the primary and secondary windings; and since ϕ_e in Fig. 176 is the phase angle between the primary current and the voltage drop due to the equivalent impedance referred to the primary circuit,

cos ϕ_e = power factor on short-circuit test,

$$= \dfrac{P_{sc}}{I_p V_{sc}}$$

If V_{sc} be the value of the primary applied voltage on the s.c. test when *full-load* currents are flowing in the primary and secondary windings, then from (203),

Per-unit voltage regulation $\Big\} = \dfrac{V_{sc} \cos (\phi_e - \phi_s)}{V_p}$. (211)

Example 46. *The following results were obtained on a 50-kVA transformer:—O.C. test: primary volts, 3300 V; secondary volts, 400 V; primary power, 430 W. S.C. test: primary volts, 124 V; primary current, 15·3 A; primary power, 525 W; secondary current, full-load value. Calculate: (a) the efficiencies at full load and at half load for 0·7 power factor; (b) the voltage regulations for power factor 0·7 (i) lagging, (ii) leading; and (c) the secondary terminal voltages corresponding to (i) and (ii).*

(a)   Core loss $=430$ W,

$$\left. \begin{array}{c} \text{copper loss on} \\ \text{full load} \end{array} \right\} = 525 \text{ W}$$

$\therefore$ $\left. \begin{array}{c} \text{total loss on} \\ \text{full load} \end{array} \right\} = 955$ W $= 0·955$ kW

and $\left. \begin{array}{c} \text{efficiency on} \\ \text{full load} \end{array} \right\} = \dfrac{50 \times 0·7}{(50 \times 0·7) + 0·955}$

$$= \left(1 - \frac{0·955}{35·95} \right) = 0·9734 \text{ per unit}$$
$$= 97·34 \text{ per cent.}$$

$\left. \begin{array}{c} \text{Copper loss on} \\ \text{half load} \end{array} \right\} = 525 \times (0·5)^2 = 131$ W,

$\therefore$ $\left. \begin{array}{c} \text{total loss on} \\ \text{half load} \end{array} \right\} = 430 + 131 = 561$ W $= 0·561$ kW

and $\left. \begin{array}{c} \text{efficiency on} \\ \text{half load} \end{array} \right\} = \dfrac{25 \times 0·7}{(25 \times 0·7) + 0·561}$

$$= \left(1 - \frac{0·561}{18·06} \right) = 0·969 \text{ per unit}$$
$$= 96·9 \text{ per cent.}$$

(b) $\cos \phi_e = \dfrac{525}{124 \times 15·3} = 0·2765$

$\therefore$ $\phi_e = 73° 57'$

For $\cos \phi_s = 0·7$, $\phi_s = 45° 34'$.

From (211), for power factor 0·7 lagging,

$$\text{voltage regulation} = \frac{124 \cos (73° 57' - 45° 34')}{3300}$$
$$= 0·033 \text{ per unit}$$
$$= 3·3 \text{ per cent.}$$

For power factor 0·7 leading,

$$\text{voltage regulation} = \frac{124 \cos (73° 57' + 45° 34')}{3300}.$$
$$= -0·0185 \text{ per unit}$$
$$= -1·85 \text{ per cent.}$$

125. Three-phase Core-type Transformers. Modern large transformers are of the three-phase core-type shown in Fig. 179. Three similar limbs are connected by top and bottom yokes, each limb having primary and secondary windings, arranged concentrically. In Fig. 179 the primary is shown star-connected and the secondary mesh-connected. Actually, the windings may be connected star-delta, delta-star, star-star or delta-delta, depending upon the conditions under which the transformer is to be used.

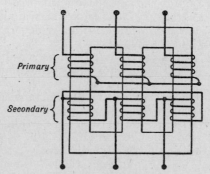

FIG. 179.—Three-phase core-type transformer.

Example 47. *A three-phase transformer has* 420 *turns on the primary and* 36 *turns on the secondary winding. The supply voltage is* 3300 *V. Find the secondary line voltage on no load when the windings are connected* (a) *star-delta and* (b) *delta-star.*

(a)   Primary phase voltage = 3300/1·73 = 1908 V,

∴   secondary phase voltage = $1908 \times \dfrac{36}{420} = 163·5$ V

                = secondary line voltage.

(b)   Primary phase voltage = 3300 V,

∴   secondary phase voltage = $3300 \times \dfrac{36}{420} = 283$ V,

∴   secondary line voltage = 283 × 1·73 = 490 V.

126. Cooling of Transformers. It is necessary to limit the temperature rise of the transformer core and windings to a safe value—the actual value depends upon the insulating materials employed; and since the transformer has no rotating component to induce a draught, natural air cooling is only suitable with very small sizes. The usual practice is to immerse the transformer in a tank filled with a mineral oil. The latter assists in maintaining the insulation of the windings and, by convection, it transfers heat from the windings and the core to the cooling surfaces. The principal methods of dissipating the heat are:

(a) By making the tank with plain sheet steel. This is satisfactory for transformers up to about 25 kVA.

(b) By fitting the tank with vertical tubes or radiators. The latter are joined to the tank near the bottom and just below the oil level near the top of the tank. The oil circulates by natural convection, i.e. the heated oil rises alongside the windings and core and flows down the cooling tubes or radiators.

(c) By pumping the oil through an external water-cooled radiator. This method is used for very large transformers.

127. Auto-transformers. An auto-transformer is a transformer having a part of its winding common to the

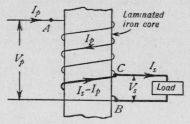

Fig. 180.—An auto-transformer.

primary and secondary circuits; thus, in Fig. 180, winding AB has a tapping at C, the load being connected across CB and the supply voltage applied across AB.

Let V_p and V_s = primary and secondary voltages respectively,

I_p and I_s = primary and secondary currents respectively,

N_p = no. of turns between A and B,

N_s = no. of turns between C and B

and n = ratio of the *smaller* voltage to the *larger* voltage.

Neglecting the losses and the magnetizing current, we have for Fig. 180,

$$n = \frac{V_s}{V_p} = \frac{I_p}{I_s} = \frac{N_s}{N_p}.$$

The current in section CB of the winding is the resultant of I_p and I_s; and since these currents are practically in phase opposition and I_s is greater than I_p, the resultant current is $(I_s - I_p)$.

Let l = mean length per turn

and J = current density throughout the winding,

∴   cross-sectional area of conductor in $AC = I_p/J$

and   cross-sectional area of conductor in $CB = (I_s - I_p)/J$

Hence,   volume of copper in $AC = l(N_p - N_s)I_p/J$

$$= lN_p(1 - n)I_p/J$$

and   volume of copper in $CB = lN_s(I_s - I_p)/J$

$$= lN_s I_s(1 - n)/J$$

$$= lN_p I_p(1 - n)/J$$

∴   total volume of copper in auto-transformer $\Big\} = 2lN_p I_p(1 - n)/J.$

If the two-winding transformer to perform the same duty has the same voltage per turn and therefore the same flux, we can assume the mean length per turn to remain unaltered. Hence, for the same current density J,

total volume of copper in two-winding transformer $\Big\} = lN_p I_p/J + lN_s I_s/J$

$$= 2lN_p I_p/J$$

Hence, $\dfrac{\text{volume of copper in auto-transformer}}{\text{volume of copper in two-winding transformer}}$

$$=\frac{2lN_pI_p(1-n)/J}{2lN_pI_p/J}=1-n \quad . \quad . \quad (212)$$

and saving of copper effec-
ted by using an $\Big\}=n\times\Big($ volume of copper in the two-winding transformer $\Big)$
auto-transformer

Thus, if $n=0\cdot1$, saving of copper is only $0\cdot1$ per unit; but if $n=0\cdot9$, saving of copper is $0\cdot9$ per unit.   Hence the nearer the ratio of transformation is to unity, the greater is the economy of copper.

Example 48.   *Capacitors are often made for a working voltage of 600 V.   It is required to supply such capacitors from a 400-V system.   Find the economy of copper effected by using an auto-transformer instead of a two-winding transformer.*

In this example, $n=400/600=0\cdot667$

$\therefore \dfrac{\text{volume of copper in auto-transformer}}{\text{volume of copper in two-winding transformer}}$

$$=1-0\cdot667=0\cdot333$$

and   economy of copper$=0\cdot667$ per unit
$$=66\cdot7 \text{ per cent.}$$

Auto-transformers are mainly used for (a) inter-connecting systems that are operating at roughly the same voltage and (b) starting squirrel-cage induction motors (Art. 156).   Should an auto-transformer be used to supply a low-voltage system from a high-voltage system, it is essential to earth the common connection, for example, B in Fig. 180, otherwise there is a risk of serious shock.   In general, however, it is better not to use an auto-transformer for interconnecting high-voltage and low-voltage systems.

128. Current Transformers.   It is difficult to construct ammeters and the current coils of wattmeters, watthour-meters and relays to carry alternating currents greater than about 100 A.   Furthermore, if the voltage of the system exceeds 500 V, it is dangerous to connect such instruments directly to the high-voltage conductors. These difficulties are overcome by using current transformers. Fig. 181 shows an ammeter A supplied through a current transformer. The ammeter is usually arranged to give full-scale deflection with 5 A, and the ratio of the primary to secondary turns must be such that full-scale ammeter reading is obtained with full-load current in the primary. Thus, if the primary has 4 turns and the full-load primary current is 50 A, the full-load primary ampere-turns are 200; consequently, to circulate 5 A in the secondary, the number of secondary turns must be 200/5, namely 40.

If the number of primary turns were reduced to *one*

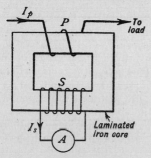

FIG. 181.—A current transformer.

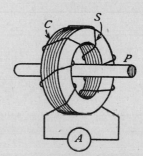

FIG. 182.—A bar-primary current transformer.

and the secondary winding had 40 turns, the primary current to give full-scale reading of 5 A on the ammeter would be 200 A. Current transformers having a single-turn primary are usually constructed as shown in Fig. 182, where P represents the primary conductor passing through the centre of a laminated iron ring. The secondary winding S is wound uniformly around the ring.

The vector diagram for a current transformer is given in Fig. 183, where:

$I_s N_s$ represents the secondary ampere-turns,

$I'_p N_p$ represents the component of the primary ampere-turns to neutralize the secondary ampere-turns and is equal and opposite to $I_s N_s$,

$I_{mag}N_p$ represents the component of the primary ampere-turns to produce the magnetic flux,

I_cN_p represents the component of the primary ampere-turns to supply the hysteresis and eddy-current losses in the core,

I_pN_p represents the actual primary ampere-turns and is the resultant of $I_p'N_p$, $I_{mag}N_p$ and I_cN_p.

In an actual transformer, I_{mag} and I_c are far smaller compared with I_p than is indicated in Fig. 183, being usually less than 1 per cent of I_p. The flux density in the core is, in consequence, very low, being usually less than $0 \cdot 1$ Wb/m² on full load. Hence I_s is practically proportional and almost in phase opposition to I_p.

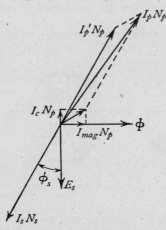

FIG. 183.—Vector diagram for a current transformer.

The secondary circuit of a current transformer must on no account be opened while the primary winding is carrying a current, since all the primary ampere-turns would then be available to produce flux. The iron loss due to the high flux density would cause excessive heating of the core and windings and a dangerously high e.m.f. might be induced in the secondary winding. Hence if it is desired to remove the ammeter from the secondary circuit, the secondary winding must first be short-circuited. This will not be accompanied by an excessive secondary current, since the latter is proportional to the primary current; and since the primary winding is in *series* with the load, the primary current is determined by the value of the load and not by that of the secondary current.

Fig. 184 shows the connections of a wattmeter W (or of a watthour meter) to a high-voltage circuit. The conventional method of representing a current transformer is indicated by CT and VT is a voltage transformer supplying the voltage circuit of the meter, usually at 110 V. As a safety precaution the secondary

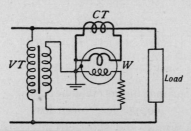

FIG. 184.—A wattmeter supplied through current and voltage transformers.

circuits of the instrument transformers and the metal casing of the meter should be earthed as shown.

Summary of Important Formulae in Chapter VII

$$\frac{V_s}{V_p} \simeq \frac{N_s}{N_p} \simeq \frac{I_p}{I_s} \quad . \quad . \quad . \quad (192)$$

$$E_p = 4 \cdot 44 N_p f \Phi_m \quad . \quad . \quad . \quad (193)$$

$$E_s = 4 \cdot 44 N_s f \Phi_m \quad . \quad . \quad . \quad (194)$$

Equivalent resistance referred to primary $\Big\} = R_e = R_p + R_s (V_p/V_s)^2 \quad (198)$

Equivalent reactance referred to primary $\Big\} = X_e = X_p + X_s (V_p/V_s)^2 \quad (199)$

Equivalent impedance referred to primary $\Big\} = Z_e = \sqrt{(R_e^2 + X_e^2)} \quad . \quad (200)$

Per-unit voltage regulation of a transformer

$$= \frac{\text{no-load voltage} - \text{full-load voltage}}{\text{no-load voltage}} \quad (201)$$

For load having power factor $=\cos \phi_s$ lagging,

$$\left.\begin{array}{c}\text{per-unit voltage} \\ \text{regulation}\end{array}\right\} = \frac{I_p Z_e \cos (\phi_e - \phi_s)}{V_p} \qquad . \quad . \quad (203)$$

$$= \frac{I_p (R_e \cos \phi_s + X_e \sin \phi_s)}{V_p} \quad . \quad (204)$$

$$\left.\begin{array}{c}\text{and per-unit} \\ \text{efficiency}\end{array}\right\} = \frac{I_s V_s \times \text{power factor}}{(I_s V_s \times \text{p.f.}) + P_i + I_p^2 R_p + I_s^2 R_s} \quad (205)$$

$$= \left(1 - \frac{\text{losses}}{\text{input power}}\right) \qquad . \quad . \quad . \quad (206)$$

Condition for maximum efficiency:
$$\text{copper loss} = \text{iron loss} \qquad . \quad . \quad (208)$$

From open-circuit and short-circuit tests:
Per-unit efficiency at $n \times$ full load

$$= \frac{n \times \text{full-load VA} \times \text{p.f.}}{n \times \text{full-load VA} \times \text{p.f.} + P_{oc} + n^2 P_{sc}} \quad (210)$$

$$\left.\begin{array}{c}\text{and per-unit voltage} \\ \text{regulation}\end{array}\right\} = \frac{V_{sc} \cos (\phi_e - \phi_s)}{V_p} \quad . \quad . \quad (211)$$

$$\frac{\text{Volume of copper in auto-transformer}}{\text{Volume of copper in two-winding transformer}}$$
$$= (1 - n) \qquad . \quad (212)$$

where $n = \dfrac{\text{the smaller voltage}}{\text{the larger voltage}}$.

EXAMPLES VII

1. Assuming sinusoidal flux variation with time, derive an expression for the induced e.m.f. of a transformer, having given the frequency, number of turns per winding, maximum flux density and effective core cross-sectional area.

A 3300/250-V, 50-c/s, single-phase transformer is built on a core having an effective cross-sectional area of 125 cm^2 and 70 turns on the low-voltage winding. Calculate (a) the value of the maximum flux density, (b) the number of turns on the high-voltage winding.
(U.E.I.)

2. A 10-kVA, single-phase transformer has a turns ratio of 300/23. The primary is connected to a 1500-V, 60-c/s supply. Find the secondary volts on open-circuit and the approximate values of the currents in the two windings on full load. Find, also, the maximum value of the flux.
(U.L.C.I.)

3. A transformer for a radio receiver has a 230-V, 50-c/s primary and three secondary windings as follows: a 1000-V winding with a centre

tapping, a 4-V winding with a centre tapping and a 6·3-V winding. The nett area of cross-section of the core is 14 cm². Calculate the number of turns on each winding if the maximum flux density is to be approximately 1 Wb/m². Prove any formula used.

4. Upon what factors does the no-load current of a transformer depend? Why does the primary current increase when the secondary current increases?

A transformer takes 10 A on no load, at a power factor of 0·1. The turn ratio is 4 : 1 (step-down). If a load is supplied by the secondary at 200 A and at a power factor of 0·8, find the primary current and power factor. (Internal voltage drops in the transformer are to be ignored.) (Joint Section A)

5. A 50-c/s, three-phase, core-type transformer is star/delta connected and has a line voltage ratio of 6600/440 V. The cross-section of the core is square with a circumscribing circle diameter of 60 cm. If the maximum flux density is about 1·2 Wb/m², calculate the turns per phase on the low-voltage and on the high-voltage windings.

6. Draw the vector diagram of a single-phase transformer on no load. A 1 : 1 ratio can be assumed.

A 400/200-V, single-phase transformer is supplying a load of 25 A at a power factor of 0·866 lagging. On no load the current and power factor are 2 A and 0·208 respectively. Obtain graphically, or by calculation, the current taken from the supply. The effects of resistance and reactance of the windings can be neglected; a vector diagram is required. (U.E.I.)

7. A three-phase, star-connected alternator generates 6360 V per phase and supplies 500 kW at power factor 0·9 lagging to a load through a step-down transformer of turns ratio 40 : 1. The transformer is delta-connected on the primary side and star-connected on the secondary side. Draw a connection diagram and calculate the value of the line volts at the load. Calculate also the currents in (a) alternator windings; (b) transformer primary windings; (c) transformer secondary windings. (U.L.C.I.)

8. A 400-V, three-phase supply is connected through a three-phase loss-free transformer of 1 : 1 ratio, which has its primary connected in mesh and secondary in star, to a load comprising three 10-Ω resistors connected in mesh. Calculate the currents in the transformer windings, in the resistors and in the lines to the supply and the load. Find also the total power supplied and the power dissipated by each resistor. Sketch the circuit diagram. (Joint Section A)

9. If three transformers, each with a turns-ratio of 12 : 1, are connected star-delta and the primary line voltage is 6600 V, what is the secondary voltage?

If the transformers are reconnected delta-star with the same primary voltage, what is the secondary line voltage?

10. Draw a simple vector diagram of a transformer (a) on open-circuit, (b) on load, indicating in each case what the various vectors represent. The no-load current of a transformer is 5·0 A at 0·3 power factor when supplied at 230 V, 50 c/s. The number of turns on the primary winding is 200. Calculate (i) the maximum value of the flux in the core; (ii) the core loss; (iii) the magnetizing current. (N.C.T.E.C.)

11. Calculate (a) the number of turns required for a choke to absorb 200 V on a 50-c/s circuit, (b) the length of air-gap required if the coil is to take a magnetizing current of 3 A (r.m.s.) and (c) the phase difference between the current and the terminal voltage. Mean length of iron

path, 50 cm; maximum flux density in core, 1 Wb/m^2; sectional area of core, 30 cm^2; maximum ampere-turns/cm for the iron, 2·5; iron loss, 0·8 watt/lb; density of iron, 7·8 g/cm^3. Neglect the resistance of the winding and any magnetic leakage and fringing.

12. Calculate the no-load current and power factor for the following 60-c/s transformer: mean length of iron path, 70 cm; maximum flux density, 1·1 Wb/m^2; maximum ampere-turns/m for the iron, 300; iron loss, 1·1 W/lb. All the joints may be assumed equivalent to a single air-gap of 0·2 mm. Number of primary turns, 120; primary voltage, 230 V. Neglect the resistance of the primary winding.

13. Explain the action of a transformer (a) at no load, (b) when loaded.

The ratio of turns of a single-phase transformer is 8, the resistances of the primary and secondary windings are 0·85 Ω and 0·012 Ω respectively, and the leakage reactances of these windings are 4·8 Ω and 0·07 Ω respectively. Determine the voltage to be applied to the primary to obtain a current of 150 A in the secondary when the secondary terminals are short-circuited. Ignore the magnetizing current. (App. El., L.U.)

14. Draw and explain the complete vector diagram for a transformer supplying a lagging-current load. Deduce a simple expression for the voltage regulation and calculate its value at 0·8 lagging power factor for a transformer which has an equivalent resistance of 2 per cent and an equivalent reactance of 4 per cent.
(C. & G., El. Eng. Pract., Int.)

15. The s.c. test on a single-phase transformer, with the primary winding short-circuited and 30 V applied to the secondary, gave a wattmeter reading of 60 W and secondary current of 10 A. If the normal applied primary voltage is 200, the transformation ratio 1 : 2 and the full-load secondary current is 10 A, calculate the secondary terminal p.d. at full-load current for (a) unity power factor, (b) power factor 0·8 lagging.

If any approximations are employed, they must be explained.
(U.E.I.)

16. Develop the equivalent circuit of a transformer referred to its primary side.

A single-phase transformer operates from a 220-V supply. It has an equivalent resistance of 0·1 Ω and an equivalent reactance of 0·5 Ω referred to the primary. The secondary is connected to a load having a resistance of 200 Ω and a reactance of 100 Ω. Calculate the secondary terminal voltage. The secondary winding has five times as many turns as the primary. Neglect no-load current.
(Assoc. Mem., I.E.E.)

17. Explain the action of a transformer (a) at no load and (b) when loaded. Draw a vector diagram for the loaded condition and explain the steps in its construction.

A 10-kVA single-phase transformer, for 2000/400 V at no load, has resistances and leakage reactances as follows. *Primary winding*: resistance, 5·5 Ω; reactance, 12 Ω. *Secondary winding*: resistance, 0·2 Ω; reactance, 0·45 Ω. Determine the approximate value of the secondary voltage at full load, 0·8 power factor (lagging), when the primary supply voltage is 2000 V. (App. El., L.U.)

18. The primary and secondary windings of a 30-kVA, 6000/230-V transformer have resistances of 10 and 0·016 Ω respectively. The reactance of the transformer referred to the primary circuit is 34 Ω. Calculate (a) the primary voltage required to circulate full-load current

when the secondary is short-circuited and (b) the percentage voltage regulation of the transformer for a load of 30 kVA having a power factor of 0·8 lagging.   (App. El., L.U.)

19. A 200-kVA, single-phase transformer gives a full-load secondary voltage of 230 V.   The equivalent resistance and reactance referred to the secondary winding are 0·005 Ω and 0·012 Ω, respectively. With the secondary winding open-circuited and normal voltage and frequency applied to the primary winding, the input power is 2·0 kW. Calculate the efficiency at full-load output at unity power factor.   If the primary voltage and frequency are maintained at normal value, estimate the probable change in secondary voltage when full load at 0·8 power factor lagging is switched off.   (N.C.T.E.C.)

20. A 75-kVA transformer, rated at 6600/230 V on no load, requires 310 V across the primary to circulate full-load currents on short-circuit, the power absorbed being 1·6 kW.   Determine (a) the percentage voltage regulation and (b) the full-load secondary terminal voltage for power factors of (i) unity, (ii) 0·8 lagging and (iii) 0·8 leading.
If the input power to the transformer on no load is 0·9 kW, calculate the per-unit efficiency at full load and at half load for power factor 0·8 and find the kVA at which the efficiency is a maximum.

21. A single-phase transformer has a voltage ratio on open-circuit of 3300/660 V.   The primary and secondary resistances are 0·8 Ω and 0·03 Ω respectively, the corresponding leakage reactances being 4 Ω and 0·12 Ω.   The load is equivalent to a coil of resistance 4·8 Ω and inductive reactance 3·6 Ω.   Determine the terminal voltage of the transformer and the output in kW.   (U.L.C.I., Adv. El. Tech.)

22. Explain with the aid of circuit diagrams how (a) the core loss, (b) the copper loss of a transformer may be determined.   A 100-kVA, single-phase transformer has an iron loss of 600 W and a copper loss of 1·5 kW at full-load current.   Calculate the efficiency at (a) 100 kVA output at 0·8 power factor lagging, (b) 50 kVA output at unity power factor.   (N.C.T.E.C.)

23. Discuss fully the energy losses in single-phase transformers. Such a transformer working at unity power factor has an efficiency of 90 per cent at both one-half load and at the full load of 500 W.   Determine the efficiency at 75 per cent of full load.   (App, El, L,U,)

24. Enumerate the losses which occur in a transformer and explain how each loss varies with the load current.
A single-phase transformer is rated at 10 kVA, 230/100 V.   When the secondary terminals are open-circuited and the primary winding is supplied at normal voltage (230 V), the current input is 2·6 A at a power factor of 0·3.   When the secondary terminals are short-circuited, a voltage of 18 V applied to the primary causes the full-load current (100 A) to flow in the secondary, the power input to the primary being 240 W.   Calculate (a) the efficiency of the transformer at full load, unity power factor, (b) the load at which maximum efficiency occurs, (c) the value of the maximum efficiency.
                                                        (App. El., L.U.)

25. Enumerate the losses which occur in a loaded transformer. Show how the losses are affected by variations in the load, the supply voltage and frequency being constant.   Deduce the relationship between the losses for maximum efficiency.
A 200-kVA single-phase transformer has an efficiency of 98 per cent at full load.   If the maximum efficiency occurs at three-quarters of

full load, calculate (a) the iron loss, (b) the copper loss at full load, (c) the efficiency at half load. Ignore magnetizing current and assume a power factor of 0·8 at all loads. (App. El., L.U.)

26. Draw to scale the no-load vector diagram for a 10-kVA, 440/3300-V, single-phase transformer which, when tested on open circuit, gave the following figures on the primary side: 440 V, 1·3 A, 115 W.

When tested on short circuit with full-load current flowing, the power input was 140 W. Calculate the efficiency of the transformer at (a) full load, unity p.f., (b) one-quarter full load, 0·8 p.f.

(U.L.C.I.)

27. What are the principal sources of energy loss in a transformer, and how do they vary with the load? A 500-kVA transformer has an iron loss of 2·5 kW and the maximum efficiency at 0·8 power factor occurs when the load is 268 kW.

Calculate (a) the maximum efficiency at unity power factor and (b) the efficiency on full load at 0·71 power factor.

(U.L.C.I., Adv. El. Tech.)

28. Each of two transformers, A and B, has an output of 40 kVA. The core losses in A and B are 500 and 250 W respectively, and the full-load copper losses are 500 and 750 W respectively. Tabulate the losses and efficiencies at quarter, half and full load for a power factor of 0·8. For each transformer, find the load at which the efficiency is a maximum.

29. If the transformers referred to in Q. 28 be used for supplying a lighting load (unity power factor) and have their primaries permanently connected to the supply system, compare the all-day efficiencies of the two transformers, assuming the output to be 4 hours at full load, 8 hours at half load and the remaining hours on no load. What would be the saving effected in 12 weeks (7 days per week) with the better transformer if the charge for electrical energy be 2d. per kWh?

Note. All-day efficiency $= \dfrac{\text{output energy in kWh in 24 hours}}{\text{input energy in kWh in 24 hours}}$.

30. Give an account of the losses which occur in a transformer and how each loss is reduced to a minimum in practice.

A 100-kVA lighting transformer has a full-load loss of 3 kW, the losses being equally divided between the iron and copper. During a day the transformer operates on full load for 3 hours, on half load for 4 hours, the output being negligible for the remainder of the day. Calculate the all-day efficiency. (C. & G., El. Eng. Pract., Int.)

31. A certain transformer core has a measured total iron loss of 50 W at 25 c/s and $B_m = 1$ Wb/m^2. At 50 c/s and the same value of B_m, the iron loss becomes 125 W. Estimate the total loss if the frequency were 50 c/s and $B_m = 0·8$ Wb/m^2. Take the hysteresis index as 1·7.

Note. For a given specimen, with maximum flux density B_m, hysteresis loss $= k_h f B_m^x$ and eddy current loss $= k_e f^2 B_m^2$ (Art. 27, 76), where k_h, k_e and x are constants.

∴ total iron loss $= P = k_h f B_m^x + k_e f^2 B_m^2$

For a given B_m, $P = k_h' f + k_e' f^2$

Hence, if the total iron loss for a given maximum flux density is known at two frequencies, k_h' and k_e' can be calculated and the hysteresis and eddy-current components of the iron loss determined at any desired frequency.

32. What is meant by the term "magnetic hysteresis"? Explain why, when iron is subjected to alternating magnetization, energy losses occur due to both hysteresis and eddy-currents. The iron loss in a transformer core at normal flux density was measured at frequencies of 30 and 50 c/s, the results being 30 W and 54 W respectively. Calculate (a) the hysteresis loss, (b) the eddy-current loss at 50 c/s.

(App. El., L.U.)

33. Give an account of the iron losses in dynamo-electric machinery and how each loss may be reduced to a minimum in practice.

The following results were obtained on an iron-cored choking coil: input when connected across (a) 250-V, 50-c/s supply, 10 A, 500 W, (b) 500-V, 100-c/s supply, 900 W, (c) 20-V d.c. supply, 10 A. Calculate the approximate values of the hysteresis and eddy-current losses in case (a). (C. & G., El. Eng. Pract., Final Part I.)

34. The following table gives the relationship between the flux and the magnetizing current in the primary winding of a transformer:

Current (amperes)	0	0·25	0·5	0·75	1	1·25	1·5	1·75
Flux (milliwebers)	−1·76	−1·48	−0·8	1·0	1·56	1·88	2·08	2·17
Current (amperes)	2	1·5	1	0·5	0			
Flux (milliwebers)	2·24	2·2		2·14	2·04	1·76		

Plot the above values and derive the waveform of the magnetizing current of the transformer assuming the flux to be sinusoidal and to have a peak value of 2·24 milliwebers.

35. Derive an expression for the saving in copper effected by using an auto-transformer instead of a two-winding transformer.

The primary and secondary voltages of an auto-transformer are 500 and 400 V respectively. Show, with the aid of a diagram, the current distribution in the windings when the secondary current is 100 A, and calculate the economy of copper in this particular case.

What are the disadvantages of auto-transformers? (N.C.T.E.C.)

36. A 10-kVA, single-phase, step-up auto-transformer has 1000 turns in its winding and a turns ratio of 1 : 5. When connected to a 440-V, 50-c/s supply, the no-load current is 1·2 A at 0·25 p.f. lagging. Calculate the magnetizing current, the iron loss and the maximum flux in the core.

Explain the effect on the magnetizing current and iron loss of building the core from alloy sheet-steel and making close-fitting joints between core and yoke.

What are the uses of the auto-transformer, and its advantages compared with the double-wound transformer? (U.L.C.I.)

CHAPTER VIII

ALTERNATORS

129. General Arrangement of Alternators. In Art. 100 it was explained how three-phase e.m.f.'s could be generated by rotating three loops in a magnetic field, the loops being attached to one another at 120°. We will now consider the arrangement of an actual three-phase alternator, so let us first consider why alternators are usually constructed with a stationary a.c. winding and rotating poles. Suppose we have a 20,000-kVA, 11,000-V, three-phase alternator; then from (184),

$$20,000 \times 1000 = 1 \cdot 73 \times I_l \times 11,000$$
$$\therefore \qquad \text{line current} = I_l = 1050 \text{ A.}$$

Hence if the machine was made with stationary poles and a rotating three-phase winding, three slip-rings would be required, each capable of dealing with 1050 A and the insulation of each ring together with that of the brushgear would have to stand a working voltage of 11,000/1·73, namely 6350 V. Further, it is usual to connect alternator windings in star and to join the star-point through a suitable resistance to a metal plate embedded in the ground so as to make good electrical contact with earth; consequently a fourth slip-ring would be required.

By using a stationary a.c. winding and a rotating field system, only two slip-rings are necessary and these have only to deal with the exciting current. Assuming the power required for exciting the poles of the above machine to be 150 kW and the voltage to be 400 V,

$$\text{exciting current} = \frac{150 \times 1000}{400} = 375 \text{ A.}$$

In other words, the two slip-rings and brushgear would only have to deal with 375 A and be insulated for merely 400 V. Hence, by using a stationary a.c. winding and

rotating poles, the construction is considerably simplified and the slip-ring losses are reduced.

Further advantages of this arrangement are: (a) The
extra space available for the a.c. winding makes it
possible to use more insulation and to enable voltages up
to 30 kV to be generated. (b) With the simpler and
more robust mechanical construction of the rotor, a
higher speed is possible, so that a greater output is
obtainable from a machine of given dimensions.

The slots in the laminated stator core of an alternator
are usually semi-enclosed, as shown in Fig. 185, so as to

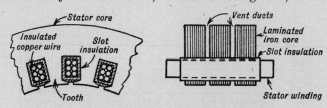

FIG. 185.—Portion of an alternator stator.

distribute the magnetic flux as uniformly as possible in
the air-gap, thereby minimizing the ripple that would
appear in the e.m.f. waveform if open slots were used.

In Art. 80 it was explained that if an alternator has
p pairs of poles and the speed is N revolutions/minute,

$$\text{frequency} = f = \frac{Np}{60} \qquad . \qquad . \qquad (138)$$

Hence for a 50-c/s supply, a two-pole alternator must be
driven at 3000 r.p.m., a four-pole alternator at 1500
r.p.m., etc.

130. Types of Rotor Construction. Alternators can be
divided into two categories: (a) those with salient or
projecting poles; and (b) those with cylindrical rotors.

Salient-pole construction is used in comparatively
small machines and machines driven at a relatively low
speed. For instance, if a 50-c/s alternator is to be driven
by an oil engine at, say, 375 r.p.m., then, from (138), the
machine must have 16 poles; and to accommodate all
these poles, the alternator must have a comparatively

10

large diameter. Since the output of a machine is roughly proportional to its volume, such an alternator would have a small axial length. Fig. 186 shows one arrangement of salient-pole construction. The poles are made of fairly thick steel laminations, L, riveted together and bolted to a steel yoke wheel Y, a bar of mild steel B being inserted to improve the mechanical strength. The exciting winding W is usually an insulated copper strip wound on edge, the coil being held firmly between the pole tips and the yoke wheel. The pole

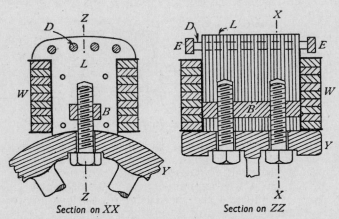

Section on XX Section on ZZ

FIG. 186.—Portion of a salient-pole rotor.

tips are well rounded to as to make the flux distribution around the periphery nearer a sine wave and thus improve the waveform of the generated e.m.f. Copper rods D, short-circuited at each end by copper bars E, are usually inserted in the pole-shoes, their function being to improve the parallel operation of alternators.

In this country alternators are generally driven by steam turbines, and these are essentially high-speed machines. The centrifugal force on a high-speed rotor is enormous: for instance, a mass of 1 lb on the outside of a rotor of 1 yard diameter rotating at a speed of 3000 r.p.m. has a centrifugal force of 4600 lb (about

2 tons) acting upon it. To withstand such a force the rotor is usually made of a solid steel forging with longitudinal slots cut as indicated in Fig. 187, which shows a two-pole rotor with 8 slots and 2 conductors per slot. In an actual rotor there are more slots and far more conductors per slot; and the winding is in the form of insulated copper strip held securely in position by phosphor-bronze wedges. The regions forming the centres of the poles are usually left unslotted. The horizontal dotted lines joining the conductors in Fig. 187

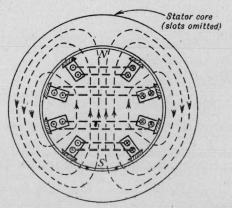

FIG. 187.—A cylindrical rotor.

represent the end connections. If the rotor current has the direction represented by the dots and crosses in Fig. 187, the flux distribution is indicated by the light dotted lines. In addition to its mechanical robustness, this cylindrical construction has the advantage that the flux distribution around the periphery is much nearer a sine wave than is the case with the salient-pole machine. Consequently, a better e.m.f. waveform is obtained.

131. Stator Windings. In this book we shall consider only two types of three-phase winding, namely (a) single-layer winding and (b) double-layer winding; and of these types we shall consider only the simplest forms.

Single-layer winding. The main difficulty with single-layer windings is to arrange the end-connections so that they do not obstruct one another. Fig. 188 shows one of the most common methods of arranging these end-connections for a four-pole, three-phase alternator having 2 slots per pole per phase, i.e. 6 slots per pole or a total of 24 slots. In Fig. 188 all the end-connections are shown bent outwards for clearness; but in actual

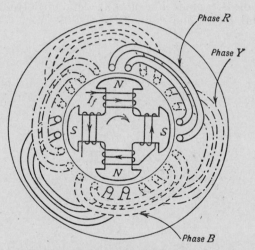

FIG. 188.—End connections of a three-phase single-layer winding.

practice the end-connections are usually shaped as shown in Fig. 189 and in section in Fig. 190. This method has the advantage that it requires only two shapes of end-connections, namely those marked *C* in Fig. 190, which are brought straight out of the slots and bent so as to lie on a cylindrical plane, and those marked *D*. The latter, after being brought out of the slots, are bent outwards roughly at right angles, before being again bent to form an arch alongside the core.

The connections of the various coils are more easily indicated by means of the developed diagram of Fig. 191.

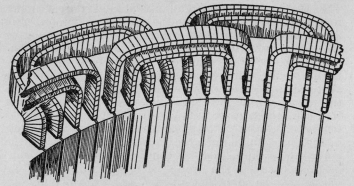

FIG. 189.—End-connections of a three-phase single-layer winding.

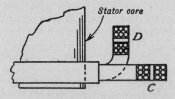

FIG. 190.—Sectional view of end-connections.

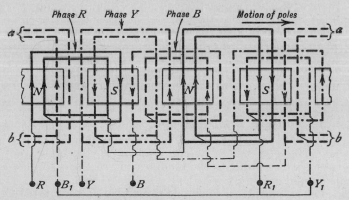

FIG. 191.—Three-phase single-layer winding.

The heavily lined rectangles (full and dotted lines) represent the coils, each coil consisting of a number of turns; and the thin lines—other than those representing the poles—indicate the connections between the various coils. The width of the pole-face has been made two-thirds of the pole pitch. The poles in Fig. 191 are assumed to be *behind* the winding and moving towards the right. From the right-hand rule—bearing in mind that the thumb represents the direction of *motion of the conductor relative to the flux*, namely towards the left in Fig. 191—the e.m.f.'s in the conductors opposite the poles are as indicated by the arrowheads. The connections between the groups of coils forming any one phase must be such that all the e.m.f.'s are helping one another.

Since the alternator has 6 slots per pole and since the rotation of the poles through one pole pitch corresponds to half a cycle of the e.m.f. wave, it follows that the spacing between two adjacent slots corresponds to 180/6, namely 30 electrical degrees. Hence, if the wire forming the beginning of the coil occupying the first slot is taken to the "red" terminal R, the connection to the "yellow" terminal Y must be a conductor from a slot 4 slot-pitches ahead, namely from the 5th slot, since this allows the e.m.f. in phase Y to lag 120° behind that in phase R. Similarly, the connection to the "blue" terminal B must be taken from the 9th slot in order that the e.m.f. in phase B may lag 120° behind that in phase Y. Ends R_1, Y_1 and B_1 of the three phases can be joined together to form the neutral point of a star-connected system. If the windings are to be mesh-connected, end R_1 of phase R is joined to the beginning of Y, end Y_1 to the beginning of B and end B_1 to the beginning of R, as shown in Fig. 192.

Double-layer winding. The general arrangement of a double-layer winding was fully discussed in Chap. XIV of *Principles of Electricity* and it is therefore only necessary to indicate the modification required to give a three-phase supply.

Let us consider a four-pole three-phase alternator with 2 slots per pole per phase and 2 conductors per slot.

Fig. 193 shows the simplest arrangement of the end-connections of one phase, the thick lines representing the conductors (and their end-connections) occupying, say, the outer halves and the thin lines representing conductors occupying the inner halves. The coils are assumed full-pitch, i.e. the spacing between the two

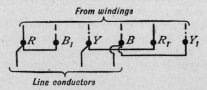

FIG. 192.—Mesh-connection of windings.

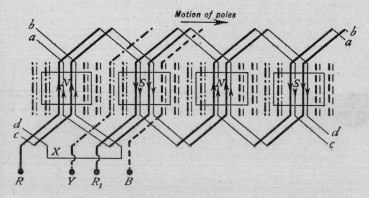

FIG. 193.—One phase of a three-phase double-layer winding.

sides of each turn is exactly a pole pitch. The main feature of the end-connections of a double-layer winding is the strap X, which enables the coils of any one phase to be connected so that all the e.m.f.'s of that phase are assisting one another.

Since there are 6 slots per pole, the phase difference between the e.m.f.'s of adjacent slots is 180/6, namely 30 electrical degrees; and since there is a phase difference of 120° between the e.m.f.'s of phases R and Y, there

must be 4 slot spans between the first conductor of phase
R and that of phase Y. Similarly, there must be 4 slot
spans between the first conductors of phases Y and B.
Hence, if the outer conductor of the third slot is connected to terminal R, the corresponding conductor in
the seventh slot, in the direction of rotation of the poles,
is connected to terminal Y and that in the eleventh slot
to terminal B.

In general, the single-layer winding is employed where
the machine has a large number of conductors per slot,
whereas the double-layer winding is more convenient
when the number of conductors per slot does not
exceed 8.

132. E.M.F. Equation of an Alternator.

Let Z =no. of conductors in series per *phase*,

Φ =useful flux per pole, in webers,

p =no. of pairs of poles

and N =speed in r.p.m.

$$\left.\begin{array}{l}\text{Magnetic flux cutting}\\\text{a conductor in 1 rev}\end{array}\right\} = \Phi \times 2p$$

$$\left.\begin{array}{l}\text{Magnetic flux cutting}\\\text{a conductor in 1 sec}\end{array}\right\} = 2\Phi p \times N/60$$

$$\therefore \quad \left.\begin{array}{l}\text{average e.m.f. generated}\\\text{in 1 conductor}\end{array}\right\} = 2\Phi p \times \frac{N}{60} \text{ volts.}$$

If the stator of a three-phase machine had only 3 slots
per pole, i.e. 1 slot/p/ph,* and if the coils were full-pitch,
the e.m.f.'s generated in all the conductors of one phase
would be in phase with one another and could therefore
be added arithmetically. Hence, for a winding concentrated in 1 slot/p/ph,

$$\text{average e.m.f. per phase} = Z \times 2\Phi p \times \frac{N}{60} \text{ volts.}$$

If the e.m.f. wave be assumed to be sinusoidal,
r.m.s. value of e.m.f. per phase for 1 slot/p/ph,

$$= 1 \cdot 11 \times 2Z \times \frac{Np}{60} \times \Phi \quad . \quad . \quad (213)$$

* " /p/ph" is an abbreviation for "per pole per phase."

A winding concentrated in 1 slot/p/ph would have two disadvantages:

(a) The size of such slots and the number of conductors per slot would be so great that it would be difficult to prevent the insulation on the conductors in the centre of the slot becoming overheated, since most of the heat generated in the slots has to flow radially outwards to the iron core.

(b) The waveform of the e.m.f. would be similar to that of the flux distribution around the inner periphery of the stator; and, in general, this would not be sinusoidal.

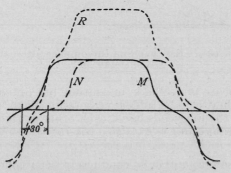

FIG. 194.—E.M.F. waveforms of a salient-pole alternator.

By distributing the winding in 2 or more slots/p/ph, the number of conductors per slot is reduced, thereby reducing the temperature rise in the centre of the slot. Also, the e.m.f. waveform is improved; for instance, consider a three-phase winding distributed in 2 slots/p/ph, such as that shown in Fig. 188. With a salient-pole alternator having a uniform gap-length over the greater part of the pole-face, the waveform of the e.m.f. generated in one conductor is represented by curve M in Fig. 194; and that of the e.m.f. generated in the adjacent slot is represented by a similar curve N displaced 30 electrical degrees from M. The resultant waveform R is obtained by adding curves M and N; and it is evident from

10*

Fig. 194 that curve R, though not sinusoidal, is a much closer approximation to a sine wave than the original waves M and N.

Let us consider how the magnitude of the e.m.f. is affected when the winding is distributed in 2 slots per pole per phase; and for simplicity it will be assumed that the e.m.f. generated in each conductor is sinusoidal. Since the e.m.f.'s in the two adjacent slots M and N of

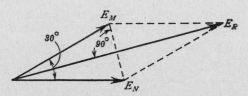

FIG. 195.—E.M.F.'s in a three-phase alternator with 2 slots/p/ph.

any one phase are equal in magnitude but differ in phase by 30°, they can be added vectorially as in Fig. 195; and since the diagonals bisect each other at right angles,

$$\text{resultant e.m.f.} = E_R = 2E_M \cos 15° = 2 \times 0{\cdot}966 E_M$$
$$= 1{\cdot}932 E_M$$

Had the same number of conductors been concentrated in 1 slot/p/ph, the resultant e.m.f. would have been $2E_M$.

Hence, $\dfrac{\text{e.m.f. with winding in 2 slots/p/ph}}{\text{e.m.f. with winding in 1 slot/p/ph}} = \dfrac{1{\cdot}932 E_M}{2 E_M}$
$$= 0{\cdot}966.$$

If the three-phase winding is distributed in 3 slots/p/ph the e.m.f.'s in adjacent slots differ by $180/(3 \times 3)$, namely 20 electrical degrees; and by adding 3 vectors spaced 20° apart, it can be shown that:

$$\dfrac{\text{e.m.f. with winding in 3 slots/p/ph}}{\text{e.m.f. with winding in 1 slot/p/ph}} = 0{\cdot}960$$

The ratio $\dfrac{\text{e.m.f. with a distributed winding}}{\text{e.m.f. with a concentrated winding}}$ is termed the *distribution* or *breadth factor* of the winding and may be represented by k_d, where

$k_d = 0 \cdot 966$ for three-phase winding with 2 slots/p/ph
$\quad = 0 \cdot 960$ for three-phase winding with 3 slots/p/ph
$\quad = 0 \cdot 958$ for three-phase winding with 4 slots/p/ph
$\quad = 0 \cdot 955$ for three-phase winding with very large number of slots/p/ph.

Hence, for a distributed winding, expression (213) becomes:

$$\left.\begin{array}{l}\text{R.M.S. value of}\\\text{e.m.f. per phase}\end{array}\right\} = 2 \cdot 22 k_d Z \frac{Np}{60} \times \Phi \quad . \quad . \quad (214)$$

$$= 2 \cdot 22 k_d Z f \Phi \quad . \quad . \quad . \quad (215)$$

Example 49. *A three-phase star-connected alternator on open-circuit is required to generate a line voltage of 3600 V, 50 c/s, when driven at 500 r.p.m. The stator has 3 slots/ p/ph and 10 conductors per slot. Calculate: (a) the number of poles and (b) the useful flux per pole. Assume all the conductors per phase to be connected in series.*

(a) From (138), $\quad 50 = \dfrac{500 \times p}{60}$

$\therefore \qquad$ no. of poles $= 2p = 12$.

(b) $\qquad$ No. of slots per phase $= 3 \times 12 = 36$

$\therefore \quad$ no. of conductors per phase $= 36 \times 10 = 360$

$$\text{E.M.F. per phase} = \frac{3600}{1 \cdot 73} = 2080 \text{ V.}$$

Substituting in (215), we have:

$$2080 = 2 \cdot 22 \times 0 \cdot 96 \times 360 \times 50 \times \Phi$$

$\therefore \qquad \Phi = 0 \cdot 0543 \text{ weber.}$

Summary of Important Formulae in Chapter VIII

$$f = \frac{Np}{60} \quad . \quad . \quad . \quad . \quad (138)$$

$$\left.\begin{array}{l}\text{R.M.S. value of}\\\text{e.m.f. per phase}\end{array}\right\} = 2 \cdot 22 k_d Z \times \frac{Np}{60} \times \Phi \quad . \quad (214)$$

$$= 2 \cdot 22 k_d Z f \Phi \quad . \quad . \quad (215)$$

$$\left.\begin{array}{l}\text{Distribution fac-}\\\text{tor of a winding}\end{array}\right\} = \frac{\text{e.m.f. with a distributed winding}}{\text{e.m.f. with a concentrated winding}}$$

EXAMPLES VIII

1. Draw a developed diagram for a concentric winding for a three-phase, six-pole alternator having 2 slots per pole per phase. The winding is to have only two shapes of end-connection. Show how the winding would be connected (a) in star, (b) in mesh.

Note. From Fig. 191 it will be seen that this type of winding has three groups of coils per pair of poles; hence a six-pole machine must have nine groups of coils—four arched, four straight and a "skewed" or "cranked" coil which is partly arched and partly straight.

2. Draw a developed diagram of one phase of a double-layer winding of a three-phase four-pole alternator having 3 slots per pole per phase and 2 conductors per slot.

3. The flux density in an alternator air-gap at equal intervals is as follows:

Angle (elect. degrees)	.	.	0	15	30	45	60	75	90
Flux density (Wb/m²)	.	.	0	0·1	0·4	0·9	1·0	1·0	1·0

Find the shape of the waveform of the resultant e.m.f. of a single-phase alternator having 6 slots/pole when the winding is (a) concentrated in 1 slot per pole, (b) distributed in 2 adjacent slots/pole and (c) distributed in 4 adjacent slots/pole.

4. Describe briefly the construction of a simple alternator, noting the essential parts.

A four-pole alternator, on open circuit, generates 200 V at 50 c/s when its field current is 4 A. Determine the generated e.m.f. at a speed of 1200 r.p.m. and a field current of 3 A, neglecting saturation in the iron parts. (N.C.T.E.C.)

5. Show that the waveform of the e.m.f. induced in a full-pitch coil on the stator of an alternator will be identical with the air-gap flux-distribution curve.

A four-pole alternator having a stator bore of 50 cm and a core length of 35 cm is wound with single-turn full-pitch coils. The r.m.s. value of the e.m.f. induced in each coil is 18 V when the speed is 1500 r.p.m. and the e.m.f. is constant over the middle two-thirds of each half cycle and varies uniformly over the remainder. Calculate the maximum flux density in the air-gap and the total flux per pole.
(App. El., L.U.)

6. The field-form of an alternator taken from the pole centre line in electrical degrees is given below, the points being joined by straight lines. Obtain the r.m.s. value of this wave and its form-factor.
Distance from pole centre, degrees:

0	20	45	60	75	90	105	120	135	

Flux density, Wb/m²:

0·7   0·7   0·6   0·15   0   0   0   −0·15   −0·6 } etc.

7. Show that the resultant of two out-of-phase sinusoidal voltages of the same frequency connected in series is also a sine wave of the same frequency as the constituent voltages.

A part of an alternator winding consists of six coils in series, each coil having an e.m.f. of 10 V (r.m.s.) induced in it. The coils are placed in successive slots and between each slot and the next there is an electrical phase displacement of 30°. Find, graphically or by calculation, the e.m.f. of the six coils in series. (U.E.I.)

8. Describe briefly the construction of a small salient-pole alternator. Upon what do its frequency and voltage depend? What is the

effect on the e.m.f. generated if the winding is distributed in more than 1 slot per pole per phase? The e.m.f. generated in a coil on an alternator is 20 V. Calculate the e.m.f. between the ends of two such coils connected in series if they are separated on the alternator core by 30 electrical degrees.   (N.C.T.E.C.)

9. A four-pole, single-phase alternator has a flux per pole of 0·02 weber and is wound with 14 conductors per slot. If the alternator has 16 slots wound and 8 slots unwound, calculate the e.m.f. when the speed is 1500 r.p.m. Assume that all conductors are joined in series and that each coil is full pitch.

10. A three-phase, star-connected alternator driven at 900 r.p.m. is required to generate a line voltage of 460 V at 60 c/s when on open-circuit. The stator has 2 slots per pole per phase and 4 conductors per slot. Calculate (a) the number of poles and (b) the useful flux per pole. Assume all the conductors per phase to be connected in series.

11. Find the number of stator conductors per slot for a three-phase, 50-c/s alternator if the winding is star-connected and has to give a line voltage of 13,000 V when the machine is on open-circuit. The flux per pole is about 0·15 weber. Assume full-pitch coils and the stator to have 3 slots per pole per phase. The speed is 300 r.p.m.

12. The following figures refer to a three-phase generator: number of poles, 8; flux per pole, 0·1 weber; number of slots, 96; conductors per slot, 6; speed, 750 r.p.m. Determine the e.m.f. across the terminals of the machine if the windings are star-connected and all the conductors in each phase are in series.

13. A four-pole, 50-c/s, three-phase mesh-connected alternator has a one-layer stator winding carried in 36 slots, each slot containing 16 conductors. The flux per pole is 0·04 weber. Calculate the e.m.f. between the terminals.

14. A four-pole machine has an armature with 60 slots and 8 conductors per slot and revolves at 1500 r.p.m., the flux per pole being 0·05 weber. Calculate the e.m.f. generated (a) as a d.c. machine if the winding is lap-connected and (b) as a three-phase star-connected machine, if the winding factor is 0·96 and all the conductors in each phase are in series.

CHAPTER IX

PRODUCTION OF A ROTATING MAGNETIC FLUX

133. Introductory. It was pointed out in Art. 99 that one of the main advantages of the three-phase over the single-phase system is that three-phase motors are more satisfactory than single-phase motors. One reason for this superiority is that three-phase currents can be arranged to produce a resultant magnetic flux that remains constant in magnitude and rotates at a uniform speed. This property of three-phase currents is applicable to alternators as well as to motors, and is therefore dealt with at this stage.

134. Distribution of the Resultant Magnetic Flux due to Three-phase Currents. Let us consider a two-pole, three-phase stator winding having, for simplicity, only 1 slot per pole per phase, as shown in Fig. 196. The end-connections of the coils are not shown, but are assumed to be similar to those already shown in Fig. 188; thus R and R_1 represent the "start" and the "finish" of the "red" phase, etc. It will be noted that R, Y and B are displaced 120 electrical degrees relative to one another. Let us also assume that the current is positive when it is flowing inwards in conductors R, Y and B, and therefore outwards in R_1, Y_1 and B_1. As far as the present discussion is concerned, the rotor core need only consist of circular iron laminations to provide a path of low reluctance for the magnetic flux.

Suppose the currents in the three phases to be represented by the curves in Fig. 197; then at instant a the current in phase R is positive and at its maximum value, whereas in phases Y and B the currents are negative and each is half the maximum value. These currents are represented in direction by dots and crosses in

Fig. 196 (a) and in magnitude by the size of these dots
and crosses.   These currents produce the magnetic flux
represented by the dotted lines in Fig. 196 (a).   At
instant *b* in Fig. 197, the currents in phases *R* and *B* are
each 0·866 of the maximum; and the distribution of the
magnetic flux due to these currents is shown in Fig.
196 (b).   It will be seen that the axis of this field is in

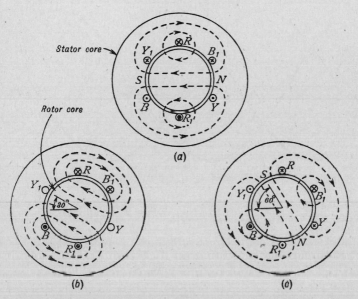

FIG. 196.—Distribution of magnetic flux due to three-phase
currents.

line with coil YY_1 and therefore has turned clockwise
through 30° from that of Fig. 196 (a).   At instant *c* in
Fig. 197, the current in phase *B* has attained its maximum negative value while the currents in *R* and *Y* are
both positive and each is half the maximum value.
These currents produce the magnetic flux shown in Fig.
196 (c), the axis of this flux being displaced clockwise by
another 30° compared with that in Fig. 196 (b).

   These three cases are sufficient to prove that for every

interval of *time* corresponding to 30° along the horizontal axis of Fig. 197, the axis of the magnetic flux in a two-pole stator moves forward 30° in *space*. Consequently, in 1 cycle, the flux rotates through 1 revolution or 2 pole pitches. If the stator is wound for 4 poles, the magnetic flux rotates through half a revolution in 1 cycle. Hence, if the stator is wound for p pairs of poles, the magnetic

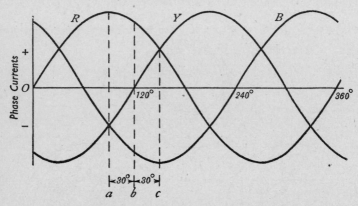

FIG. 197.—Three-phase currents in windings.

flux rotates through $1/p$ revolution in 1 cycle and therefore through f/p revolutions in 1 second.

If N is the speed of the magnetic flux in r.p.m.,

$$N = 60f/p \quad . \quad . \quad . \quad . \quad (216)$$

or

$$f = \frac{Np}{60}$$

which is the same as expression (138) derived for an alternator in Art. 80. It follows that if the stator in Fig. 196 had the same number of poles as the alternator supplying the three-phase currents, the magnetic flux in Fig. 196 would rotate at *exactly* the same speed as the poles of the alternator. It also follows that when a three-phase alternator is supplying a balanced load, the stator currents of that alternator set up a resultant magnetic flux that rotates at exactly the same speed as the poles. Hence the magnetic flux due to three-phase currents is said to rotate at *synchronous speed*.

135. Mathematical Derivation of the Magnitude and Speed of the Resultant Magnetic Flux due to Three-phase Currents. Suppose RR_1, YY_1 and BB_1 in Fig. 198 to be three coils of a two-pole stator, the coils being spaced 120° apart. It is immaterial whether the coils are assumed to be wound on a stator core as in Fig. 196 or to be situated in air as in Fig. 198. Each coil, when carrying a current alone, gives rise to a magnetic flux the axis of which is at right angles to the plane of the coil. For instance the axis of the magnetic flux due to current

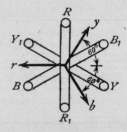

FIG. 198.—Fluxes due to currents in a three-phase winding.

FIG. 199.—Horizontal and vertical components of the resultant magnetic flux.

in coil RR_1 is horizontal; and if the current in RR_1 is assumed positive when flowing inwards in R, the positive direction of the flux is represented by arrowhead r. Similarly, the current in YY_1 is assumed positive when flowing inwards in Y so that the positive direction of the flux due to current in YY_1 is represented by arrowhead y. In the same way, arrowhead b represents the positive direction of the flux due to current in BB_1. If Φ is the maximum value of the magnetic flux due to one phase *alone*, then:

instantaneous flux due to $RR_1 = r = \Phi \sin \omega t$

instantaneous flux due to $YY_1 = y = \Phi \sin (\omega t - 2\pi/3)$

and instantaneous flux due to $BB_1 = b = \Phi \sin (\omega t - 4\pi/3)$

where $\omega = 2\pi f$ radians/second.

The resultant flux at any instant is the combination of the above fluxes, the directions as well as the magnitudes of the fluxes being taken into account. Thus if h and $v*$ in Fig. 199 be the instantaneous values of the horizontal and vertical components respectively of the resultant flux, it follows from Fig. 198 that:

$$h = r - (y + b) \cos 60°$$
$$= \Phi [\sin \omega t - \tfrac{1}{2}\{\sin (\omega t - 2\pi/3) + \sin (\omega t - 4\pi/3)\}]$$
$$= \tfrac{3}{2}\Phi \sin \omega t \quad . \quad . \quad . \quad . \quad . \quad . \quad (217)$$

and $v = b \cos 30° - y \cos 30°$

$$= \frac{\sqrt{3}}{2} \Phi \left[\sin (\omega t - 4\pi/3) - \sin \left(\omega t - \frac{2\pi}{3} \right) \right]$$
$$= \tfrac{3}{2}\Phi \cos \omega t \quad . \quad . \quad . \quad . \quad . \quad . \quad (218)$$

The instantaneous value of the resultant flux is represented by the diagonal m of the parallelogram drawn on h and v.

i.e. $m^2 = h^2 + v^2 = \left(\dfrac{3\Phi}{2} \right)^2 (\sin^2 \omega t + \cos^2 \omega t) = (1 \cdot 5\Phi)^2$

$$\therefore \quad m = 1 \cdot 5\Phi \quad . \quad . \quad . \quad . \quad . \quad . \quad . \quad (219)$$
$$= 1 \cdot 5 \times \text{maximum flux due to one phase alone.}$$

Since there is no term involving "ωt" in (219), it follows that the resultant flux remains constant in value from instant to instant. If α be the instantaneous value of the phase displacement of the resultant flux relative to the vertical axis, namely the angle between m and v,

$$\tan \alpha = \frac{h}{v} = \frac{1 \cdot 5\Phi \sin \omega t}{1 \cdot 5\Phi \cos \omega t} = \tan \omega t$$
$$\therefore \qquad \alpha = \omega t = 2\pi ft.$$

Hence the axis of the resultant flux in the above two-pole machine rotates clockwise at a uniform angular velocity of ω radians per second. For a value of t equal to the duration of 1 cycle, namely $1/f$ second,

corresponding value of $\alpha = 2\pi$ radians,

* It is convenient to draw v in the same direction as the vertical component of b, thereby avoiding a negative value for v in (218). It is also more convenient to take α as the angle between m and v than between m and h.

i.e. the resultant magnetic flux of a two-pole machine
rotates through 2π radians or 1 revolution in 1 cycle,
which is the same result as that deduced by a different
method in Art. 134.   Hence if the stator has p pairs of
poles, the speed of the rotating flux is given by:

$$N = \frac{60f}{p} \text{ r.p.m.}$$

**136. Reversal of Direction of Rotation of the Magnetic
Flux produced by Three-phase Currents.**   Suppose the
stator winding to be connected as in Fig. 200 (a) and that

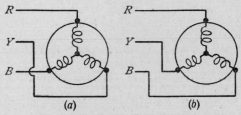

Fig. 200.—Reversal of direction of rotation.

this arrangement corresponds to that already shown in
Fig. 196 and discussed in Art. 134.   The resultant magnetic flux was found to rotate clockwise.   Let us inter-
change the connections between two of the supply lines,
say Y and B, and the stator windings, as shown in
Fig. 200 (b).   The distribution of currents at instant a
in Fig. 197 will be exactly as shown in Fig. 196 (a); but
at instant b, the current in the winding that was originally
the "yellow" phase is now 0·866 of the maximum and
the distribution of the resultant magnetic flux is as
shown in Fig. 201.   From a comparison of Fig. 196 (a)
and 201 it is seen that the axis of the magnetic flux is now
rotating anti-clockwise.   The same result may be represented thus:

	becomes		or		or	
R		R		Y		B
$B \quad Y$		$Y \quad B$		$B \quad R$		$R \quad Y$
Original sequence		Inter- changing Y and B		Inter- changing R and Y		Inter- changing R and B

From the above table it can be seen that the direction of rotation of the resultant magnetic flux can be reversed by reversing the connections to any two of the three

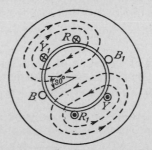

FIG. 201.—Distribution of magnetic flux at instant *b* of Fig. 197.

terminals of the motor. The ease with which it is possible to reverse the direction of rotation constitutes one of the advantages of three-phase motors.

EXAMPLES IX

1. The stator of an a.c. machine is wound for 6 poles, three-phase. If the supply frequency is 25 c/s, what is the value of the synchronous speed?

2. A stator winding supplied from a three-phase, 60-c/s system is required to produce a magnetic flux rotating at 1800 r.p.m. Calculate the number of poles.

3. A three-phase, two-pole motor is to have a synchronous speed of 9000 r.p.m. Calculate the frequency of the supply voltage.

CHAPTER X

ALTERNATORS (*continued*)

137. Armature Reaction in a Three-phase Alternator.
By "armature reaction" is meant the influence of the
stator ampere-turns upon the value and the distribution
of the magnetic flux in the air-gaps between the poles and
the stator core. It has already been explained in Chap.
IX that balanced three-phase currents in a three-phase
winding give rise to a resultant magnetic flux of constant
magnitude rotating at synchronous speed. We will now
consider the application of this principle to an alternator.

Case (a). *When the current and the generated e.m.f.**
are in phase. Consider a two-pole, three-phase alternator with 2 slots per pole per phase. If the alternator is
on open-circuit, there is no stator current and the magnetic flux due to the rotor current is distributed symmetrically as shown in Fig. 202. If the direction of
rotation of the poles be clockwise, the e.m.f. generated in
phase RR_1 is at its maximum and is towards the paper
in conductors R and outwards in R_1.

Let us next consider the distribution of flux (Fig. 203)
due to the stator currents alone at the instant when the
current in phase R is at its maximum positive value
(instant a in Fig. 197) and when the rotor (unexcited) is
in the position shown in Fig. 202. This magnetic flux
rotates clockwise at synchronous speed and is therefore
stationary relative to the rotor.

We can now derive the resultant magnetic flux due to
the rotor and stator currents by superimposing the fluxes
of Fig. 202 and 203 on each other. Comparison of these

---

* For simplicity this generated e.m.f. is taken as that due to
the flux produced by the field current alone. The effect of
armature reaction in case (a) is to distort the magnetic flux so
that the resultant e.m.f. lags behind the e.m.f. due to the field
current alone.

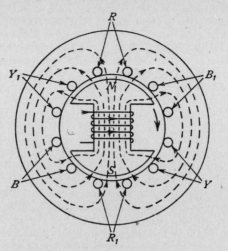

FIG. 202.—Magnetic flux due to rotor current alone.

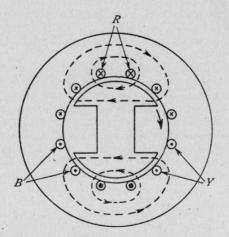

FIG. 203.—Magnetic flux due to stator currents alone.

figures shows that over the leading half of each pole-face the two fluxes are in opposition, whereas over the trailing half of each pole-face they are in the same direction. Hence the effect is to distort the magnetic flux as shown in Fig. 204. If the effect of magnetic saturation is negligible, the increase of flux over the trailing half of the pole-face is the same as the decrease over the leading half, so that the total flux per pole remains unaltered. It will be noticed, however, that the direction of most of

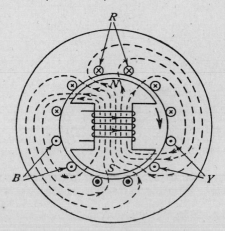

FIG. 204.—Resultant magnetic flux for case (a).

the lines of flux in the air-gaps has been skewed and thereby lengthened. But lines of flux behave like stretched elastic cords and consequently in Fig. 204 they exert a backward pull on the rotor; and to overcome the tangential component of this pull, the engine driving the alternator has to exert a larger torque than that required on no load. Since the magnetic flux due to the stator currents rotates synchronously with the rotor, the flux distortion shown in Fig. 204 remains the same for all positions of the rotor.

Case (b). *When the current lags a quarter of a cycle behind the generated e.m.f.* When the e.m.f. in phase R is at its maximum value, the poles are in the position shown in Fig. 202. By the time the current in phase R reaches its maximum value, the poles will have moved forward through half a pole pitch to the position shown in Fig. 205. A reference to Fig. 203 shows that the stator ampere-turns, acting alone, would send a flux from right to left through the rotor, namely in direct opposition to the flux produced by the rotor ampere-turns. Hence it follows that the effect of armature reaction due to a

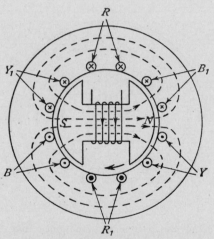

Fig. 205.—Resultant magnetic flux
for case (b).

current lagging 90° behind the e.m.f. is to reduce the flux per pole. The resultant distribution of the flux, however, is symmetrical over the two halves of the pole-face, so that no torque is required to drive the rotor, apart from that to overcome losses.

Case (c). *When the current leads a quarter of a cycle in front of the generated e.m.f.* In this case the current in phase R is a positive maximum when the N and S poles of the rotor are in the positions occupied by the S and N poles respectively in Fig. 205. Consequently the flux due to the stator ampere-turns is now in the same direction as that due to the rotor ampere-turns, so that the effect of armature reaction due to a leading current is to increase the flux per pole.

The influence of armature reaction upon the variation of terminal voltage with load is shown in Fig. 206, where it is assumed that the field current is maintained constant at a value giving an e.m.f. OA on open-circuit. When the power factor of the load is unity, the fall in voltage with increase of load is comparatively small. With an inductive load, the demagnetizing effect of armature reaction causes the terminal voltage to fall much more rapidly. The graph for 0·8 power factor is roughly mid-

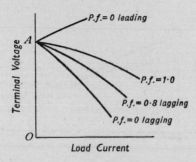

FIG. 206.—Variation of terminal voltage with load.

way between those for 1·0 and 0. With a capacitive load, the magnetizing effect of armature reaction makes the terminal voltage increase with increase of load.

138. Voltage Regulation of an Alternator. An a.c. generator is always designed to give a certain terminal voltage when supplying its rated current at a specified power factor—usually unity or 0·8 lagging. For instance, suppose OB in Fig. 207 to represent the full-load current and OA the rated terminal voltage of an alternator. If the field current is adjusted to give the terminal voltage OA when the alternator is supplying current OB at unity power factor, then when the load is removed but with the field current and speed kept unaltered, the terminal voltage rises to *OC*. This variation of the terminal voltage between full load and no load, expressed as a per-unit value or a percentage of the full-load voltage, is termed the per-unit or the percentage *voltage regulation* of the alternator; thus:

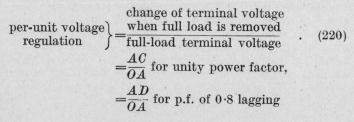

$$\left.\begin{array}{c}\text{per-unit voltage}\\ \text{regulation}\end{array}\right\} = \dfrac{\begin{array}{c}\text{change of terminal voltage}\\ \text{when full load is removed}\end{array}}{\text{full-load terminal voltage}} \quad (220)$$

$$= \frac{AC}{OA} \text{ for unity power factor,}$$

$$= \frac{AD}{OA} \text{ for p.f. of } 0\cdot 8 \text{ lagging}$$

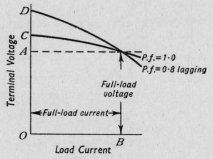

Fig. 207.—Variation of terminal voltage with load.

The voltage regulation for a power factor of $0\cdot 8$ lagging is usually far greater than that at unity power factor, and it is therefore important to include the power factor when stating the voltage regulation. (See Example 50.)

139. Synchronous Impedance. In Fig. 204 and 205, the resultant flux was shown as the combination of the flux due to the stator ampere-turns alone and that due to the rotor ampere-turns alone. For the purpose of deriving the effect of load upon the terminal voltage, however, it is convenient to regard these two component fluxes as if they existed independently of each other and to consider the cylindrical-rotor type rather than the salient-pole type of alternator (see Art. 130). Thus the flux due to the rotor ampere-turns may be regarded as generating an e.m.f., E, due to the rotation of the poles, this e.m.f. being a maximum in any one phase when the conductors of that phase are opposite the centres of the poles; and the rotating field due to the stator currents may be regarded as generating an e.m.f. lagging a quarter of a cycle behind the current. For instance, in Fig. 196 (a), the current in R is at its maximum value flowing towards the paper, but the e.m.f. induced in R by the rotating flux due to the stator currents is zero at that instant. A quarter of a cycle later this rotating flux will have turned clockwise through 90°; and since we are considering an alternator having a cylindrical rotor and therefore a uniform air-gap, R is then being cut at the maximum rate by flux passing from the rotor to the stator, so that the e.m.f. induced in R is at that instant at its maximum value acting towards the paper. Since the e.m.f. induced by the rotating flux in any one phase lags a quarter of a cycle behind the current in that phase, the effect is exactly similar to that of inductive reactance, i.e. the rotating magnetic flux produced by the stator currents may be regarded as being responsible for the reactance of the stator winding. Furthermore, since the rotating flux revolves synchronously with the poles, this reactance is referred to as the *synchronous reactance* of the winding.

By combining the resistance with the synchronous reactance of the winding, we obtain its *synchronous impedance*. Thus,

if X_s = synchronous reactance/phase,

$\quad\quad R$ = resistance/phase

and $\quad Z_s$ = synchronous impedance/phase.

then $\quad\quad\quad Z_s = \sqrt{(R^2 + X_s^2)}$.

In alternator windings, R is usually very small compared with X_s, so that for many practical purposes Z_s can be assumed to be the same as X_s.

The relationship between the terminal voltage V of the alternator and the e.m.f. E generated by the flux due to the rotor ampere-turns alone can now be derived. Thus in Fig. 208, S represents *one* phase of the stator winding and R and X_s represent the resistance and synchronous reactance of that phase. If the load takes a current I at

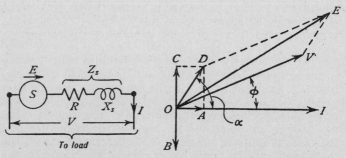

FIG. 208.—Equivalent circuit of an alternator.

FIG. 209.—Vector diagram for an alternator.

a lagging power factor cos ϕ, the various quantities can be represented vectorially as in Fig. 209, where:

OI = current/phase,

OV = terminal voltage/phase,

$OA = IR$ = component of the generated e.m.f. E absorbed in sending current through R,

OB = e.m.f./phase induced by the rotating flux due to stator currents and lags 90° behind OI,

OC = component of the generated e.m.f. E required to neutralize OB,

= voltage drop due to synchronous reactance X_s

= IX_s

OD = component of the generated e.m.f. absorbed in sending current through the synchronous impedance Z_s,

α = phase angle between OI and OD = $\tan^{-1} X_s/R$

and OE = resultant of OV and OD

= e.m.f./phase generated by the flux due to the rotor ampere-turns.

From Fig. 209,

$$OE^2 = OV^2 + OD^2 + 2 \cdot OV \cdot OD \cdot \cos(\alpha - \phi)$$

i.e. $E^2 = V^2 + (IZ_s)^2 + 2V \cdot IZ_s \cos(\alpha - \phi)$

from which the e.m.f. E generated by the flux due to the rotor ampere-turns, namely the open-circuit voltage, can be calculated. It follows that if V is the rated terminal voltage per phase of the alternator and I is the full-load current per phase, the terminal voltage/phase obtained when the load is removed and the exciting current left unaltered is given by E, and from (220):

$$\text{Per-unit voltage regulation} = \frac{E - V}{V}.$$

The synchronous impedance is important when we come to deal with the parallel operation of alternators and with synchronous motors (Chap. XI); but numerical calculations involving synchronous impedance are usually unsatisfactory, owing mainly to magnetic saturation in the poles and stator teeth and, in the case of salient-pole machines, to the value of Z_s varying with the p.f. of the load and with the excitation of the poles. One method of estimating the value of the synchronous impedance is to run the alternator on open-circuit and measure the generated e.m.f., and then short-circuit the terminals through an ammeter and measure the short-circuit current, the exciting current and speed being kept constant. Since the e.m.f. generated on open-circuit may be regarded as being responsible for circulating the short-circuit current through the synchronous impedance of the winding, the value of the synchronous impedance is given by the ratio of the open-circuit voltage/phase to the short-circuit current/phase.

Example 50. *A three-phase, 600-kVA alternator has a rated terminal voltage of 3300 V (line). The stator winding is star-connected and has a resistance of 0·37 Ω/phase and a synchronous impedance of 4·3 Ω/phase. Calculate the voltage regulation for a load having a power factor of (a) unity and (b) 0·8 lagging.*

(a) Since $600 \times 1000 = 1 \cdot 73 I_l \times 3300$

$\therefore$ line current $= I_l = 105$ A $=$ phase current.

Terminal voltage/phase on full load $\Big\} = 3300/1 \cdot 73 = 1910$ V

Voltage drop/phase on full load due to synchronous impedance $\Big\} = 105 \times 4 \cdot 3 = 452$ V.

From Fig. 209 it follows that at unity power factor,

$$OV = 1910; \quad OD = 452; \quad \text{and} \quad \phi = 0.$$

Also, $\cos \alpha = OA/OD = R/Z_s = 0 \cdot 37/4 \cdot 3 = 0 \cdot 086,$

$\therefore \quad OE^2 = (1910)^2 + (452)^2 + 2 \times 1910 \times 452 \times 0 \cdot 086$
$= 4 \times 10^6$

$\therefore \quad OE = 2000$ V,

and voltage regulation at unity power factor $\Big\} = \dfrac{2000 - 1910}{1910}$

$= 0.047$ per unit

$= 4 \cdot 7$ per cent.

(b) Since the rating of the alternator is 600 kVA, the full-load current is the same whatever the power factor.

For power factor of $0 \cdot 8$, $\phi = 36° 52'$

Also $\alpha = \cos^{-1} 0 \cdot 086 = 85° 4',$

so that $(\alpha - \phi) = 48° 12'$ and $\cos 48° 12' = 0 \cdot 666.$

Hence, $OE^2 = (1910)^2 + (452)^2 + 2 \times 1910 \times 452 \times 0 \cdot 666$
$= 5 \cdot 006 \times 10^6$

$\therefore \quad OE = 2240$ V,

and voltage regulation for power factor $0 \cdot 8$ lagging $\Big\} = \dfrac{2240 - 1910}{1910}$

$= 0 \cdot 173$ per unit

$= 17 \cdot 3$ per cent.

140. Synchronizing of Alternators. For simplicity, let us assume single-phase alternators; thus, in Fig. 210 A represents an alternator already connected to the busbars and B is an alternator to be connected in parallel.

To enable this to be done, the following conditions must be fulfilled:

(a) the frequency of B must be the same as that of A,
(b) the e.m.f. generated in B must be equal to the busbar voltage,
(c) the e.m.f. of B must be in phase with the busbar voltage.

The procedure is to start up the engine driving alternator B and adjust its speed to about its correct value.

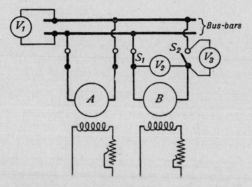

FIG. 210.—Synchronizing of alternators.

The excitation of B is then adjusted so that the reading on voltmeter V_2 is the same as the busbar voltage given by voltmeter V_1. Switch S_1 is closed and voltmeter V_3 connected across switch S_2. The pointer of V_3 will then oscillate between zero and twice the busbar voltage at a frequency equal to the difference between the frequencies of A and B. This will be evident from Fig. 211, where curves E_A and E_B represent the e.m.f.'s of A and B respectively, the frequencies being assumed such that E_B varies through 4 cycles for every 3 cycles of E_A. The p.d. across switch S_2 is the difference between E_A and E_B and Fig. 211 (b) represents two "beats" of this voltage. If the frequency of A is 50 c/s and that of B is 50·5 c/s, the beat frequency is 0·5 c/s and the pointer of V_3 makes one complete oscillation in 2 seconds.

The speed of B is adjusted until the pointer of volt-meter V_3 oscillates very slowly and switch S_2 is closed just as the pointer is reaching zero, i.e. when the e.m.f.'s of A and B are in phase opposition relative to each other but in phase with each other relative to the busbars.

The above method of paralleling two alternators does not indicate whether the frequency of the incoming alternator B is higher or lower than that of A. In actual practice it is customary to use an instrument, called a

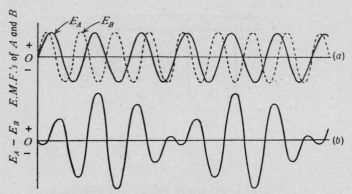

Fig. 211.—Curves of E_A, E_B and $(E_A - E_B)$.

synchroscope, which shows whether the incoming machine is running too fast or too slow as well as indicating the correct moment for closing switch S_2.

141. Parallel Operation of Alternators. It is not obvious why two alternators continue running in synchronism after they have been paralleled; so let us consider the case of two similar single-phase alternators, A and B, connected in parallel to the busbars, as shown in Fig. 212, and let us, for simplicity, assume that there is no external load connected across the busbars. We will consider two separate cases:

(a) the effect of varying the torque of the driving engine, e.g. by varying the steam supply,

(b) the effect of varying the exciting current.

Effect of varying the driving torque. Let us first assume that each engine is exerting exactly the torque required by its own alternator and that the field resistances R_A and R_B are adjusted so that the generated e.m.f.'s E_A and E_B are equal. Suppose the arrows in Fig. 212 to represent the *positive* directions of these e.m.f.'s. It will be seen that, *relative to the busbars*, these e.m.f.'s are acting in the same direction, i.e. when the e.m.f. generated in each machine is positive, each e.m.f. is making the top busbar positive in relation to the bottom busbar. But *in relation to each other*, these e.m.f.'s are in opposition, i.e. if we trace the closed circuit

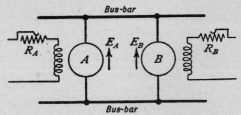

FIG. 212.—Two alternators in parallel.

formed by the two alternators, we find that the e.m.f.'s oppose each other.

In the present discussion we want to find out if any current is being circulated in this closed circuit. It is therefore more convenient to consider these e.m.f.'s in relation to each other rather than to the busbars. This condition is shown vectorially in Fig. 213 (a) when E_A and E_B are in exact phase opposition relative to each other; and since they are equal in magnitude, their resultant is zero and consequently no current is circulated.

Let us next assume the driving torque of B's engine to be reduced, e.g. by a reduction of its steam supply. The rotor of B falls back in relation to that of A, and Fig. 213 (b) shows the conditions when B's rotor has fallen back by an angle θ. The resultant e.m.f. in the closed circuit formed by the alternator windings is

11

represented by E_z, and this e.m.f. circulates a current I lagging by an angle α behind E_z,

where $\quad I = \dfrac{E_z}{2Z_s} \quad$ and $\quad \alpha = \tan^{-1} X_s/R,$

$\qquad R =$ resistance of each alternator,

$\qquad X_s =$ synchronous reactance of each alternator,

and $\quad Z_s =$ synchronous impedance of each alternator.

Since the resistance is very small compared with the synchronous reactance, α is nearly 90°, so that the current I is almost in phase with E_A and in phase opposition to

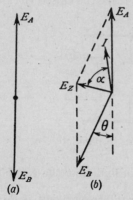

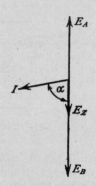

Fig. 213.—Effect of varying the driving torque.

Fig. 214.—Effect of varying the excitation.

E_B. This means that A is generating and B is motoring, and the power supplied from A to B tends to compensate for the reduction of the power supplied by B's engine.

The larger the value of θ (so long as it does not exceed about 80°), the larger is the circulating current and the greater is the power supplied from A to B. Hence machine B falls back in relation to A until the power taken from the latter exactly compensates for the reduction in the driving power of B's engine. Once this balance has been attained, B and A continue to run in synchronism.

Effect of varying the excitation. Let us again revert to Fig. 213 (a) and assume that each engine is exerting the torque required by its alternator and that the e.m.f.'s, E_A and E_B, are equal. The resultant voltage is zero and there is therefore no circulating current.

Suppose the exciting current of alternator B to be increased so that the corresponding open-circuit e.m.f. is represented by E_B in Fig. 214. The resultant e.m.f. E_Z ($=E_B-E_A$) circulates a current I through the synchronous impedances of the two alternators; and since the machines are assumed similar, the impedance drop per machine is $\frac{1}{2}E_Z$, so that:

$$\text{terminal voltage} = E_B - \tfrac{1}{2}E_Z$$
or
$$= E_A + \tfrac{1}{2}E_Z.$$

Hence one effect has been to increase the terminal voltage. Further, since angle α is nearly 90°, the circulating current I is almost in quadrature with the generated e.m.f.'s, so that very little power is circulated from one machine to the other.

In general, we may therefore conclude:

(1) the distribution of load between alternators operating in parallel can be varied by varying the driving torques of the engines and only slightly by varying the exciting currents,

(2) the terminal voltage is controlled by varying the exciting currents.

EXAMPLES X

1. A single-phase alternator has a rated output of 500 kVA at a terminal voltage of 3300 V. The stator winding has a resistance of $0 \cdot 6$ Ω and a synchronous reactance of 4 Ω. Calculate the percentage voltage regulation at power factor of (a) unity, (b) $0 \cdot 8$ lagging and (c) $0 \cdot 8$ leading.

2. Explain what is meant by the synchronous impedance of an alternator.

A single-phase alternator with a synchronous reactance of $5 \cdot 5$ Ω and a resistance of $0 \cdot 6$ Ω delivers a current of 100 A. What will be the voltage induced in the armature if the p.d. at the terminals is 2000 V and the power factor of the external load is $0 \cdot 8$ lagging? If the terminals of the machine are short-circuited, what will the armature current become? State all the assumptions made.

(C & G., El. Eng. Pract., Int.)

3. A three-phase star-connected 50-c/s alternator has 96 conductors per phase and a flux per pole of 0·1 weber. Its terminals are connected to non-inductive resistances of 10 Ω per phase connected in star. Calculate the terminal voltage.

The alternator has a synchronous reactance of 5 Ω per phase. The distribution factor for the alternator winding is 0·96.

4. Explain the term "synchronous reactance" with reference to an alternator and show how it can be measured.

A 1500-kVA, 6600-V, three-phase star-connected alternator has a resistance of 0·5 Ω per phase and a synchronous reactance of 5 Ω per phase. Find the percentage change of voltage when the full rated output at power factor 0·8 lagging is switched off.

(C. & G., El. Eng. Pract., Int.)

5. Two single-phase alternators are connected in parallel and the excitation of each machine is such as to generate an open-circuit e.m.f. of 3500 V. Each machine has a stator resistance of 2·5 Ω and a synchronous reactance of 30 Ω. If there is a phase displacement of 40 electrical degrees between the e.m.f.'s, calculate the synchronizing current and the terminal voltage. Also, find the power in kilowatts supplied from one machine to the other and the total I^2R loss in the stator windings.

6. Two similar three-phase star-connected alternators are connected in parallel. Each machine has a resistance of 0·37 Ω/phase and a synchronous impedance of 4·3 Ω/phase. If the machines have a phase displacement of 30 electrical degrees relative to each other and if each machine is excited to generate an e.m.f. of 1910 V per phase on open circuit, calculate (a) the circulating current, (b) the terminal voltage per phase, (c) the power supplied from one machine to the other and (d) the I^2R loss in the stator winding of one alternator.

7. If the two alternators of Q. 6 are adjusted to be in exact phase opposition relative to each other and if the excitation of one alternator is adjusted to give an open-circuit voltage of 2240 V per phase and that of the other alternator adjusted to give an open-circuit voltage of 1600 V per phase, calculate (a) the circulating current, (b) the terminal voltage, (c) the power supplied from one machine to the other and (d) the I^2R loss in the stator winding of one alternator.

CHAPTER XI

SYNCHRONOUS MOTORS

142. Principle of Action. In Art. 141 it was explained that when two alternators, A and B, are in parallel, with no load on the busbars, a reduction in the driving torque applied to B causes the latter to fall back by some angle θ (Fig. 213) in relation to A, thereby causing power

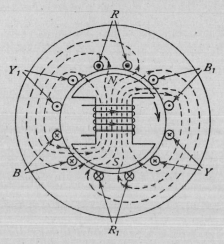

Fig. 215.—Principle of action of a three-phase synchronous motor.

to be supplied from A to B. Machine B is then operating as a synchronous motor.

It will also be seen from Fig. 213 that the current in a synchronous motor is approximately in phase opposition to the e.m.f. generated in that machine. We may represent this effect as in Fig. 215, where the rotor poles are shown in the same position relative to the three-phase winding as in Fig. 204. The latter represented an alternator with the current in phase with the generated e.m.f., whereas Fig. 215 represents a synchronous motor with the current in phase opposition to this generated e.m.f. A diagram similar to Fig. 203 could be drawn showing the flux distribution due to the stator currents alone, but a comparison with Fig. 202, 203 and 204 will undoubtedly be sufficient to indicate that in Fig. 215 the effect of armature reaction is to increase the flux in the leading half of each pole and to reduce it in the trailing half. Consequently the flux is distorted in the direction of rotation and the lines of flux in the gap are skewed in such a direction as to exert a clockwise torque on the rotor. Since the magnetic flux due to the stator currents rotates at synchronous speed, the rotor must also rotate at exactly the same speed in order that the flux distribution shown in Fig. 215 shall remain unaltered.

143. Effect of Varying the Load on a Synchronous Motor.

Fig. 216 represents diagrammatically a three-phase, star-connected synchronous motor connected to the supply mains and excited by a field winding F in series with a regulating resistance.

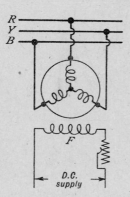

FIG. 216.—Connections of a three-phase synchronous motor.

Suppose V in Fig. 217 to represent the voltage *applied* to one phase and E the e.m.f.* *generated* in that phase. Angle θ represents the displacement of E from exact phase opposition to V. Let us assume that E is exactly equal to V in magnitude. Consequently, if E had been in exact phase opposition to V, i.e. if $\theta=0$, there would have been no stator current and therefore no power taken from the a.c. supply. The

* This e.m.f. is the open-circuit voltage of the machine when driven as an alternator at the same speed with the same field current.

motor would have to slow down and the phase of the generated e.m.f. E would fall back in relation to the applied voltage V by some angle θ, the value of which depends upon the load.

Let us first assume that the load is small so that θ is also small, as shown in Fig. 217 (a). The resultant voltage available to send a current I through the syn-

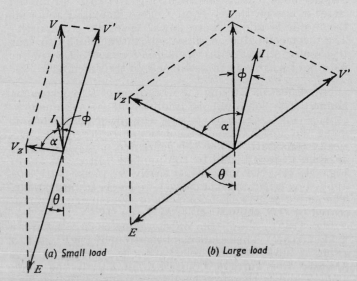

(a) Small load   (b) Large load

FIG. 217.—Vector diagrams for a synchronous motor.

chronous impedance of the winding is represented by V_Z, the resultant of V and E. Alternatively, we may regard the applied voltage V as having to provide two components:

(a) V' to neutralize the generated e.m.f. E, and
(b) V_Z to provide the voltage drop due to the synchronous impedance of the stator winding.

If the synchronous impedance per phase is Z_s, the current is V_Z/Z_s and lags behind V_Z by an angle α approximating $90°$, since the resistance is very small compared with the synchronous reactance. If the phase angle between I and the supply voltage is ϕ,

power factor of motor $=\cos \phi$

and power/phase taken by motor $=IV \cos \phi$.

Let us next consider the effect of an increase in load. The rotor of the motor slows down momentarily until the displacement θ is as shown in Fig. 217 (b). From the latter it is seen that V_Z and I have increased and that the motor is taking more power from the a.c. supply. The displacement θ adjusts itself automatically so that the motor takes from the supply exactly the power required by the load plus that lost in the machine.

144. Effect of Varying the Excitation of a Synchronous Motor. The load on the motor will be assumed to remain constant; consequently the phase displacement θ and the power component of the current remain practically constant. When the generated or back e.m.f. E is equal in magnitude to the applied voltage V, as in Fig. 218 (a), the current is nearly in phase with the applied voltage and the power factor is almost unity. The active or power component of the current is represented by OP, the projection of OI on OV.

Fig. 218 (b) shows the effect of increasing the rotor field current. The result has been to increase V_Z and to swing it anti-clockwise relative to its position in Fig. 218 (a). The current I lags behind V_Z by the same angle α and is therefore leading in front of the applied voltage by an angle ϕ. Since the active component OP remains unaltered—any alteration in the losses being neglected—the extremity of the current vector lies on the dotted line drawn through P at right angles to OP.

The effect of reducing the excitation is shown in Fig. 218 (c), from which it is seen that the current is now lagging behind the terminal voltage. It follows from these vector diagrams that the power factor of a synchronous motor can be controlled by varying the field current, as indicated in Fig. 219, the actual range of power factor variation being dependent upon the value of the load.

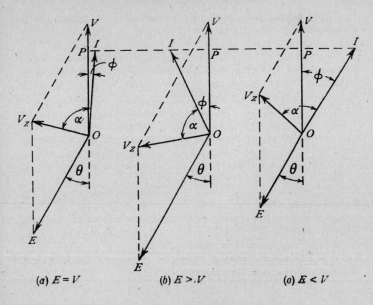

(a) $E = V$ (b) $E > V$ (c) $E < V$

FIG. 218.—Effect of varying the excitation of a synchronous motor.

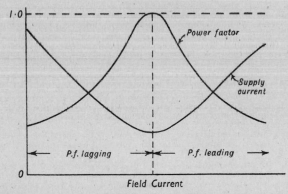

FIG. 219.—Variation of supply current and power factor with field current for a constant load on a synchronous motor.

11*

145. Advantages and Disadvantages of the Synchronous Motor. The principal advantages of the synchronous motor are:

(1) The ease with which the power factor can be controlled. An over-excited synchronous motor having a leading power factor can be operated in parallel with induction motors having lagging power factor, thereby improving the power factor of the supply system.

(2) The speed is constant and independent of the load. This characteristic is mainly of use when the motor is required to drive another alternator to generate a supply at a different frequency, as in frequency-changers.

The principal disadvantages are:

(1) The cost per horsepower is higher than that of an induction motor.

(2) A d.c. supply is necessary for the rotor excitation. This is usually provided by a small d.c. shunt generator carried on an extension of the shaft.

(3) Some arrangement must be provided for starting and synchronizing the motor.

EXAMPLES XI

1. A single-phase synchronous motor is connected across a 2200-V supply. It has a resistance of $0 \cdot 4$ Ω and a synchronous impedance of 5 Ω. If the input power remains constant at 100 kW, calculate the generated e.m.f. when the power factor is (a) unity, (b) $0 \cdot 8$ lagging and (c) $0 \cdot 8$ leading.

2. A three-phase star-connected synchronous motor is connected across a 400-V supply. It has a resistance of $0 \cdot 1$ Ω/phase and a synchronous reactance of $0 \cdot 8$ Ω/phase. If the input power remains constant at 30 kW, calculate the generated e.m.f. per phase when the power factor is (a) unity, (b) $0 \cdot 7$ lagging and (c) $0 \cdot 7$ leading.

3. A 200-V, single-phase synchronous motor takes a current of 10 A at unity power factor from the supply. Calculate the e.m.f. and the angle of retard if the synchronous reactance is 5 Ω and the resistance is negligible.

If the e.m.f. is decreased by 10 per cent, calculate the current and power factor. Assume the angle of retard to remain unaltered.

(E.M.E.U., Grade IV)

4. An alternator supplying 2800 kW at power factor $0 \cdot 7$ lagging is loaded to its full kVA capacity. If the power factor is raised to unity by means of an over-excited synchronous motor, how many more kilowatts can the alternator supply and what must be the power factor of the synchronous motor, assuming that the latter absorbs all the extra power obtainable from the alternator?

5. A three-phase factory load of 600 kVA at 0·6 lagging power factor is to be increased by an additional 300 h.p. Calculate the kVA rating and the operating power factor of a synchronous motor which would supply the additional load and improve the overall power factor of the whole factory load to 0·9 lagging. Assume a motor efficiency of 85 per cent.

Find also the line current before and after the extension, assuming the supply voltage to be 6·6 kV.

(C. & G., El. Eng. Pract., Int.)

6. A three-phase, star-connected induction motor takes 200 kW at a power factor of 0·8 lagging and operates on a 3300-V three-phase supply in parallel with a three-phase, star-connected synchronous motor taking 250 kVA at 0·9 power factor leading. Find the line current and power factor of the load. Draw a vector diagram, not necessarily to scale, to illustrate your answer. (U.E.I.)

7. An installation operates on full-load kVA with lagging power factor of 0·6. The cost of increasing the power plant to deal with an increase of load having the *same* power factor is £15 per kVA. By raising the power factor of the whole installation to 0·8 lagging by means of capacitors, the same increase of load could be supplied by the original power plant operating at its full-load kVA. Determine the limit of cost per kVA of capacitor that would justify its installation.

CHAPTER XII

INDUCTION MOTORS

146. Principle of Action. The stator of an induction motor is similar to that of an alternator; and in the case of a machine supplied with three-phase currents, a rotating magnetic flux is produced, as already explained in Chap IX. The rotor core is laminated and the winding, in its simplest form, usually consists of copper

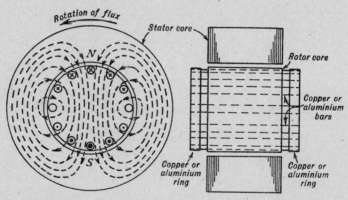

FIG. 220.—Induction motor with a squirrel-cage rotor.

or aluminium bars short-circuited at each end by heavy rings as shown in Fig. 220. This type is known as the *squirrel-cage* or *short-circuited* rotor. The air-gap between the rotor and the stator is uniform and very narrow. For simplicity, the stator slots and winding have been omitted in Fig. 220. If the stator is wound for two poles, the distribution of the magnetic flux due to the stator currents at a particular instant is shown in Fig. 220. The e.m.f. generated in a rotor conductor is a

332

maximum in the region of maximum flux density; and if the flux be assumed to rotate anti-clockwise, the directions of the e.m.f.'s generated in the stationary rotor conductors can be determined by the right-hand rule and are indicated by the crosses and dots in Fig. 220. If we were to consider a single con-

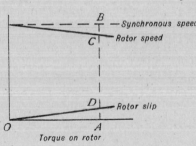

FIG. 221.—Force on rotor.

ductor on the rotor (Fig. 221), the generated e.m.f. would circulate a current the effect of which would be to strengthen the flux density on the right-hand side and weaken it on the left-hand side; i.e. the flux in the gap would be distorted as indicated by the dotted lines in Fig. 221. Consequently, a force is exerted on the rotor tending to drag it in the direction of the rotating flux.

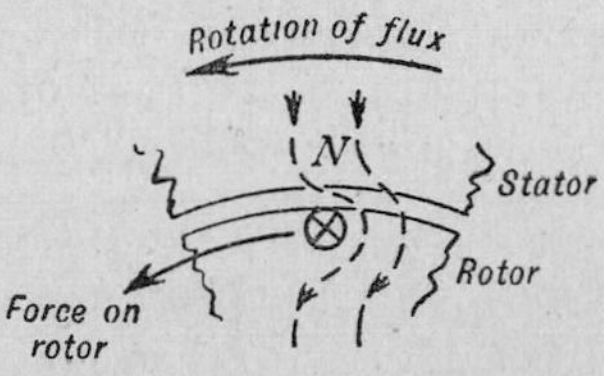

The higher the speed of the rotor, the lower is the speed of the rotating field relative to the rotor winding and the smaller is the e.m.f. generated in the latter. Should the speed of the rotor attain the synchronous value, the rotor conductors would be stationary in relation to the rotating flux. There would therefore be no e.m.f. and no current in the rotor conductors and consequently no torque on the rotor. Hence the latter could not continue rotating at synchronous speed. As the rotor speed falls more and more below the synchronous speed, the values of the rotor e.m.f. and current and therefore of the torque continue to increase until the latter is equal to that required by the load.

FIG. 222.—Slip and rotor speed of an induction motor.

The speed of the rotor relative to that of the rotating

flux is termed the *slip*; thus for a torque OA in Fig. 222, the rotor speed is AC and the slip is AD, where

$$AD = AB - AC = CB.$$

For torques varying between zero and the full-load value, the slip is practically proportional to the torque. It is usual to express the slip either as a per-unit value or as a percentage of the synchronous speed; thus in Fig. 222,

$$\left.\begin{array}{c}\text{per-unit}\\ \text{slip}\end{array}\right\} = \frac{\text{slip in r.p.m.}}{\text{synchronous speed in r.p.m.}} = \frac{AD}{AB}$$

$$= \frac{\text{synchronous speed} - \text{rotor speed}}{\text{synchronous speed}} \quad . \quad (221)$$

and percentage slip = per-unit slip $\times 100 = \dfrac{AD}{AB} \times 100.$

The value of the slip at full load varies from about 6 per cent for small motors to about 2 per cent for large machines. The induction motor may therefore be regarded as practically a constant-speed machine; and the difficulty of varying its speed economically constitutes one of its main disadvantages (see Art. 155).

147. Rotor Frequency. It was shown in Art. 134 that for a three-phase winding with p pairs of poles supplied at a frequency of f cycles per second, the speed of the rotating flux is given by N r.p.m., where

$$f = \frac{Np}{60}.$$

If N_r is the rotor speed in r.p.m., the speed at which the rotor conductors are being cut by the rotating flux is $(N - N_r)$ r.p.m.

$\therefore$ frequency of rotor e.m.f. $= f_r = \dfrac{(N - N_r)p}{60}.$

If $= \text{per-unit slip} = \dfrac{N - N_r}{N}$

then $N - N_r = sN$

and $f_r = \dfrac{sNp}{60} = sf \quad . \quad . \quad . \quad . \quad (222)$

148. Rotor E.M.F. and Current.

Let V_p =voltage per phase applied to stator winding.

  Z_s =no. of stator conductors in series/phase,

  k_d =distribution factor of winding

and Φ =flux/pole, i.e. total flux entering or leaving the stator over one pole pitch, namely the distance between 2 adjacent points of zero flux density.

Since the back e.m.f. generated in the stator winding is approximately equal to the applied voltage, then from expression (215) we have:

$$V_p \simeq 2 \cdot 22 k_d Z_s f \Phi \quad . \quad . \quad . \quad (223)$$

When the rotor is at standstill, the rotating flux Φ cuts the rotor at the same speed as it cuts the stator winding, so that the frequency of the rotor e.m.f. is then the same as the supply frequency, namely f cycles/second. Hence:

if E_o =rotor e.m.f. generated per phase* at standstill,

and Z_r =no. of rotor conductors in series/phase,

then $E_o = 2 \cdot 22 k_d Z_r f \Phi \quad . \quad . \quad . \quad (224)$

Assuming the distribution factor to be the same for the stator and rotor windings, we have from (223) and (224):

$$E_o \simeq V_p \times \frac{Z_r}{Z_s} \quad . \quad . \quad . \quad (225)$$

If E_r is the rotor e.m.f. generated per phase when the per-unit slip is s and the rotor frequency is $f_r = sf$,

$$E_r = 2 \cdot 22 \times k_d Z_r f_r \Phi$$
$$= s E_o \quad . \quad . \quad . \quad . \quad (226)$$

* In the squirrel-cage rotor, the number of bars is usually a prime number, such as 47. Consequently the e.m.f.'s in all the rotor bars differ from one another in phase, so that the number of phases is the same as the number of rotor bars. The rotor winding may also be of the three-phase type, star- or delta-connected, with its ends joined to 3 slip-rings, already described in Art. 131. The relative advantages and usually tages of the two types of rotor are discussed in Art. 157.

If R=resistance/phase of the rotor winding

and X_o=leakage reactance/phase of rotor winding at standstill

$=2\pi f \times$leakage   inductance/phase   of   rotor winding,

then for per-unit slip s,

corresponding reactance/phase $\Big\} = X_r = sX_o$

and corresponding impedance/phase $\Big\} = Z_r = \sqrt{[R^2+(sX_o)^2]}$ (227)

If I_o=rotor current/phase at standstill,

and I_r=rotor current/phase at slip s,

$$I_o = \frac{E_o}{\sqrt{(R^2+X_o^2)}}$$

and $$I_r = \frac{E_r}{\sqrt{[R^2+(sX_o)^2]}} = \frac{sE_o}{\sqrt{[R^2+(sX_o)^2]}}$$.   (228)

Finally, if ϕ_r be the phase difference between E_r and I,

$$\tan \phi_r = X_r/R = sX_o/R \quad . \quad . \quad (229)$$

and $$\cos \phi_r = \frac{R}{\sqrt{(R^2+X_r^2)}} \quad . \quad . \quad (230)$$

Example 51. *A three-phase induction motor is wound for 4 poles and is supplied from a 50-c/s system. Calculate:* (a) *the synchronous speed,* (b) *the speed of the rotor when the slip is 4 per cent and* (c) *the rotor frequency when the speed of the rotor is 600 r.p.m.*

(a) From (216), synchronous speed $\Big\} = \dfrac{60f}{p} = \dfrac{60 \times 50}{2}$

$=1500$ r.p.m.

(b) From (221), $0 \cdot 04 = \dfrac{1500 - \text{rotor speed}}{1500}$

∴   rotor speed$=1440$ r.p.m.

(c) Also from (221), per-unit slip $\Big\} = \dfrac{1500 - 600}{1500} = 0 \cdot 6$

Hence, from (222), rotor frequency $\Big\} = 0 \cdot 6 \times 50 = 30$ c/s.

Example 52. *The stator winding of the motor of Example* 51 *is delta-connected with* 240 *conductors per phase and the rotor winding is star-connected with* 48 *conductors per phase. The rotor winding has a resistance of* 0·013 Ω/*phase and a leakage reactance of* 0·048 Ω/*phase at standstill. The supply voltage is* 400 *V. Assuming the distribution factor to be* 0·96 *for each winding, calculate:* (a) *the flux per pole,* (b) *the rotor e.m.f. per phase at standstill with the rotor on open-circuit,* (c) *the rotor e.m.f. and current per phase at* 4 *per cent slip and* (d) *the phase difference between the rotor e.m.f. and current for a slip of* (i) 4 *per cent and* (ii) 100 *per cent. Assume the impedance of the stator winding to be negligible.*

(a) From (223), $400 = 2 \cdot 22 \times 0 \cdot 96 \times 240 \times 50 \times \Phi$

$\therefore \qquad \Phi = 0 \cdot 01565$ weber.

(b) From (224), $E_o = 2 \cdot 22 \times 0 \cdot 96 \times 48 \times 50 \times 0 \cdot 01565$
$= 80$ V.

Alternatively, $\qquad E_o = 400 \times \dfrac{48}{240} = 80$ V.

(c) From (226),

$\left.\begin{array}{l}\text{rotor e.m.f. for} \\ \text{4 per cent slip}\end{array}\right\} = 80 \times 0 \cdot 04 = 3 \cdot 2$ V.

From (227),

$\left.\begin{array}{l}\text{impedance/phase} \\ \text{for 4 per cent slip}\end{array}\right\} = \sqrt{[(0 \cdot 013)^2 + (0 \cdot 04 \times 0 \cdot 048)^2]}$
$= 0 \cdot 01314 \ \Omega.$

$\therefore \qquad \text{rotor current} = \dfrac{3 \cdot 2}{0 \cdot 01314} = 243 \cdot 5$ A.

(d) From (229), it follows that for 4 per cent slip,

$$\tan \phi_r = \frac{0 \cdot 04 \times 0 \cdot 048}{0 \cdot 013} = 0 \cdot 1477$$

$\therefore \qquad \phi_r = 8° \ 24'$

For 100 per cent slip, $\tan \phi_r = \dfrac{0 \cdot 048}{0 \cdot 013} = 3 \cdot 692,$

$\therefore \qquad \phi_r = 74° \ 51'.$

This example shows that the slip has a considerable effect upon the phase difference between the rotor e.m.f.

and current—a fact that is very important when we come to discuss the variation of torque with slip.

149. Relationship between the Rotor I^2R Loss and the Rotor Slip. The following table indicates concisely what becomes of the power supplied to the stator of the induction motor:

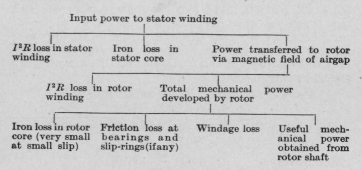

If T=torque in newton-metres exerted on the rotor by the rotating flux

and n_s=synchronous speed in revolutions/second,

power transferred from stator to rotor $=2\pi T n_s$ watts.

This input power to the rotor is often referred to as the *torque in synchronous watts*.

If n_r=rotor speed in revolutions/second,

$$\left.\begin{array}{l}\text{total mechanical power}\\ \text{developed by rotor}\end{array}\right\}=2\pi T n_r \text{ watts.}$$

But from the above table it is seen that:

Total I^2R loss in rotor

$$=\left(\begin{array}{c}\text{power transferred from}\\ \text{stator to rotor}\end{array}\right)-\left(\begin{array}{c}\text{total mechanical power}\\ \text{developed by rotor}\end{array}\right)$$

$$=2\pi T(n_s-n_r) \text{ watts}$$

$$\therefore\quad \frac{\text{total rotor } I^2R \text{ loss}}{\text{input power to rotor}}=\frac{2\pi T(n_s-n_r)}{2\pi T n_s}=s \quad . \quad (231)$$

$$\therefore\quad \begin{array}{cc}\text{rotor } I^2R \text{ loss}=s\times\text{input power to rotor}\\ \text{(in watts)}\qquad\qquad\text{(in watts)}\end{array}$$

150. Factors determining the Torque.

If $m=$ number of rotor phases,

then, using the symbols given in Art. 148, we have:

electrical power generated in rotor $= mI_rE_r \cos \phi_r$ watts

$$= \frac{ms^2E_o^2R}{R^2+(sX_o)^2}.$$

All this power is dissipated as I^2R loss in the rotor circuits.

Since input power to rotor $= 2\pi Tn_s$ watts,

hence, from (231), we have:

$$s \times 2\pi Tn_s = \frac{ms^2E_o^2R}{R^2+(sX_o)^2}$$

Consequently, for given synchronous speed and number of rotor phases,

$$T \propto \frac{sE_o^2R}{R^2+(sX_o)^2} \propto \frac{s\Phi^2R}{R^2+(sX_o)^2} \qquad . \quad (232)$$

since $E_o \propto \Phi$.

151. Variation of Torque with Slip, other Factors remaining Constant.

If the impedance of the stator winding is negligible, then for a given supply voltage, Φ and E_o remain constant,

$$\therefore \qquad \text{torque} \propto \frac{sR}{R^2+(sX_o)^2} \qquad . \quad . \quad (233)$$

The value of X_o is usually far greater than the resistance of the rotor winding; so let us for simplicity assume $R=1\ \Omega$ and $X_o=8\ \Omega$, and calculate the value of $sR/(R^2+s^2X_o^2)$ for various values of the slip between 1 and 0. The results are represented by curve A in Fig. 223. It will be seen that for small values of the slip, the torque is almost directly proportional to the slip; whereas for slips between about 0·2 and 1, the torque is almost inversely proportional to the slip. These relationships can be easily deduced from expression (233). Thus, in the case of the squirrel-cage rotor, R is small compared with X_o; but for values of the slip less than about $0 \cdot 1$ per unit, $(sX_o)^2$ is very small compared with R^2, so that:

$$\text{torque} \propto \frac{sR}{R^2} \propto \frac{s}{R} \quad . \quad . \quad (234)$$

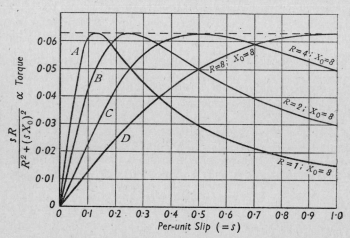

FIG. 223.—Torque/slip curves for an induction motor.

i.e. the torque is directly proportional to the slip when the latter is very small.

For large values of the slip, R^2 is very small compared with $(sX_o)^2$ in the case of the squirrel-cage rotor,

$$\therefore \qquad \text{torque} \propto \frac{sR}{(sX_o)^2} \propto \frac{R}{s} \quad . \quad . \quad (235)$$

since X_o is constant for a given motor; i.e. the torque is inversely proportional to the slip when the latter is large. The term R has been left in the above expressions as it is referred to in the next Article.

152. Effect of Rotor Resistance upon the Torque/Slip Relationship. From expression (235) it is seen that when R is small compared with sX_o, the torque for a given slip is directly proportional to the value of R; whereas from (234) it follows that when R is large compared with sX_o, the torque for a given slip is inversely proportional to the value of R. The simplest method of demonstrating this effect is to repeat the calculation of $sR/(R^2+s^2X_o^2)$ with $R=2\ \Omega$, $R=4\ \Omega$ and then with $R=8\ \Omega$. The results are represented by curves B, C and D respectively in Fig. 223. It will be seen that for a slip of, say, 0·05 p.u., the effect of doubling the rotor resistance is to reduce the torque by about 0·45 per unit, whereas for a slip of 1, the effect of increasing the resistance from 1 to 2 Ω is to increase the torque by about 0·9 per unit. Hence if a large starting torque is required, the rotor must have a high resistance.

It will also be noticed from Fig. 223 that the maximum value of the torque is the same for the four values of R and that the larger the resistance the greater is the slip at maximum torque. The condition for maximum torque can be derived by differentiating (233) with respect to s, assuming R to remain constant, or with respect to R, assuming s to remain constant. Both methods give the same result; thus with the first method, the torque is maximum when:

$$\frac{d}{ds}\left(\frac{sR}{R^2+s^2X_o^2}\right)=\frac{(R^2+s^2X_o^2)R-sR\times 2sX_o^2}{(R^2+s^2X_o^2)^2}=0$$

i.e. $\qquad\qquad s^2X_o^2=R^2$

so that $\qquad\qquad sX_o=R$ . . . . (236)

Hence the torque is a maximum when the reactance is equal to the resistance. For instance, with $R=1\ \Omega$ and $X_o=8\ \Omega$, maximum torque occurs when $s=0\cdot125$ p.u.; whereas with $R=8\ \Omega$ and $X_o=8\ \Omega$, maximum torque occurs when $s=1$, namely when the rotor is at standstill.

For a given motor operating at a given voltage,

$$\text{maximum torque} \propto \frac{sR}{2R^2}$$

$$\propto \frac{1}{2X_o}.$$

But X_o, the reactance at standstill, is a constant for a given rotor; hence the maximum torque is the same whatever the value of the rotor resistance.

153. Starting Torque.   At the instant of starting, $s = 1$, and it will be seen from Fig. 223 that with a motor having a low-resistance rotor, such as the usual type of squirrel-cage rotor, the starting torque is small compared with the maximum torque available.   On the other hand, if the bars of the cage rotor were made of sufficiently high resistance to give the maximum torque at standstill, the slip with full-load torque—usually about one-third to one-half of the maximum torque—would be relatively large and the I^2R loss in the rotor winding would be high, with the result that the efficiency would be low; and if this load was maintained for an hour or two, the temperature rise would be excessive.   Also the variation of

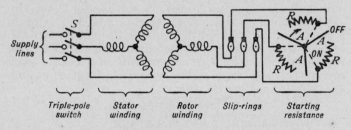

Fig. 224.—Induction motor with slip-ring rotor.

speed with load would be large (see Art. 155).   Hence, when a motor is required to exert its maximum torque at starting, the usual practice is to insert extra resistance into the rotor circuit and to cut this resistance out as the motor accelerates.   Such an arrangement involves a three-phase winding on the rotor, the three ends of the winding being connected via slip-rings on the shaft to an external star-connected resistance R, as shown in Fig. 224.   The three arms, A, are mechanically and electrically connected together.

The starting procedure is to close the triple-pole switch S and then move arms A clockwise as the motor accelerates, until, at full speed, the arms are in the *ON* position shown dotted in Fig. 224, and the starting resistances have been cut out of the rotor circuit.   Many large motors are fitted with a short-circuiting and brush-lifting device which first short-circuits the three slip-rings and then lifts the brushes off the rings, thereby eliminating losses due to the brush-contact resistance and the brush friction and reducing the wear of the brushes and of the slip-rings.

154. Variation of Torque with Stator Voltage, other Factors remaining Constant. From expression (232), it is seen that for given values of the slip and of the rotor resistance and reactance,

$$\text{torque on rotor} \propto \Phi^2.$$

But for a given stator winding, it follows from expression (223) that Φ is approximately proportional to the voltage applied to the stator winding:

$$\therefore \text{ torque on rotor} \propto (\text{stator applied voltage})^2 \quad (237)$$

This relationship will be referred to in Art. 156 in connection with methods of starting up squirrel-cage motors.

155. Speed Control by means of External Rotor Resistance. From expression (231), it follows that for a given input power to the rotor and therefore for a given torque exerted by the rotor, the total rotor I^2R loss is proportional to the slip. Thus, if a motor has 100 kW transferred from the stator to the rotor when the slip is 5 per cent, the total rotor I^2R loss is 5 kW and the mechanical power developed by the rotor is 95 kW. But if the slip is increased to, say, 40 per cent by the addition of external resistance in the rotor circuit and if the *torque developed by the rotor remains unaltered*, the I^2R loss in the rotor circuit increases to 40 kW and the mechanical power developed by the rotor decreases to 60 kW. Hence the efficiency of the motor has been considerably reduced.

Speed control by means of external rotor resistance has the following disadvantages:

(1) reduction of speed is accompanied by reduced efficiency,

(2) with a large resistance in the rotor circuit, the

speed varies considerably with variation of torque (see Fig. 223),

(3) the external rotor resistance is comparatively bulky and expensive as it may have to dissipate a good deal of power without becoming overheated.

The main advantage of this method of speed control is its simplicity.

Example 53. *The power supplied to a three-phase induction motor is* 40 *kW and the corresponding stator losses are* 1·5 *kW. Calculate:* (a) *the total mechanical power developed and the rotor* I^2R *loss when the slip is* 0·04 *per unit,* (b) *the output horsepower of the motor if the friction and windage losses are* 0·8 *kW and* (c) *the efficiency of the motor. Neglect the rotor iron loss.*

(a)   Input power to rotor $= 40 - 1·5 = 38·5$ kW.
From (231),

$$\frac{\text{rotor } I^2R \text{ loss in kW}}{38·5} = 0·04$$

$\therefore$ rotor I^2R loss $= 1·54$ kW

so that mechanical power $\left.\right\}= 38·5 - 1·54 = 36·96$ kW
developed by the rotor

$$= \frac{36·96}{0·746} = 49·5 \text{ h.p.}$$

(b) Output power of motor $= 36·96 - 0·8 = 36·16$ kW

$$= \frac{36·16}{0·746} = 48·5 \text{ b.h.p.}$$

(c)   Efficiency of motor $= 36·16/40 = 0·904$ p.u.
$$= 90·4 \text{ per cent.}$$

Example 54. *If the speed of the motor of Example* 53 *is reduced to* 40 *per cent of its synchronous speed by means of external rotor resistance, calculate:* (a) *the total rotor* I^2R *loss and* (b) *the efficiency, assuming the torque and the stator losses to remain unaltered. Also, assume that the increase in the rotor iron loss is equal to the reduction in the friction and windage loss.*

(a)   New slip $= \dfrac{100 - 40}{100} = 0·6$ p.u.

and   input power to rotor $= 38·5$ kW

From (231), total rotor$\left.\begin{array}{c}\\ I^2R \text{ loss}\end{array}\right\}$ $=0\cdot6\times38\cdot5=23\cdot1$ kW.

(b) Total losses in rotor$=23\cdot1+0\cdot8=23\cdot9$ kW

∴ output power of motor$=38\cdot5-23\cdot9=14\cdot6$ kW

and efficiency of motor$=14\cdot6/40=0\cdot365$ p.u.

$=36\cdot5$ per cent.

156. Starting of a Three-phase Induction Motor fitted with a Squirrel-cage Rotor. If this type of motor is started up by being switched directly across the supply, the starting current is about 4 to 7 times the full-load current, the actual value depending upon the size and design of the machine. Such a large current may cause a relatively large voltage drop in the cables and thereby produce an objectionable momentary dimming of the lamps in the vicinity. Consequently it is usual to start squirrel-cage motors—except small machines—with a reduced voltage, using one of the following methods:

(1) *Star-delta starter.* The two ends of each phase of the stator winding are brought out to the starter which, when moved to the "starting" position, connects the winding in star. After the motor has accelerated, the starter is quickly moved to the "running" position, thereby changing the connections to delta. Hence the voltage per phase at starting is $1/\sqrt{3}$ of the supply voltage, and the starting torque is therefore one-third of that obtained if the motor were switched directly across the supply with its stator winding delta-connected. Also, the starting current per phase is $1/\sqrt{3}$ and that taken from the supply is one-third of the corresponding value with direct switching.

(2) *Auto-transformer starter.* In Fig. 225, T represents a three-phase star-connected auto-transformer (see Art. 127) with a mid-point tapping on each phase so that the voltage applied to motor M is half the supply voltage. With such tappings, the supply current and the starting torque are only a quarter of the values when the full voltage is applied to the motor.

After the motor has accelerated, the starter is moved to the "running" position, thereby connecting the motor directly across the supply and opening the star-connection of the auto-transformer.

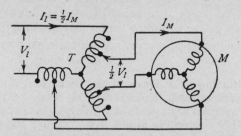

Fig. 225.—Starting connections of an auto-transformer starter.

157. Comparison of Squirrel-cage and Slip-ring Rotors. The squirrel-cage rotor possesses the following advantages:

(1) cheaper and more robust,
(2) slightly higher efficiency and power factor,
(3) explosion proof, since the absence of slip-rings and brushes eliminates risk of sparking.

The advantages of the slip-ring rotor are:

(1) the starting torque is much higher and the starting current much lower,
(2) the speed can be varied by means of an external rotor resistance (see Art. 155).

Summary of Important Formulae in Chapter XII

$$\text{Synchronous speed} = \frac{60f}{p} \qquad (216)$$

$$\text{Per-unit slip, } s \Big\} = \frac{\text{synchronous speed} - \text{rotor speed}}{\text{synchronous speed}} \qquad (221)$$

$$\text{Rotor frequency} = f_r = sf \qquad (222)$$

$$\text{Rotor e.m.f./phase} = E_r = sE_o \qquad (226)$$

where $\qquad E_o = 2 \cdot 22 k_d Z_r f \Phi \qquad (224)$

Rotor impedance/phase $= Z_r = \sqrt{[R^2 + (sX_o)^2]}$. (227)

$$\text{Per-unit slip} = \frac{\text{total rotor } I^2R \text{ loss}}{\text{input power to rotor}} \quad (231)$$

$$\text{Torque on rotor} \propto \frac{\Phi^2 s R}{R^2 + (sX_o)^2} \quad (232)$$

For small slip, torque $\propto s/R$ . . . (234)

For large slip and low rotor resistance,

torque $\propto R/s$ . . . (235)

For maximum torque, $R = sX_o$ . . . . (236)

Starting torque $\propto$ (stator applied voltage)^2 (237)

EXAMPLES XII

1. Describe briefly, with sketches, the construction of a three-phase squirrel-cage induction motor.

A three-phase, twelve-pole, 60-c/s induction motor runs at 570 r.p.m. on full load. Find the frequency of the rotor e.m.f. Give the no-load speed of the motor and sketch the speed-load curve and state with which type of d.c. motor it compares. (U.E.I.)

2. Explain, with sketches, why the torque developed by the rotor of a three-phase induction motor is in the same direction as the rotating field set up by the stator currents. Why does the rotor normally run at a speed slightly less than that of the rotating field?

A twelve-pole, three-phase induction motor runs at 485 r.p.m. on a 50-c/s supply. Calculate its slip and the frequency of the rotor e.m.f. (U.L.C.I.)

3. If a six-pole induction motor supplied from a three-phase 50-c/s supply has a rotor frequency of 2·3 c/s, calculate (a) the percentage slip and (b) the speed of the rotor in r.p.m.

4. Show how a rotating magnetic field can be produced by three-phase currents.

A fourteen-pole, 50-c/s induction motor runs at 415 r.p.m. Deduce the frequency of the currents in the rotor winding and the slip. (App. Elect., L.U.)

5. What is meant by *slip* in an induction motor? If a three-phase motor with 6 poles runs at 970 r.p.m. when connected to a 50-c/s supply, calculate (i) the percentage slip and (ii) the frequency of the rotor currents.

Explain the effect of inserting resistance in the rotor circuit of an induction motor and give the reasons for doing this when starting a motor of the slip-ring type. (U.E.I.)

6. (i) A 60-b.h.p., 400-V, 50-c/s, eight-pole induction motor has a delta-connected stator and a star-connected rotor. The full-load efficiency is 0·9 per unit and the power factor is 0·85. There are 192 conductors in series per phase on the stator and 96 on the rotor.

Calculate (a) the full-load current in the stator windings and (b) the rotor e.m.f. per phase at standstill.

(ii) If the resistance/phase of the rotor winding is $0 \cdot 08$ Ω and the reactance negligible, and if the full-load rotor current is 85 A, find (a) the rotor e.m.f. per phase and (b) the slip and the rotor speed at full load. Assume the impedance drop in the stator winding to be negligible.

(iii) If the leakage reactance of the rotor winding at standstill be $0 \cdot 5$ Ω/phase, calculate the external rotor resistance/phase required to give maximum starting torque.

(iv) Calculate the rotor speed with an external resistance of $0 \cdot 2$ Ω/phase when the rotor current is 85 A.

(v) Calculate the slip for maximum torque when there is no external resistance in circuit.

7. If the star-connected rotor winding of a three-phase induction motor has a resistance of $0 \cdot 01$ Ω/phase and a standstill reactance of $0 \cdot 08$ Ω/phase, what must be the value of the resistance per phase of a starter to give the maximum starting torque? What is the percentage slip when the starting resistance has been reduced to $0 \cdot 02$ Ω/phase, if the motor is still exerting its maximum torque?

8. A 30-b.h.p., three-phase, 50-c/s, six-pole induction motor has a full-load slip of $0 \cdot 04$ per unit. The frictional loss is 250 W. Find (a) the rotor speed and (b) the rotor I^2R loss.

9. Explain the advantages gained by using a slip-ring rotor instead of a cage-rotor for a three-phase induction motor.

A three-phase, four-pole induction motor works on 200-V, 50-c/s mains. On full load of 10 h.p. its speed is 1440 r.p.m. (Frictional losses total $0 \cdot 5$ h.p.) Determine approximately (a) its speed at 200 V and half-full load and (b) its speed with an output of 10 h.p. at 190 V, 50 c/s.   (App. Elect., L.U.)

10. Define the term "slip" as applied to a three-phase induction motor. Explain how currents are produced in the rotor.

If at standstill the rotor voltage is 100 V, the rotor reactance is 10 Ω and its resistance is $0 \cdot 2$ Ω, calculate the value of the rotor current when the slip is 4 per cent. Prove the formula employed.

(Assoc. Mem., I.E.E.)

11. The star-connected rotor of a three-phase induction motor has a standstill reactance of 2 Ω and a resistance of $0 \cdot 4$ Ω. The induced e.m.f. between the slip-rings at standstill is 90 V. Find (a) the current in each rotor phase when the rings are short-circuited and the machine is running with a slip of 4 per cent and (b) the slip and rotor current when the rotor is developing maximum torque.

(C. & G., El. Eng. Pract., Final, Part I)

12. Describe briefly the construction of the stator and slip-ring rotor of a three-phase induction motor. Illustrate your answer with appropriate sketches. Explain the action of the motor and why the rotor is provided with slip-rings.

A three-phase, 50-c/s induction motor has 4 poles and runs at a speed of 1440 r.p.m. when the gross torque is 50 lb.ft. Calculate (a) the total input (in watts) to the rotor, (b) the rotor copper loss in watts.   (App. El., L.U.)

13. A three-phase 50-c/s induction motor with its rotor star-connected gives 500 V (r.m.s.) at standstill between the slip-rings on open-circuit. Calculate the current and power factor at standstill when the rotor winding is joined to a star-connected external circuit, each phase of which has a resistance of 10 Ω and an inductance of

0·04 H.   The resistance per phase of the rotor winding is 0·2 Ω and its inductance is 0·04 H.   Also calculate the current and power factor when the slip-rings are short-circuited and the motor is running with a slip of 5 per cent.   Assume the flux to remain constant.

(App. Elect., L.U.)

14.   Sketch the usual form of the torque-speed curve for a polyphase induction motor and explain the factors which determine the shape of this curve.

In a certain eight-pole, 50-c/s machine the rotor resistance per phase is 0·04 Ω and the maximum torque occurs at a speed of 645 r.p.m. Assuming that the air-gap flux is constant at all loads, determine the percentage of maximum torque (a) at starting and (b) when the slip is 3 per cent.   (App. Elect., L.U.)

CHAPTER XIII

THERMIONICS

158. The Two-electrode Vacuum Tube or Diode. If a metal cylinder A is placed around an incandescent filament C in an evacuated glass bulb G, as shown in Fig. 226, it is found that if a battery B is connected in series with a milliammeter D between the cylinder and one end of the filament, an electric current flows through the milliammeter when the cylinder is made positive relative to the filament; but when the connections to battery B are reversed, so as to make A negative relative to C, there is no current through D.

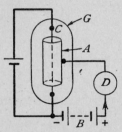

Fig. 226.—A vacuum diode.

Let us now consider the reason for this behaviour.

An electrical conductor contains a large number of mobile electrons that are not attached to any particular atom of the material, but move about from one atom to another within the boundary of the conductor; and the higher the temperature of the conductor, the greater is the velocity attained by these electrons. In the case of an incandescent tungsten filament, for instance, some of these free electrons may acquire sufficient momentum to overcome the forces tending to hold them within the boundary of the filament. Consequently they escape outwards; but if there is no p.d. between the filament and the surrounding cylinder, the electrons emitted from the filament form a cloud or *space charge* around the wire. Consequently, the electrons that are emitted after the formation of the space charge are repelled back into the filament, so that the net number of electrons leaving the latter is zero.

If cylinder *A* is made positive in relation to the filament, electrons are attracted outwards from the space charge, as indicated by the dotted radial lines in Fig. 227, and fewer of the electrons emitted from the filament are repelled back into the latter. The number of electrons reaching the cylinder increases with increase in the positive potential of the cylinder, as shown in Fig. 228, until ultimately all the electrons emitted from the filament travel to the cylinder. The corresponding rate of flow of electrons is referred to as the *saturation current*.

If the cylinder is made negative in relation to the filament, the electrons of the space charge are repelled

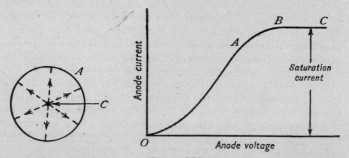

FIG. 227.—Electron paths from cathode to anode.

FIG. 228.— Anode current/anode voltage characteristic of a vacuum diode.

towards the latter, so that none reaches the cylinder and the reading on milliammeter *D* (Fig. 226) is zero.

Since current flows through *D* only when the cylinder is positive and the filament negative, the former is termed the *anode* and the latter the *cathode*; and since current can flow in one direction only, the arrangement is termed a *thermionic valve* or merely a *valve*. When a valve contains only an anode and a cathode it is referred to as a *diode*. The p.d. between the anode and the cathode is termed the *anode voltage* and the rate of flow of electrons from cathode to anode constitutes the *anode current*. The *conventional* direction of the anode current is from the positive of battery *B* via the anode to the cathode, as indicated by the arrowhead in Fig. 226; but it is important to realize that the anode current is actually a movement of electrons in the reverse direction.

The thermionic emission from a metallic surface is given approximately by Richardson's formula:

$$I = A T^2 e^{-b/T} \text{ amperes/cm}^2$$

where $\qquad T =$ absolute temperature

$$= 273 + \text{temperature in } °C,$$

$$e = \text{Napierian base} = 2 \cdot 718$$

and $\qquad A$ and $b =$ constants for a given material.

The current represented by the above expression is the saturation current, namely the anode current when all the electrons emitted from the cathode are attracted to the anode. This condition is represented by range BC of the characteristic in Fig. 228; and the corresponding value of the anode current is referred to as the *temperature-limited current*, since, for a given cathode, it depends only upon the temperature of the latter.

Over the range OB, the same number of electrons are being emitted from the cathode, but the number which reaches the anode depends upon the combined effect of the space charge and the anode voltage. The lower the anode voltage, the more effective is the opposition of the space charge to the movement of electrons from the cathode to the anode. Over range OA, the value of this *space-charge limited current* is represented approximately by the expression:

$$I_a = k V_a^{3/2}$$

where $k =$ a constant for a given valve.

159. Construction of a Diode. The anode is stamped out of nickel sheet and the cathode may be either of the directly-heated or of the indirectly-heated type. In the former, the cathode is a filament heated by current passing through it. There are three types of directly-heated filaments:

(a) *Pure tungsten filament*, which has to be operated at the relatively high temperature of about 2200°C in order that it may give an emission of about 3 mA per watt absorbed by the filament. It has the advantage, however, of being able to withstand positive-ion bombardment due to any residual gas (see Art. 163) far better than any other type of cathode. It is therefore used for valves operated with very high anode voltages.

(b) *Thoriated-tungsten filament*, containing a small quantity (about 1 to 2 per cent) of thorium oxide together with a reducing agent—usually carbon. By a special activating process the impregnated carbon reduces some of the thorium oxide to metallic thorium which diffuses to the surface, where it forms a layer, one molecule deep, capable of emitting about 30 mA/W at about 1600°C. Thoriated tungsten can withstand positive-ion bombardment better than the oxide-coated cathode and is used for valves working at moderate anode voltages of about 500 to 5000 V.

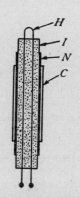

(c) *Oxide-coated filament*, consisting of a mixture of barium and strontium oxides on a nickel wire. Such a cathode is operated at about 750°C and is capable of emitting about 100 mA/W absorbed by the filament.

In the *indirectly-heated* type, the cathode C consists of a mixture of barium and strontium oxides sprayed on a hollow nickel cylinder N, as in Fig. 229. The cathode is heated by a tungsten filament H, known as the *heater*, embedded in an insulator I to prevent the heater making electrical contact with the cathode. Oxide emitters must be activated by special heat-treatment to produce a layer of metallic molecules on the surface of the oxide. The oxide-coated cathode has a higher efficiency and, in the absence of positive-ion bombardment, has a longer life than the other types of cathode and is almost universally used in small valves.

Fig. 229.—An indirectly-heated cathode.

160. Static Characteristic of a Vacuum Diode. The static* characteristic of a diode gives the relationship

* The "dynamic" characteristic of a diode gives the relationship between the anode current and the *supply* voltage when a load, such as a resistance, is connected in a series with the anode.

12

between the anode current and the anode voltage for a given filament voltage and therefore for a given filament temperature.   A convenient circuit arrangement for determining the characteristic of a directly-heated

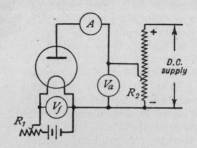

Fig. 230.—Determination of the static characteristic of a vacuum diode.

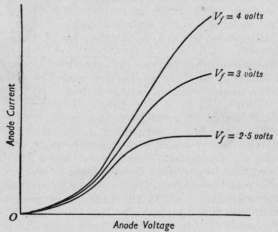

Fig. 231.—Static characteristics of a vacuum diode.

vacuum diode is shown in Fig. 230.   The filament voltage is given by voltmeter V_f and its value can be varied by means of R_1.   The anode voltage can be varied between zero and any desired maximum by means of a resistance R_2 arranged as a voltage divider. Fig. 231 shows typical results obtained with different filament voltages. It will be seen that with a relatively large anode voltage, a further increase of anode voltage produces only a relatively small increase of anode current, i.e. the valve is reaching a state of saturation, when practically all the electrons emitted by the cathode are being attracted to the anode. The smaller the filament voltage and therefore the lower the cathode temperature, the smaller is the saturation current.

161. The Vacuum Diode as a Half-wave Rectifier.
In Fig. 232 a transformer T is arranged with two secondary windings, one giving a low-voltage supply for the filament and the other giving a suitable high-voltage supply for the anode circuit. One end of the high-voltage winding is connected to a mid-point tapping M on the low-vol-

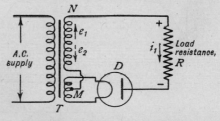

FIG. 232.—Half-wave rectifier.

tage winding. When the e.m.f. induced in winding $M N$ is in the direction represented by e_1 in Fig. 232 and 233, the anode is positive in relation to the filament, and a current i_1 flows through the load resistance R. But when the e.m.f. of MN is in the reverse direction, as shown by e_2, the anode is negative in relation to the filament and there is no current. Hence the waveform of the load current is represented by the lower curve in Fig. 233.

162. Full-wave Rectification by means of Two Vacuum Diodes.
The high-voltage secondary winding PQ in Fig. 234 has a mid-point tapping N connected to one end of the load resistance R, the other end of which is connected to the mid-point tapping M of the low-voltage winding. To the latter are connected the

filaments of two diodes, the two anodes being connected
to the two ends of the high-voltage winding, as shown
in Fig. 234.

During the half-cycle OC (Fig. 235), the e.m.f. induced
in PQ is assumed to be acting in the direction of arrow e_1,
thereby making anode B positive and anode A negative

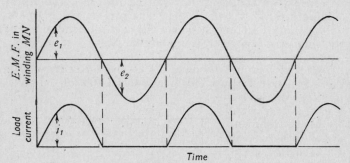

FIG. 233.—Waveforms of input voltage and output current of
a half-wave rectifier.

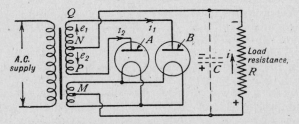

FIG. 234.—Full-wave rectifier.

in relation to their filaments.   Consequently current i_1
flows via B and none via A.   During the second half-
cycle CD, the e.m.f. in PQ is in the direction shown by
arrow e_2, so that current i_2 flows via A and none via B.
Hence the current through the load is unidirectional as
represented in Fig. 235 (b).   For many purposes this
fluctuation of current is very undesirable, and we will
now consider how it may be reduced.

Let us first consider the effect of connecting a capacitor C, as shown dotted in Fig. 234, *without any load resistance*. During the first half-cycle, Q is assumed to be positive in relation to P, so that electrons are being withdrawn from the lower plate of C and flow via anode B and winding QN towards the upper plate of C. Thus the capacitor is charged to the maximum value of the e.m.f. induced

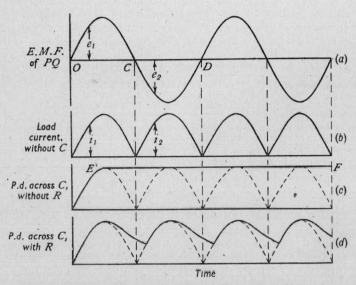

FIG. 235.—Waveforms for a full-wave rectifier.

in winding NQ. As the e.m.f. of NQ decreases to zero, the electrons assembled on the upper plate of C are unable to return to the lower plate (the insulation resistance of C being assumed infinite). Consequently the p.d. across C remains constant at the peak value of the alternating e.m.f., as shown by the horizontal line EF in Fig. 235 (c).

When a load R is connected in parallel with C, the latter discharges through R during the time when the e.m.f. induced in NQ or NP is less than the p.d. across C

and is recharged when the induced e.m.f. exceeds the p.d. across C. Consequently the terminal voltage varies as shown in Fig. 235 (d). The larger the capacitance of C and the higher the resistance of the load R, the smaller is the fluctuation of the terminal voltage. This fluctuation can be practically eliminated by adding an iron-cored choke L and another capacitor C_2, as shown in Fig. 236. In this diagram the two anodes are assembled in one bulb with a common cathode. Such a valve is termed a *double-diode*. The inductance of L is usually about 10 henrys and C_1 and C_2 may each be 8 μF.

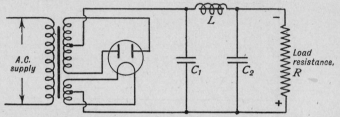

FIG. 236.—Double-diode with smoothing capacitors and choke.

163. Gas-filled Diode or Rectifier. This type of rectifier consists of a glass bulb with an oxide-coated cathode and an anode, as already described for the vacuum diode, but the bulb contains either a small amount of an inert gas such as argon or a small globule of mercury which is vaporized by the heat of the filament.

An atom of argon or mercury vapour normally contains equal amounts of positive and negative electricity, and the atom, as conceived by the late Lord Rutherford, consists of a central dense nucleus containing a positive charge of electricity surrounded—at distances relatively great compared with its diameter—by planetary electrons, i.e. by electrons circling around the nucleus. The outermost electrons are loosely held to the atom and can be easily detached. An atom, or a group of atoms forming a molecule, that has lost one or more electrons is therefore deficient in negative electricity, i.e. its positive charge is greater than its negative charge

Such an atom or molecule is termed a *positive ion* and behaves as a positively charged body.

One method of detaching these loosely held electrons is by bombardment by other electrons; but in order to be capable of causing this detachment, the bombarding electrons must have attained a certain velocity before impact. This process of detaching electrons from molecules and forming positive ions is known as *ionization*.

In the gas-filled rectifier, the electrons emitted from the cathode are attracted towards the anode when the latter is positive in relation to the cathode; and the greater the p.d. between the anode and the cathode, the greater is the acceleration of the electrons. When an electron has attained a certain velocity, its collision with

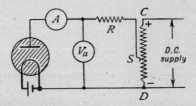

FIG. 237.—Determination of anode voltage/anode current characteristic of a gas-filled rectifier.

a molecule results in the liberation of one or more electrons and the formation of a positive ion. Once ionization commences, the electrons released from molecules join those emitted from the cathode and thus increase the number of electrons travelling towards the anode. Consequently the number of collisions between these electrons and other molecules will be increased, with the result that still more electrons will be released and more positive ions formed. For this reason the ionization tends to increase indefinitely and has to be limited by a resistance R in series with the anode, as shown in Fig. 237. It will be noticed that the circle representing the glass bulb is cross-hatched. This is the convention used to distinguish a gas-filled tube from a vacuum tube.

The relationship between the anode-cathode p.d. and

the anode current is shown in Fig. 238, from which it is seen that, once ionization commences, the p.d. is practically independent of the anode current. Consequently the effect of moving slider S towards C in Fig. 237 is merely to cause such an increase of anode current that the increase of voltage drop in R absorbs the increase of voltage between S and D.

The ionizing p.d. is usually about 15 to 20 V and the presence of ionization is indicated by a glow in the space between the anode and the cathode. The bombardment of the cathode by the positive ions may be sufficiently severe to disintegrate the electrode; and in order that the cathode may have a reasonably long life, it is necessary to limit the maximum value of the anode current, the actual value being dependent upon the area of the cathode surface.

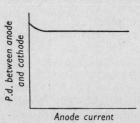

FIG. 238.—Anode voltage/anode current characteristic of a gas-filled rectifier.

The circuit diagrams for a gas-filled diode are similar to those already given for the diode. The advantages of the gas-filled diode over the vacuum diode are:

(1) the anode-cathode voltage is much smaller than that normally required for the vacuum valve, so that the efficiency of the gas-filled diode is much higher than that of the vacuum diode,

(2) owing to ionization, the anode current is far greater than that obtainable when there is no gas present.

The main disadvantage of the gas-filled rectifier is its shorter life due to the disintegration of the cathode by positive-ion bombardment.

164. Full-wave Mercury-arc Rectifier.

A glass bulb B, shaped as in Fig. 239, has a mercury pool C and two electrodes A_1 and A_2, made of graphite in small rectifiers and iron in large rectifiers. The bulb is thoroughly evacuated before being sealed. These electrodes are connected to the two ends of the secondary winding of transformer T and a mid-point tapping M is connected through an inductance L to one side of the load, the other side of which is connected to pool C.

The essential features of one method of starting the arc between the anodes $A_1 A_2$ and the cathode C is shown in Fig. 239. A flexible metal electrode F carries an iron

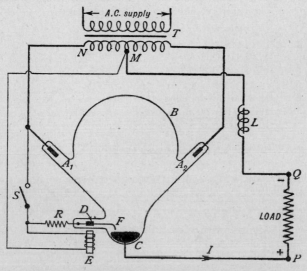

FIG. 239.—Full-wave mercury-arc rectifier.

core D, and an electromagnet E is situated directly under D. When switch S is closed, D is attracted downwards each time the flux in E grows from zero to a maximum. Consequently, strip F vibrates at twice the supply frequency, and the tip of F makes and breaks contact with the mercury pool C, the current being limited by resistance R to a relatively small value. Each time the circuit is broken, the arc between F and C vaporizes some of the mercury and also forms an incandescent spot on the surface of C, sufficiently to emit

12*

electrons. The latter are attracted towards the main electrode that happens to be positive in relation to the cathode C and thus produce ionization. The positive ions produced by this ionization bombard the surface of the mercury sufficiently to maintain the incandescent spot and enable the supply of electrons to be continued from the cathode. Switch S is then opened. If the load current is less than a certain critical value, the ionization is insufficient to maintain the incandescent spot; consequently, the arc is extinguished.

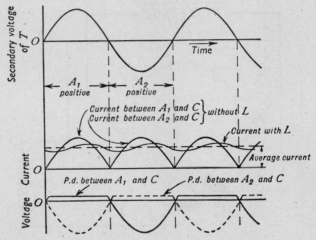

FIG. 240.—Waveforms of voltages and currents for a full-wave rectifier.

If inductance L were not in circuit, the current through the load would vary between zero and a maximum every half-cycle, as shown in Fig. 240. With L in circuit, the effect of the e.m.f. induced in L is to delay the decrease of the current at one anode until the potential of the other anode is sufficiently high to take over the arc from the first anode, thereby reducing the fluctuation of the current, as indicated in Fig. 240.

The function of the large glass dome B is to provide the

cooling surface necessary to prevent excessive temperature rise of the rectifier. In practice, the arms containing the anodes A_1 and A_2 are made with an elbow to reduce the risk of an arc directly between these electrodes.

The p.d. across the arc remains practically constant at about 20 V over a wide variation of current, as represented by the positive portions of the bottom curves in Fig. 240 (see also Art. 163 and Fig. 238); hence:

if V = output voltage, namely the p.d. between Q and C,

    p.d. between Q and the conducting anode = $V + 20$.

But this voltage is the average value of the e.m.f. induced in one-half of the secondary winding of T, the impedance drop in the latter being assumed negligible,

i.e. $V + 20 = \left(\dfrac{\text{r.m.s. value of e.m.f. induced in } MN}{1 \cdot 11} \right)$

so that $V = \left(\dfrac{\text{r.m.s. value of e.m.f. in } MN}{1 \cdot 11} - 20 \right).$

If   output current = I amperes,

               output power = IV watts.

With the ripple in the output current reduced to a negligible value, the arc current between A_1 and C remains practically constant during alternate half-cycles, the p.d. between these electrodes being then about 20 V. Similarly, during the other half-cycles the current between A_2 and C remains practically constant. Hence, if the losses in the transformer and the smoothing coil L be neglected,

      loss in rectifier = $I \times$ voltage drop in arc

               $\simeq 20I$ watts,

and $\left. \begin{array}{l} \text{input power} \\ \text{to rectifier} \end{array} \right\} = IV + 20I$

$\therefore$ $\left. \begin{array}{l} \text{efficiency of} \\ \text{rectifier} \end{array} \right\} = \dfrac{IV}{I(V + 20)} = \dfrac{V}{V + 20}$.   .   (238)

Hence the efficiency is practically independent of the load.

If $V = 100$ volts,

$$\text{efficiency} = \frac{100}{100 + 20} = 0 \cdot 83 \text{ p.u.}$$

but if $V = 1000$ volts,

$$\text{efficiency} = \frac{1000}{1000 + 20} = 0 \cdot 98 \text{ p.u.}$$

It follows that the greater the output voltage, the higher is the efficiency of the mercury-arc rectifier.

165. Three-phase Mercury-arc Rectifier. Fig. 241 shows the principal features of a three-phase rectifier

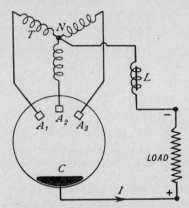

FIG. 241.—Three-phase mercury-arc rectifier.

supplied from the secondary winding T of a transformer, and the variation of the output voltage, with and without coil L, is represented in Fig. 242. In an actual rectifier, in addition to the starting electrode as described for the single-phase rectifier, it is necessary to provide two exciter electrodes, the function of which is to maintain ionization in the bulb when the rectifier is on no load and thus enable it to take instantly any load that may be switched on. The connections of these exciter electrodes are very similar to those of the full-wave rectifier described in Art. 164. In large mercury-arc rectifiers the glass bulb is replaced by a steel tank; and in this way it is possible to make rectifiers capable of supplying several thousand kilowatts.

The main advantages of the mercury-arc rectifiers are:

(a) low maintenance and operating costs, owing to the absence of any rotating machinery,

(b) the higher the output voltage, the higher is the efficiency,

(c) the ease with which they can be arranged for automatic operation or remote control.

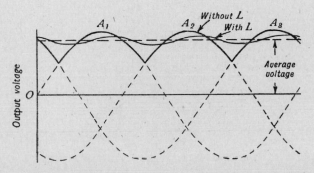

FIG. 242.—Output voltage of a three-phase mercury-arc rectifier.

166. Metal Rectifiers. This type of rectifier depends upon ionization in a *barrier-layer* between a conductor and a semi-conductor. There are two commercial types of metal rectifier: (a) the copper-oxide rectifier and (b) the selenium rectifier. Both types depend upon the behaviour of a contact-surface between a conductor and a semi-conductor—copper and cuprous oxide in type (a), a metal alloy and selenium in type (b).

The *copper-oxide rectifier* consists of copper discs, one side of each disc having a layer of cuprous oxide (Cu_2O) formed by special heat treatment.* These discs are assembled on an insulated spindle as shown in Fig. 243,

* See "Metal Rectifiers," by Williams and Thompson, *Journal of the Institution of Electrical Engineers*, Part I, October 1941.

the number of discs being dependent upon the voltage at which the rectifier is to operate. Contact is made with the external surface of the cuprous oxide either by washers of a soft metal such as lead, as in Fig. 243, or by spraying a layer of metal on the cuprous oxide, the main purpose being to make as good a contact as possible with the cuprous oxide, thereby reducing the "forward" resistance to a minimum.

The rectifying property appears to be due to a barrier-layer between the copper and the cuprous oxide. The

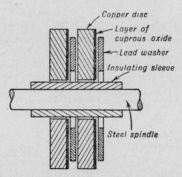

FIG. 243.—Copper-oxide rectifier.

precise nature of this layer is not known; but the existence of such a layer is suggested by the following experimental observations:

(a) The capacitance of a rectifier unit, measured between the terminals, is about $0 \cdot 01$ to $0 \cdot 02$ $\mu F/cm^2$ of contact surface. Assuming the dielectric of the barrier-layer to have a relative permittivity of $1 \cdot 0$, the calculated thickness of such a layer would be about $4 \cdot 5$ to 9×10^{-6} cm.

(b) The relationship between the current and the applied voltage for a certain rectifier unit is given in Fig. 244. It will be seen that for a current in the "forward" direction and for a p.d. greater than about $0 \cdot 2$ V, a small increase of the voltage is accompanied by relatively large increase of current. A comparison of this graph with that given in Fig. 238 for the gas-filled rectifier suggests that ionization takes place in the barrier-layer and that the latter behaves like a film of gas.

The above suggestions are inadequate to provide a full explanation of the action of the metal rectifier, but they enable a mental picture to be formed which does agree approximately with the observed facts. When the

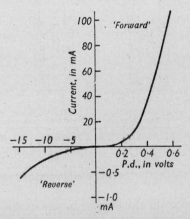

FIG. 244.—Static characteristic of a copper-oxide rectifier.

copper is negative in relation to the oxide, as in Fig. 245 (a), a p.d. of, say, 0·5 V produces a high potential gradient in the barrier-layer, thereby causing ionization in the latter. Electrons move towards the oxide and positive ions towards the copper. Since the latter contains a plentiful supply of mobile electrons, i.e. electrons that can easily be detached from their atoms, its bombardment by positive ions releases many of these electrons, which then pass across the barrier-layer to the oxide, thereby maintaining the ionization. Hence the circuit has a low resistance when the current is flowing conventionally from the oxide to the copper, as in Fig. 245 (a).

The cuprous oxide, being only a semi-conductor, has far fewer mobile electrons than the copper. Consequently, when the polarity of the applied voltage is reversed, as in Fig. 245 (b), relatively few electrons are released from the oxide into the barrier-layer by the high potential gradient in the latter, and the circuit has therefore a high resistance when the current is flowing

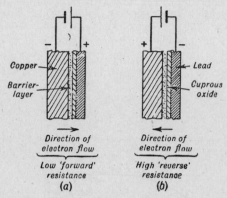

FIG. 245.—Action of the copper-oxide rectifier.

conventionally from the copper to the oxide. It follows from the above explanation that the action of the copper-oxide rectifier may be likened to that of a cold gas-filled rectifier in which the copper forms the cathode and the oxide forms the anode.

The *selenium rectifier* consists of a plate or disc of

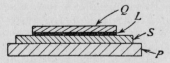

FIG. 246.—A selenium rectifier unit.

nickel-plated steel or aluminium P (Fig. 246) on the face of which is a thin layer of selenium S. A metal alloy Q is sprayed over the selenium. In Fig. 246 the thicknesses of the selenium and of the alloy are greatly exaggerated; for instance, in the actual rectifier the thickness of the selenium is only about 0·1 mm. The selenium has to be subjected to a special treatment* to produce a barrier-layer L between the selenium and the sprayed alloy (not between the selenium and the disc). The alloy contains an abundant supply of mobile electrons, whereas the selenium, being a semi-conductor, has relatively few. Consequently the rectifier has low resistance when the alloy is negative and the selenium positive, and a high resistance when the polarity of the applied voltage is reversed.

167. Full-wave Rectification with a Metal Rectifier.

The arrangement most commonly used for obtaining full-wave rectification with metal rectifiers is the bridge circuit shown in Fig. 247. The four rectifier elements are represented by the solid triangles butting against perpendicular lines. The apex of the triangle indicates the forward direction of the current, i.e. the direction in which the rectifier resistance is low. The elements are so arranged that a secondary e.m.f. in the direction represented by the full arrow sends current through B and E; whereas an e.m.f. in the reverse direction (dotted arrow) sends current through D and C. It is evident from Fig. 247 that the current through ammeter A is uni-directional.

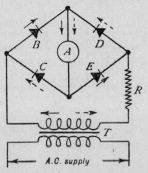

FIG. 247.—Bridge circuit for full-wave rectification.

If a resistance R is connected in series with the bridge as shown in Fig. 247 and if A is a milliammeter, the arrangement can be used as a rectifier voltmeter and the milliammeter can be calibrated to read directly the r.m.s. value of the voltage, the waveform of the latter being assumed sinusoidal. By means of suitable tappings on

* Full particulars are given in "Characteristics and Applications of the Selenium Rectifier," by E. A. Richards, *Journal of the Inst. of Electrical Engineers*, Part II, October 1941.

R, the voltmeter can be made into a multi-range instrument.

168. The Three-electrode Vacuum Tube or Triode.

Fig. 248 shows the general arrangement of a triode having a directly-heated cathode C. The anode cylinder A is shown cut to depict more clearly the internal construction. Grid G is usually a wire spiral attached to one or two supporting rods. The pitch of this spiral and the distance between the spiral and the cathode are the main factors that determine the characteristics of the triode.

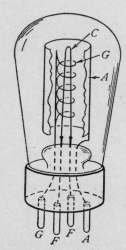

In a triode, the potential of the anode A is always positive in relation to the filament, so that electrons tend to be attracted towards A from the space charge surrounding cathode C. The effect of making the grid G positive in relation to C is to attract more electrons from the space charge. Most of these electrons pass through the gaps between the grid wires, but some of them are caught by the grid as shown in Fig. 249(a) and return to the cathode via the grid circuit. On the other hand, the effect of making the grid negative is to neutralize, partially or wholly,

FIG. 248.—A triode.

the effect of the positive potential of the anode. Consequently, fewer electrons reach the anode, the paths of these electrons being as shown in Fig. 249(b). No electrons are now reaching the grid, i.e. there is no grid current when the grid is negative. The paths of the electrons which are repelled back from the space charge into the cathode are not indicated in Fig. 249.

It will be seen that the magnitude of the anode current can be controlled by varying the p.d. between the grid and the cathode ; and since the grid is in close proximity to the space charge surrounding the cathode,

a variation of, say, 1 volt in the grid potential produces a
far greater change of anode current than that due to
1 volt variation of anode potential. The relationship
between the anode current and the grid voltage for a
given anode voltage and that between the anode current
and the anode voltage for a given grid voltage are referred

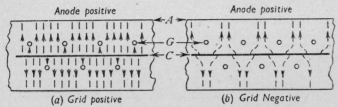

FIG. 249.—Influence of grid potential upon electron paths.

to as the *static characteristics* of the triode, and we shall
now consider how these characteristics are determined
experimentally.

**169. Determination of the Static Characteristics of a
Triode.** (a) I_a/V_g *Characteristics.* The triode is connected as shown in Fig. 250. The slider on R_1 is adjusted

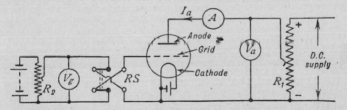

FIG. 250.—Circuit for the determination of the static characteristics of a vacuum triode.

to give a constant reading of, say, 130 V on voltmeter V_a.
The readings on milliammeter A are noted for various
positive and negative values of V_g, the polarity being
reversed by means of switch RS. The test is repeated
with V_a maintained constant at, say, 100 V and then at

70 V. The graphs of Fig. 251 are typical of the results obtained. It will be observed (a) that over an appreciable part of its length, the I_a/V_g characteristic is practically linear and (b) that graphs for equal differences of anode voltage are approximately equally spaced.

(b) *I_a/V_a Characteristics.* The slider on R_2 (Fig. 250) is set for zero voltage on voltmeter V_g and the anode current is noted for various values of the anode voltage. The test is repeated with V_g equal to, say, -2 V and

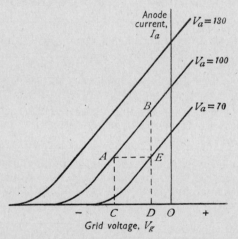

FIG. 251.—I_a/V_g characteristics of a vacuum triode.

then with V_g equal to -4 V. The graphs in Fig. 252 are typical of the results obtained. Again it will be seen (a) that the graphs are practically linear over a considerable portion of their length, and (b) that graphs for equal differences of grid voltage are approximately equally spaced.

170. Amplification Factor, Mutual Conductance and Anode Slope Resistance. Let us start with a point A on the *linear* portion of the I_a/V_g characteristic for V_a of 100 V in Fig. 251; and at A draw a horizontal dotted line to cut at E the characteristic for V_a of 70 V. With

V_a maintained constant at 100 V, it will be seen that the anode current can be increased from CA to DB by reducing the grid voltage from OC to OD; i.e. a change CD of the grid voltage produces an increase EB of the anode current. On the other hand, if the grid voltage is kept constant at OD, the anode current can be increased from DE to DB by increasing the anode voltage from 70 to 100 V: i.e. an increase of 30 V of the anode voltage produces an increase EB of the anode current. In other words, the variation CD of the grid voltage has

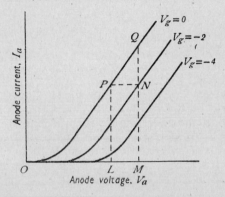

FIG. 252.—I_a/V_a characteristics of a vacuum triode.

exactly the same effect on the anode current as a variation of 30 V of the anode voltage. If CD were, say, 2 V, it would follow that a variation of 1 V on the grid would produce the same change of anode current as a variation of 15 V on the anode. Hence the *amplification factor* of such a valve is said to be 15 and is denoted by the symbol μ.

In general, let ΔV_a* be the variation of anode voltage to produce a change ΔI_a of anode current, the grid voltage being kept constant; and let ΔV_g be the variation of grid voltage to produce the same change ΔI_a of

* "ΔV_a" represents a relatively large variation of V_a, whereas "δV_a" signifies a small variation and "dV_a" an infinitesimal variation.

anode current, the anode voltage being kept constant, then:

$$\text{amplification factor} = \mu = \frac{\Delta V_a}{\Delta V_g} \quad \cdots \quad (239)$$

$$= \frac{100 - 70}{DC} \text{ in Fig. 251.}$$

The ratio of the change of anode current ΔI_a to the change of grid voltage ΔV_g, the anode voltage remaining constant, is termed the *mutual conductance** of the triode and is denoted by the symbol g_m,

$$\text{i.e. mutual conductance} = g_m = \frac{\Delta I_a}{\Delta V_g} \quad \cdots \quad (240)$$

$$= \frac{EB}{AE} \text{ in Fig. 251}$$

$$= \text{slope of } I_a/V_g \text{ characteristic.}$$

The ratio of the change of anode voltage ΔV_a to the change of anode current ΔI_a, the grid voltage remaining constant, is termed the *anode slope resistance* of the triode and is represented by the symbol r_a,

$$\text{i.e. anode slope resistance} = r_a = \frac{\Delta V_a}{\Delta I_a} \quad \cdots \quad (241)$$

$$= \frac{100 - 70}{EB} \text{ in Fig. 251.}$$

The reason for the term "slope" will be obvious from the following consideration of the I_a/V_a characteristics of Fig. 252. Taking a point P on the *linear* portion of the characteristic for $V_g = 0$, let us draw PL vertically and PN horizontally to cut the characteristic for $V_g = -2$ V at N. Draw MQ vertically through N. It follows that if the grid voltage is maintained at zero and the anode voltage increased from OL to OM, the anode current

---

* The term "conductance" is due to the fact that the quantity is a ratio of current/voltage; and the term "mutual" is intended to show that the variation of current in one circuit is due to a variation of voltage in *another* circuit, just as *mutual* inductance refers to the flux linked with one circuit due to current in another circuit (Art. 41).

increases from LP to MQ, i.e. an increase LM of the anode voltage produces an increase NQ of the anode current,

$$\therefore \text{ anode slope re-sistance, } r_a \Big\} = \frac{\Delta V_a}{\Delta I_a} \text{ (for a given grid voltage)}$$

$$= \frac{PN}{NQ} \text{ in Fig. 252} = \frac{1}{NQ/PN}$$

$$= \frac{1}{\text{slope of } I_a/V_a \text{ characteristic}}$$

$$\text{Also, mutual conduc-tance, } g_m \Big\} = \frac{\Delta I_a}{\Delta V_g} \text{ (for a given anode voltage)}$$

$$= \frac{NQ}{2} \text{ in Fig. 252}$$

$$\text{and} \quad \text{amplification factor, } \mu \Big\} = \frac{\Delta V_a}{\Delta V_g} \text{ (for a given variation* of anode current)}$$

$$= \frac{PN}{2} \text{ in Fig. 252.}$$

From the above relationships it follows that:

$$g_m \times r_a = \frac{\Delta I_a}{\Delta V_g} \cdot \frac{\Delta V_a}{\Delta I_a} = \frac{\Delta V_a}{\Delta V_g} = \mu \quad . \quad (242)$$

Example 55. *The following readings were obtained from the linear portions of the static characteristics of a triode:*

V_a (volts)	120	120	80
V_g (volts)	$-1\cdot3$	$-3\cdot8$	$-1\cdot3$
I_a (mA)	10	4	6$\cdot$2

* Instead of considering a given variation of I_a, we could have argued thus: With zero grid voltage, an increase of anode voltage from OL to OM (Fig. 252) increases the anode current from LP to MQ. With the anode voltage maintained at OM, the anode current can then be reduced from MQ to the original value MN by making the grid more negative by 2 V. Hence, making the grid more negative by 2 V has exactly neutralized the effect of making the anode more positive by PN volts, so that the corresponding amplification factor is $PN/2$. In general, $\mu = \Delta V_a/\Delta V_g$ for a given anode current, where ΔV_g is the extra *negative* grid bias required to neutralize the effect of an increase ΔV_a of the anode voltage.

Calculate: (a) *the anode slope resistance,* (b) *the mutual conductance and* (c) *the amplification factor.*

(a) With a grid voltage of $-1\cdot3$ V, a reduction of V_a from 120 to 80 V is accompanied by a reduction of I_a from 10 to $6\cdot2$ mA; i.e. $\Delta V_a=40$ V and $\Delta I_a=3\cdot8$ mA.

$$\therefore \text{ anode slope resistance }=r_a=\frac{40\times1000}{3\cdot8}=10{,}530\ \Omega.$$

(b) With V_a constant at 120 V, I_a is reduced from 10 to 4 mA by increasing the grid voltage from $-1\cdot3$ to $-3\cdot8$ V, i.e. $\Delta I_a=6$ mA and $\Delta V_g=2\cdot5$ V,

$$\therefore \text{ mutual conductance}=g_m=\frac{6}{2\cdot5}=2\cdot4\text{ mA/V}.$$

The mutual conductance could also be expressed as $2\cdot4$ milli-mhos or $0\cdot0024$ mho, but it is more commonly expressed as "milliamperes per volt."

(c) Amplification factor $=\mu=g_m r_a$
$$=\frac{2\cdot4}{1000}\times10{,}530$$
$$=25\cdot3.$$

171. Voltage Amplification by means of a Triode.

In order to obtain any useful effect from a triode, it is

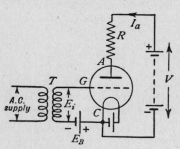

FIG. 253.—A triode with a resistive load.

necessary to insert some form of load, such as a resistance or an inductance, in series with the anode. Consequently, when an alternating voltage is applied to the grid, the variation of anode current is accompanied by a variation of p.d. across the load.

Fig. 253 shows a resistance R connected in series with the anode. Between the cathode and the grid, a battery having an e.m.f. E_B is connected in series with the secondary of a transformer T having a secondary induced e.m.f. E_i. The function of the battery is to give the grid a negative bias; and if E_B is greater than the peak value of E_i, the grid is never positive in relation to the cathode and therefore there is no grid current. Considerable distortion of the output voltage waveform can be caused by grid

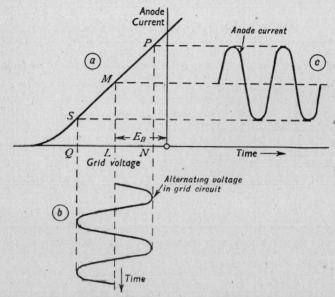

Fig. 254.—Grid voltage and anode current for Fig. 253.

current if there is appreciable resistance in the grid circuit.

Curve (a) in Fig. 254 gives the *dynamic* characteristic of the triode, namely the relationship between the anode current and the grid-cathode voltage for a given anode supply voltage V with resistance R in the anode circuit. When there is no alternating voltage applied to the grid, the anode current is LM in Fig. 254 (a). But with the alternating voltage represented in Fig. 254 (b) applied to the grid, the anode current varies between a minimum of QS and a maximum of NP. By projecting points M, S and P to the right as in Fig. 254 (c), the waveform of the anode current can be derived. It is evident that if portion SP of the dynamic characteristic is a straight line, the waveforms of the anode current and therefore of the p.d. across R are exactly the same as the waveform of the input voltage E_i.

172. Equivalent Circuit of the Triode. It was explained in Art. 170 that if the amplification factor of a valve is, say, 15, then the change of anode current due to a change of 1 V on the grid is exactly the same as that

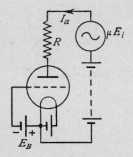

Fig. 255.—Equivalent e.m.f. generated in anode circuit of triode.

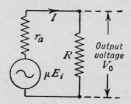

Fig. 256.—Equivalent circuit of a triode.

produced by a change of 15 V on the anode. Hence, in general, if the amplification factor is μ, the variation of anode current due to an alternating voltage E_i applied to the grid is exactly the same as that due to an alternating voltage μE_i generated in the anode circuit, as shown in Fig. 255. Also, since it is the alternating component of the anode current that produces the required alternating output voltage across the load resistance R, we can neglect the direct components of the voltages and current, thereby reducing the equivalent circuit to the very simple form shown in Fig. 256. Hence, as far as the *alternating components* of the voltages and current are concerned, the triode may be regarded as equivalent to an alternator generating an e.m.f. μE_i and having an internal resistance r_a equal to the anode slope resistance of the actual valve.

173. Voltage Amplification. If I be the current in Fig. 256, namely the r.m.s. value of the a.c. component of the actual anode current and if E_i be the r.m.s. value of the alternating voltage applied to the grid, then:

$$I = \frac{\mu E_i}{r_a + R}$$

$\therefore$ output voltage $= V_o = IR = \dfrac{\mu E_i R}{r_a + R}$

and voltage amplification

$$= \frac{\text{alternating component of p.d. across load}}{\text{alternating voltage to grid}}$$

$$= \frac{V_o}{E_i} = \mu \cdot \frac{R}{r_a + R} = \frac{\mu}{1 + r_a/R} \qquad . \qquad . \qquad (243)$$

Thus, if $R = r_a$, voltage amplification $= 0 \cdot 5 \ \mu$, and if $R = 5 r_a$, voltage amplification $= 0 \cdot 83 \ \mu$.

Hence it follows that the higher the value of the load resistance R, the greater is the voltage amplification, but the latter cannot exceed the amplification factor. The disadvantage of a high load resistance is that it necessitates a correspondingly high supply voltage for the anode circuit. The main advantage of the resistive method of loading is that the voltage amplification is independent of the frequency.

174. Resistance-capacitance Coupling of Two Triodes. Fig. 257 shows how the output voltage of triode M can be applied to the grid of a second triode N. The function of capacitor C is to prevent the d.c. component of the p.d. between the anode and cathode of M being applied to the grid of N. A bias battery B_2 is necessary to prevent the grid of N becoming positive and thus prevent any grid current flowing through R_1.

The operation of the circuit may be explained qualitatively thus: With no alternating voltage applied to the grid of M, there is a steady anode current through

M, and C is charged to approximately the anode-cathode p.d. of that valve. When the input alternating voltage E_i is positive, the anode current of M increases. The *increased* p.d. across R is accompanied by the same *decrease* of p.d. between the anode and cathode of M;

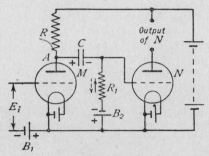

FIG. 257.—Resistance-capacitance coupling of two triodes.

consequently C discharges via M and R_1, as shown by the full arrow, so that the grid end of R_1 becomes negative in relation to the cathode end, and the anode current of N is therefore reduced. When the input voltage E_i is negative, the anode current of M is reduced, the p.d.

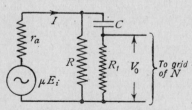

FIG. 258.—Equivalent circuit of Fig. 257.

across R decreases and that between the anode and cathode of M increases. Hence C is charged by a current that flows through R_1 in the direction indicated by the dotted arrow. The grid end of R_1 is now positive in relation to the cathode end and the anode current of N is therefore increased. It will be noticed that the variations of the anode currents of M and N are in anti-phase, i.e. when one increases, the other decreases.

The equivalent circuit of M and its coupling to N is

given in Fig. 258. The resistance of R_1 is of the order of 1 megohm and is normally far greater than that of R, so that the current through C and R_1 is then negligible compared with that through R. Also the reactance of C is usually very small compared with the resistance of R_1; consequently,

output voltage $= V_o =$ p.d. across $R_1 \simeq$ p.d. across R

$$\simeq IR \simeq \frac{\mu E_i R}{r_a + R}$$

$\therefore$ voltage amplification due to triode M $\left.\right\} \simeq \dfrac{\mu}{1 + r_a/R}$,

namely that given by expression (243).

175. Tuned-anode Coupling of Two Triodes. Fig. 259 shows a coil having an inductance L henrys and a

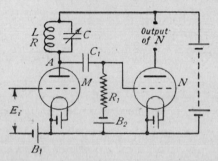

Fig. 259.—Tuned-anode coupling of two triodes.

resistance R ohms connected in parallel with a variable capacitance C. The parallel circuit forms the anode load for triode M. The method of coupling M and N is exactly the same as that shown in Fig. 257. When C is adjusted to resonance, the impedance of the parallel circuit is equivalent to a non-inductive resistance of L/CR ohms (Art. 92). By substituting this value for the load resistance in expression (243), we have:

$$\text{voltage amplification} = \frac{\mu}{1 + CRr_a/L} \qquad (244)$$

At frequencies above and below the resonance value, the impedance of the parallel circuit is much less than L/CR and the voltage amplification is therefore considerably reduced. Hence the advantage of this method is that it gives selective amplification. Its main application is in radio work when it is desired to amplify a voltage having a particular frequency, thereby enabling that voltage to be separated from voltages of other frequencies.

176. Transformer Coupling of two Triodes. A transformer T in Fig. 260 has its primary winding P connected

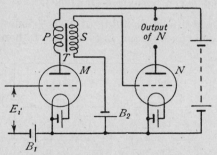

Fig. 260.—Transformer coupling of two triodes.

in the anode circuit of triode M and its secondary S to the grid of triode N, with a battery B_2 to prevent grid current. Since there is therefore no secondary current in S, P behaves as a large inductance. The equivalent circuit of triode M is given in Fig. 261. If L is the inductance in henrys of the primary winding P, its reactance is $2\pi fL$ ohms; and neglecting the resistance of P, we have:

$$I = \frac{\mu E_i}{\sqrt{[r_a^2 + (2\pi fL)^2]}}$$

and   voltage across $P = 2\pi fLI = \dfrac{\mu E_i \times 2\pi fL}{\sqrt{[r_a^2 + (2\pi fL)^2]}}.$

The p.d. across P is practically equal and opposite to the e.m.f. induced in P; and in the case of an iron-cored transformer with well-designed windings, the magnetic leakage is very small, so that the e.m.f. per turn is practically the same for the primary and secondary windings.

Hence, $\left.\begin{array}{c}\text{output} \\ \text{voltage of } T\end{array}\right\} = V_o = $ p.d. across $P \times \dfrac{\text{no. of turns on } S}{\text{no. of turns on } P}$

$$= \frac{\mu E_i \times 2\pi f L}{\sqrt{[r_a^2 + (2\pi f L)^2]}} \cdot \frac{N_s}{N_p}$$

and $\left.\begin{array}{c}\text{voltage} \\ \text{amplification} \\ \text{of triode } M\end{array}\right\} = \dfrac{V_o}{E_i} = \dfrac{\mu}{\sqrt{\left[1 + \left(\dfrac{r_a}{2\pi f L}\right)^2\right]}} \cdot \dfrac{N_s}{N_p} \quad . \quad .(245)$

By making N_s several times greater than N_p, it is possible to obtain a voltage amplification much greater than the amplification factor.

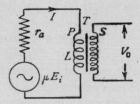

Also, since the resistance of the primary winding P is comparatively small, the supply voltage is only slightly greater than that required between the anode and cathode of the valve.

From expression (245) it is seen that the value of the voltage amplification is dependent upon the frequency and this consti-

FIG. 261.—Equivalent circuit of Fig. 260.

tutes one of the disadvantages of transformer coupling. The method is, however, widely used for audio-frequency amplification.

Example 56. *A certain triode has an amplification factor of 27 and an anode slope resistance of 18,000 Ω. Calculate the voltage amplification when the load is* (a) *a non-reactive resistance of 25,000 Ω and* (b) *a coil having an inductance of 200 μH and a resistance of 30 Ω in parallel with a capacitor which, when adjusted to give resonance, has a capacitance of 150 μμF.*

(a) From expression (243),

$$\text{voltage amplification} = \frac{27}{1 + \dfrac{18,000}{25,000}} = 15 \cdot 7$$

(b) Dynamic impedance of the resonant parallel circuit $\left. \right\} = \dfrac{L}{CR} = \dfrac{200 \times 10^{-6}}{150 \times 10^{-12} \times 30}$

$$= 44{,}400 \ \Omega.$$

$$\therefore \quad \text{voltage amplification} = \frac{27}{1 + \dfrac{18{,}000}{44{,}400}} = 19 \cdot 2$$

Example 57. *A transformer having a primary inductance of* 10 *H is connected in the anode circuit of a triode having an amplification factor of* 15 *and an anode slope resistance of* 4000 Ω. *The secondary is wound with three times as many turns as the primary. Calculate the voltage amplification when the frequency of the input voltage is* (a) 50 *c/s,* (b) 100 *c/s and* (c) 500 *c/s.*

(a) At 50 c/s,

reactance of primary $= 2 \times 3 \cdot 14 \times 50 \times 10 = 3140 \ \Omega$,

$$\therefore \quad \sqrt{\left[1 + \left(\frac{r_a}{2\pi f L}\right)^2\right]} = \sqrt{\left[1 + \left(\frac{4000}{3140}\right)^2\right]} = 1 \cdot 62.$$

From expression (245),

$$\text{voltage amplification} = \frac{15 \times 3}{1 \cdot 62} = 27 \cdot 8.$$

(b) At 100 c/s,

reactance of primary $= 6280 \ \Omega$,

$$\therefore \quad \begin{array}{c}\text{denominator of expression (245)}\end{array}\left. \right\} = \sqrt{\left[1 + \left(\frac{4000}{6280}\right)^2\right]} = 1 \cdot 186$$

and voltage amplification $= \dfrac{15 \times 3}{1 \cdot 186} = 38 \cdot 0.$

(c) At 500 c/s,

reactance of primary $= 31{,}400 \ \Omega$,

$$\therefore \quad \text{voltage amplification} = \frac{15 \times 3}{\sqrt{\left[1 + \left(\dfrac{4000}{31{,}400}\right)^2\right]}} = 44 \cdot 7.$$

It is obvious that for frequencies above 500 c/s the amplification factor will be practically 45, namely the product of the amplification factor and the ratio of the secondary to the primary turns. If the values of the voltage amplification were plotted for the various frequencies, it would be found that the voltage amplification is within 10 per cent of the maximum value of 45 for frequencies above 130 c/s.

177. Gas-filled Triode, or Thyratron.* In Art. 163 it was explained that when the p.d. between the anode and cathode of a gas-filled hot-cathode tube is raised to a certain value (the actual value being dependent upon the gas pressure and the distance between the electrodes), ionization takes place. Let us now consider the effect of introducing a grid between the cathode and the anode, thereby converting the gas-filled diode into a *gas-filled triode* or *thyratron* (*thyra* being the Greek for a door).

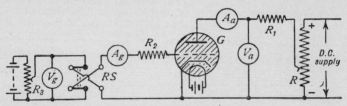

FIG. 262.—Circuit for the determination of the characteristics of a gas-filled triode.

The characteristics of this type of valve can be determined with the aid of the circuit shown in Fig. 262, where G represents a gas-filled triode having an indirectly-heated cathode. There are two important features which distinguish Fig. 262 from the arrangement shown in Fig. 250 for determining the static characteristics of a vacuum triode, namely: (1) a fairly high resistance R_1 (say, 2000 Ω) in series with the anode and (2) a very high resistance R_2 of the order of 0·1 MΩ in series with the grid. The function of these resistances is to limit the currents in the respective circuits to values that will prevent excessive bombardment of the cathode and grid by positive ions.

The procedure is to adjust the reading on V_g to, say, 4 V and then to move the slider on R so as to increase V_a from *zero* up to the value that will start ionization. This

* *Thyratron* was originally a trade name used by the B.T.H. Co.

13

value of the p.d. is termed the *striking voltage*. Immediately ionization commences, the reading on V_a falls to about 16 V, the difference between this voltage and that obtainable from R being absorbed by R_1. The slider on R is then moved backwards; the anode current decreases, but the p.d. between the anode and cathode remains

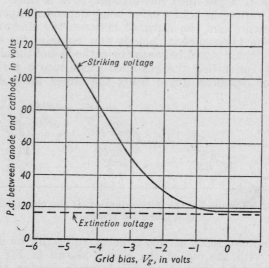

FIG. 263.—Characteristics of a gas-filled triode.

approximately constant and its value at the extinction of the glow is noted.

The test is repeated with different readings on voltmeter V_g and the graphs in Fig. 263 represent the results obtained with a GT1(B) gas-filled triode. It is seen that the larger the negative bias applied to the grid, the greater is the striking voltage. This is due to the fact that the electrons moving outwards from the cathode must reach a certain critical velocity before they can start ionization; and the more negative the grid, the greater is the positive potential that must be applied to the anode to neutralize the retarding effect of the grid upon the movement of these electrons.

The slope of the striking-voltage characteristic is termed the *control ratio*, i.e.

$$\text{control ratio} = \frac{\text{change of anode voltage at which discharge commences}}{\text{corresponding change of grid-bias voltage}}$$

For the thyratron whose characteristic is given in Fig. 263, the control ratio is about 34 for grid bias between −3 and −6 V.

An interesting characteristic of the thyratron is that *once ionization has commenced, the anode current cannot*

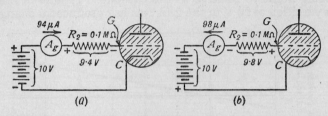

(a)   (b)

FIG. 264.—Effect of grid current on p.d. between grid and cathode.

be controlled by varying the grid voltage V_g (Fig. 262). This is a feature that is at first somewhat difficult to understand; and it was for the purpose of dealing with this problem that a microammeter A_g was inserted in the grid circuit of Fig. 262. By means of the slider on R, let us increase the anode voltage until the gas is ionized and then adjust this slider to give a convenient reading of, say, 50 mA on milliammeter A_a. Let us next adjust the reading on voltmeter V_g to, say, 10 V and then note the readings on microammeter A_g when the positive end of V_g is connected (by means of reversing switch RS) first to the grid and then to the cathode. Suppose these readings to be 94 μA and −98 μA respectively. Also, let us assume that R_2 is 0·1 MΩ.

When the positive side of V_g is connected to the grid, the effect is to attract electrons to the latter and thus produce a grid current, the conventional direction of which is indicated by the arrow in Fig. 264 (a). With

94 μA through 0·1 MΩ, the p.d. across the latter is 9·4 V, the grid end of R_2 being at the lower potential. From Fig. 264 (a), it is evident that the p.d. between G and C is (10—9·4), namely 0·6 V, the grid being positive relative to the cathode.

When the negative side of V_g is connected to the grid, the effect is to attract positive ions to the latter, thereby producing a grid current in the direction shown by the arrow in Fig. 264 (b). The p.d. across R_2 is now 9·8 V, the grid end being at the higher potential. The p.d. between G and C is (9·8—10), namely —0·2 V, the grid being negative relative to the cathode. It follows that a variation of 20 V in the grid bias has produced a change

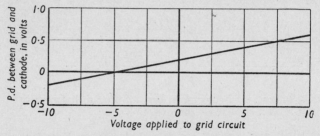

FIG. 265.—Variation of grid-cathode p.d. with grid bias applied to a gas-filled triode.

of only 0·8 V in the p.d. between the grid and the cathode. The graph in Fig. 265 shows the variation of grid-cathode p.d. for various voltages applied to the grid circuit of a GT1(B) gas-filled triode.

From the above explanation it will be seen that the effect of making the grid more positive or more negative is to attract so many electrons or positive ions to the grid that nearly the whole of the additional applied voltage is absorbed in the grid resistance R_2; and the potential of the grid merely changes by the small amount necessary to attract the required number of electrons or positive ions. The current shunted via the grid circuit is negligible compared with the anode current, so that the value of the latter is practically unaffected by a variation of the voltage applied to the grid circuit.

178. Cathode-ray Oscillographs. The cathode-ray oscillograph (usually abbreviated to "C.R.O.") is almost universally employed to reproduce the waveforms of alternating voltages and currents and has very many applications in electrical testing—especially at high frequencies. The cathode-ray tube is also an important component of the television receiver.

Fig. 266 shows the principal features of the modern cathode-ray tube. C represents an indirectly-heated cathode and G is a control grid with a variable negative bias by means of which the electron emission of C can be varied, thereby varying the brilliancy of the spot on the

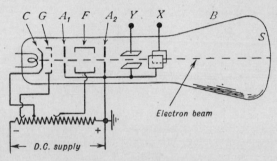

Fig. 266.—A cathode-ray tube.

fluorescent screen S. The anode discs A_1 and A_2 are usually connected together and maintained at a high potential relative to the cathode, so that the electrons passing through G are accelerated very rapidly. Many of these electrons shoot through the small apertures in the discs and their impact on the fluorescent screen S produces a luminous patch on the latter. This patch can be focused into a bright spot by varying the potential of the focusing electrode F, thereby varying the distribution of the electrostatic field in the space between discs A_1 and A_2. Electrode F may consist of a metal cylinder or of two discs with relatively large apertures. The combination of A_1, A_2 and F may be regarded as an *electron lens* and the system of electrodes producing the electron beam is termed an *electron gun*. The glass bulb B is thoroughly evacuated to prevent any ionization.

179. Deflecting Systems of a C.R.O.

(1) *Electrostatic deflection*. The electrons after emerging through the aperture in disc A_2 pass between two pairs of parallel plates, termed the X and Y plates and arranged as indicated in Fig. 267. One plate of each pair is usually connected to anode A_2 and to earth, as in Fig. 266.

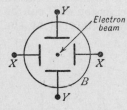

FIG. 267.—Deflecting plates of a C.R.O.

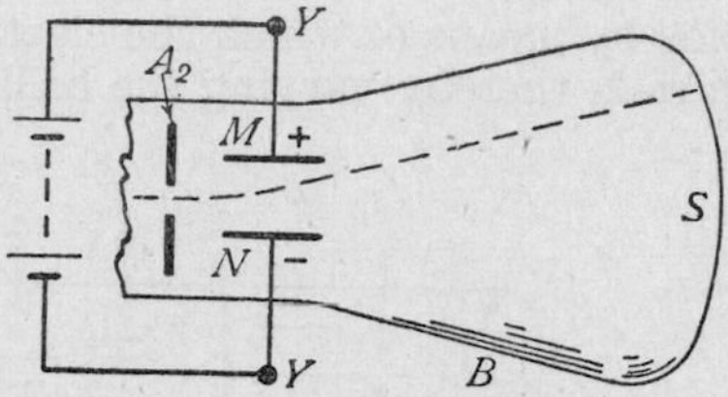

FIG. 268.—Electrostatic deflection of an electron beam.

Suppose a d.c. supply to be connected across the Y-plates, as in Fig. 268, then the electrons, being negative charges of electricity, are attracted towards the positive plate M and the beam is deflected upwards. If an alternating voltage were applied to the Y-plates, the beam would be deflected alternately upwards and downwards and would therefore trace a *vertical* line on the screen. Similarly, an alternating voltage applied to the X-plates would cause the beam to trace a horizontal line.

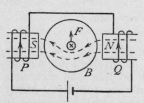

FIG. 269.—Electromagnetic deflection of an electron beam. (C.R.O. viewed from screen end).

(2) *Electromagnetic deflection*. If two coils, P and Q, were arranged outside the tube, with their axis perpendicular to the beam, and if a direct current were passed through the coils in the direction shown in Fig. 269, the beam would be deflected upwards, This is due to the fact that the electron beam behaves

as a flexible conductor and the *conventional* direction of
the current in the beam is from the screen towards the
cathode. Applying either the grip or the corkscrew rule,
we find that the magnetic flux underneath the beam is
strengthened and that above the beam is weakened, so
that the resultant flux is distorted as shown in Fig. 269.
Consequently there is a force F urging the beam upwards. An alternating current through the coils would
give a vertical line on the screen—similar to that obtained
with an alternating voltage on the Y-plates.

180. Time Base for a C.R.O. To enable the waveforms of alternating voltages and currents to be reproduced on the screen of a C.R.O., it is necessary to provide

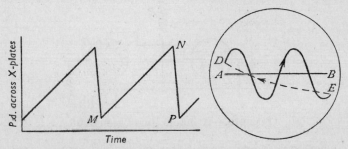

FIG. 270.—P.d. across X-plates   FIG. 271.—A waveform
        to give a time base.   on a C.R.O. screen.

a *time base*, i.e. the p.d. across the X-plates must be
made to increase uniformly from M to N and then
decrease quickly from N to P, as shown in Fig. 270.
In consequence, the spot on the screen travels at a uniform speed from left to right across the screen and then
returns quickly. The effect is to give a horizontal line
AB (Fig. 271). With an alternating voltage applied to
the Y-plates, then during time MN (Fig. 270), the spot
traces a wave such as that represented by the full line
DE; but during the short interval NP, a faint trace may
be seen, as represented by the dotted line ED in Fig. 271.
To obtain a stationary oscillogram on the screen, it is
necessary to introduce some synchronizing arrangement

to ensure that the frequency of the sweep voltage
applied to the X-plates is an exact sub-multiple of the
frequency of the voltage applied to the Y-plates so
that successive traces may be superimposed on one
another.

The circuit arrangement for a synchronized time-base
is too complicated for inclusion in this volume, but it
may be mentioned that all such circuits involve the slow
charging and quick discharging of a capacitor connected
in parallel with the X-plates. For instance, in Fig. 272,
C represents such a capacitor connected in series with a
very high resistance R across a d.c. supply. A gas-filled

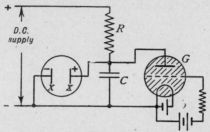

FIG. 272.—A simple time-base circuit.

triode G is also in parallel with C and the striking voltage
of G is set to any desired value by varying its grid bias,
as already explained in Art. 177. As the p.d. across C
and the X-plates increases, the spot on the screen moves
to the right; but when this p.d. reaches the striking
voltage of G (point N in Fig. 270), ionization occurs in G
so that the capacitor is quickly discharged and the p.d.
across the X-plates falls to about 20 V (point P in Fig.
270), thereby causing the spot to return rapidly to the
left. After the capacitor has been discharged, the
ionization in G ceases and the above cycle is repeated.

The sweep frequency depends upon the time constant
(see Art. 58) of circuit RC and can be increased by
reducing the value of either C or R.

The simple time-base arrangement shown in Fig. 272
has the following disadvantages:

(1) the charging current does not remain constant, so that the horizontal speed of the spot is not uniform,

(2) the time required for de-ionization in G renders it unsuitable for frequencies above about 50 kc/s,

(3) no arrangement is provided for synchronizing.

Summary of Important Formulae in Chapter XIII

$$\text{Efficiency of mercury-arc rectifier} \Big\} \simeq \frac{V}{V+20} \qquad (238)$$

$$\text{Amplification factor} = \mu = \frac{\Delta V_a}{\Delta V_g} \qquad (239)$$

$$\text{Mutual conductance} = g_m = \frac{\Delta I_a}{\Delta V_g} \qquad (240)$$

$$\text{Anode slope resistance} = r_a = \frac{\Delta V_a}{\Delta I_a} \qquad (241)$$

$$\mu = g_m r_a \qquad (242)$$

$$\text{Voltage amplification with resistive load} \Big\} = \frac{\mu}{1+r_a/R} \qquad (243)$$

$$\text{Voltage amplification with tuned-anode load} \Big\} = \frac{\mu}{1+CRr_a/L} \qquad (244)$$

$$\text{Voltage amplification with transformer load} \Big\} = \frac{\mu}{\sqrt{\left[1+\left(\dfrac{r_a}{2\pi fL}\right)^2\right]}} \cdot \frac{N_s}{N_p} \qquad (245)$$

EXAMPLES XIII

1. Describe, with the aid of a circuit diagram, how you would obtain the characteristic of a diode valve.

The following results were obtained on a diode. Obtain the anode characteristic resistance (r_a) and state the value of the saturation current.

V_a volts	0	25	40	65	90	120	145	180	210	250	275	300
I_a mA	0	2·8	5·5	9·8	14·5	20	24·5	29	30·7	31·2	31·3	31·3

(U.E.I.)

2. Describe the action of any form of rectifier and explain, with a circuit diagram, how it would be used to charge a 12-V battery from 230-V a.c. mains.

If in a half-wave rectifier the current is sinusoidal during the positive half-cycles and zero during the negative half-cycles, and a hot-wire

13*

ammeter in the circuit reads 7·5 A, what is the charge in ampere-hours given to the battery in 8 hours?   (App. El., L.U.)

3. The characteristic of each of the four elements of a copper-oxide bridge-rectifier is given by the following table:

Voltage	.	.	.	0·1	0·15	0·2	0·24	0·28	0·34	0·38	0·41
Current (mA)	.	.	.	0·2	0·4	1	2	4	8	12	16

This bridge unit is connected in series with a non-inductive resistance of 50 Ω across a 1-V (r.m.s.) a.c. supply. Find the reading on a milli-ammeter connected across appropriate points of the bridge. Neglect the instrument resistance and any reverse current in the rectifiers.

4. The slope of the I_a/V_g characteristic of a triode is 1·3 mA/V and the slope of the I_a/V_a characteristic is 0·2 mA/V. Calculate the amplification factor and the voltage amplification obtained with a load resistance of 8000 Ω.

5. The following readings were obtained with a certain triode:

Grid voltage, in volts .	.	0	−1	−2	−4	−6	−8
Anode current in mA							
with anode voltage 100	.	9·4	6·7	4·2	1·2	0·1	0
„ „ „ 150	.	15·8	13·1	10·5	5·6	2·3	0·6

Plot the characteristics and estimate (a) the mutual conductance, (b) the anode slope resistance and (c) the amplification factor for a grid bias of about −1 V and an anode voltage of about 100 V.

6. The following readings were obtained with a certain triode:

Anode voltage, in volts	.	120	100	80
Anode current in mA				
with grid voltage of 0	.	20·3	15	10
„ „ „ „ −2		12·5	7·5	3

Estimate (a) the anode slope resistance, (b) the amplification factor and (c) the mutual conductance for an anode voltage of 100 and a grid bias of about −1 V.

7. The anode current of a triode was 4 mA with an anode voltage of 130 V and a grid voltage of −2·8 V. When the grid voltage was reduced to −0·4 V, with the anode voltage unaltered, the anode current increased to 8 mA. By reducing the anode voltage to 80 V, with the grid voltage at −0·4 V, the anode current was brought back to 4 mA. Calculate the corresponding values of the anode slope resistance, the mutual conductance and the amplification factor.

8. Give a brief description of the construction of a triode thermionic valve and explain the function of each part. The following readings were obtained on a triode:
Anode voltage, 100

Grid voltage	.	.	−2·0	−1·5	−1·0	−0·5	0	0·5
Anode current (mA)	.		1·5	2·7	4·0	5·6	7·4	9·5

Anode voltage, 150

Grid voltage	.	.	−2·0	−1·5	−1·0	−0·5	0	
Anode current (mA)	.		4·0	5·7	7·6	9·6	11·8	

Plot the curves and deduce (a) the internal impedance; (b) the amplification factor; (c) the mutual conductance for the region in the neighbourhood of zero grid voltage.   (N.C.T.E.C.)

9. Explain with a sketch the construction and action of the control grid in a vacuum triode valve.

The following figures give part of the anode current/anode voltage curves of a vacuum triode:

Anode current (mA)

Anode voltage	Grid bias: 0	−2 V	−4 V
0	0	0	0
25	1·1	0	0
50	3·4	0·4	0
75	7·9	2·2	0·1
100	13·0	6·0	1·1
125	18·1	10·8	3·9
150	—	15·7	8·0

Plot these curves and hence find the anode slope resistance, mutual conductance and amplification factor for the valve when the anode voltage is 110 V and the grid bias is −2 V. (U.L.C.I.)

10. The static characteristics of a triode are as follows:

$$V_g = 0$$

V_a (volts)	.	50	100	150	200
I_a (mA)	.	3·0	6·5	10·1	13·7

$$V_g = -3·0 \text{ V}$$

V_a (volts)	.	150	200	250	300
I_a (mA)	.	1·4	5·0	8·5	12·1

This valve is used as an amplifier, with an anode resistor of 20,000 Ω, and operates on the linear portions of its characteristics. Plot the anode voltage/anode current curves and determine (a) the amplification factor, the mutual conductance and the anode slope resistance of the valve and (b) the voltage amplification.

(App. El., L.U.)

11. Define the terms amplification factor, mutual conductance and anode slope resistance as applied to a triode valve.

In a test on a triode valve, the anode voltage was held constant at 100 V while the grid voltage was varied, with the following results:

$-V_g$ (volts)	.	0	1	2	3	4	5
I_a (milliamperes)	.	3·2	1·84	0·8	0·3	0·1	0

Plot the characteristic and by calculating four or five points, draw the curve relating mutual conductance and grid voltage.

(U.L.C.I.)

12. If a triode has a mutual conductance of 1·4 mA/V and an anode slope resistance of 18,000 Ω, calculate the value of the amplification factor.

If this valve is used with a load resistance of 50,000 Ω, what is the voltage amplification?

13. A non-reactive resistance of 60,000 Ω is connected in the anode circuit of a triode having an amplification factor of 15 and an anode slope resistance of 12,000 Ω. Calculate the r.m.s. value of the a.c. component of the voltage across the load resistance when an alternating voltage of 1·5 V (r.m.s.) is applied to the grid.

14. A non-inductive resistance of 20,000 Ω is connected in the anode circuit of a triode having an amplification factor of 15 and an anode slope resistance of 12,000 Ω. If an alternating voltage having an effective value of 0·5 V is applied to the grid, what is the effective

value of the alternating voltage across the load resistance, assuming the anode voltage and the grid bias to be such as to give distortionless amplification.   Prove any formula used.

Indicate with the aid of a circuit diagram how this voltage may be applied to another triode for further amplification.

(App. El., L.U.)

15. A coil having an inductance of 400 μH and a resistance of 30 Ω is connected in the anode circuit of a triode having an amplification factor of 25 and an anode slope resistance of 20,000 Ω.   A variable capacitance is connected in parallel with the coil.   Calculate the stage gain at resonance frequency if the capacitance is then 320 $\mu\mu$F.

16. The primary of a transformer having a step-up ratio of 1 : 3 is connected in the anode circuit of a triode having an anode slope resistance of 6000 Ω and an amplification factor of 8.   The inductance of the primary is 10 H.   Calculate the voltage amplification for a frequency of (a) 50 c/s and (b) 500 c/s.

17. In a tuned-anode amplifier the coil has an inductance of 300 μH and a resistance of 10 Ω and the capacitor has a capacitance of 400 $\mu\mu$F. Calculate the output voltage at resonant frequency for an input voltage of 0·2 V if the valve has an amplification of 15 and an anode slope resistance of 20,000 Ω.

18. In a two-stage amplifier, the first valve has an amplification factor of 25, an anode slope resistance of 20,000 Ω and a load resistance of 30,000 Ω.   The second valve has an amplification factor of 10 and an anode slope resistance of 6000 Ω.   The load consists of the primary of a transformer having an inductance of 8 H.   If the transformer has a step-up ratio of 1 : 3·5, calculate the secondary voltage of the transformer for an input voltage of 0·1 V to the grid of the first valve for frequencies of (a) 100 c/s and (b) 1000 c/s.   Assume the reactance of the coupling capacitor to be negligible and the value of the coupling resistance to be very high.

CHAPTER XIV

ELECTRIC LAMPS AND ILLUMINATION

181. The Spectrum. Newton discovered that when white light, such as that given by the sun, is passed through a glass prism, a band of light is obtained having colours in the following sequence: red, orange, yellow, green, blue, violet. It is now known that light is a form of electromagnetic radiation having a velocity of 3×10^8 m/sec (or 186,000 miles/sec) and that the various colours have different frequencies ranging from about 4×10^{14} c/s for the extreme visible red end of the spectrum to about $7 \cdot 5 \times 10^{14}$ c/s for the extreme visible violet end.

Since velocity in m/sec $= \begin{cases} \text{wavelength in metres} \\ \quad \times \text{frequency in c/s} \end{cases}$

$\therefore$ wavelength of the extreme visible red end of the spectrum $\left. \right\} = \dfrac{3 \times 10^8}{4 \times 10^{14}} = 0 \cdot 75 \times 10^{-6}$ m

$= 0 \cdot 75$ micron

$= 7500$ Ångstrom units,

where 1 micron $=$ one-millionth of a metre, and 1 Ångstrom unit $= 10^{-10}$ metre and is represented by the symbol Å. Similarly,

wavelength of the extreme visible violet of the spectrum $\left. \right\} = \dfrac{3 \times 10^8}{7 \cdot 5 \times 10^{14}} = 0 \cdot 4 \times 10^{-6}$ m

$= 0 \cdot 4$ micron $= 4000$ Å.

Electromagnetic radiations that are immediately below the red and above the violet ends of the spectrum are termed *infra-red* and *ultra-violet* respectively. In the case of light emitted by incandescent solid bodies, the spectrum is continuous, but the relative intensity of the different colours depends upon the temperature of the body—the higher the temperature, the more pronounced is the violet end of the spectrum compared with the red end. When light is obtained from a gaseous discharge, the spectrum is discontinuous, i.e. it consists of one or more coloured lines. Thus in the case of the sodium lamp, the spectrum consists mainly of two yellow lines very close together with wavelengths of 5890 and 5896 Å. These two wavelengths are so close to each other that the light from a sodium lamp is said to be "monochromatic," namely a light having only one wavelength.

Fig. 273 shows how the sensitivity or the brightness sensation of the average human eye varies at different wavelengths for ordinary levels of illumination, the power radiated as light being assumed constant for the different wavelengths. It will be seen that the eye is most sensitive to light having a wavelength of about 5550 Ångstrom units in the green portion of the spectrum. The ratio of the visual effect of light of a given wavelength to that at a wavelength of 5550 Å is termed the *relative luminous efficiency of radiation*; thus, the relative luminous efficiency of light having a wavelength of either 5100 or 6100 Å is about 0·5.

The most common and useful source of light is the sun, and the graph in Fig. 274 shows the relative values of the power radiated at different wavelengths for an average summer midday sunlight. It will be seen that the maximum power is being radiated at about 5000 Å, which is approximately the wavelength at which the human eye is most sensitive. Fig. 275 gives the relative values of the power radiated from an incandescent filament at different temperatures. These curves show that the lower the temperature the lower is the amount of energy radiated in the visible range and emphasize the necessity of operating incandescent lamps at the highest practicable temperature.

182. Incandescent Electric Lamp. In this type of lamp the filament must be capable of being operated for long periods at a high temperature without appreciable deterioration; and for this duty there are only two

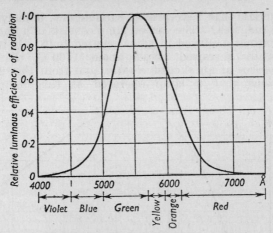

FIG. 273.—Relative luminous efficiency of the human eye.

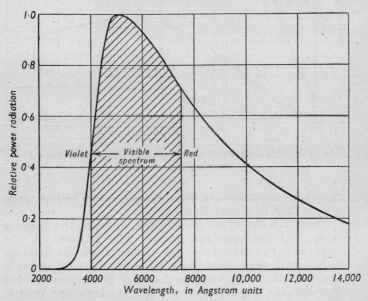

FIG. 274.—Spectral power distribution curve for sunlight.

materials that have proved satisfactory, namely carbon and tungsten. The carbon lamp consists of a fine thread of carbon mounted in an evacuated bulb. If the temperature is raised above about 1700°C, the carbon vaporizes at an excessive rate; and from Fig. 275 it is obvious that a lamp operated at this temperature

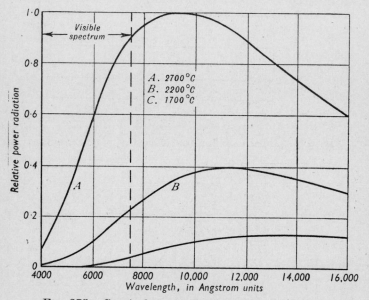

Fig. 275.—Spectral power distribution curves for an incandescent filament.

radiates comparatively little energy in the visible range and is therefore very inefficient.

There are two types of tungsten lamp: (i) the vacuum lamp, (ii) the gas-filled lamp. The purpose of the vacuum is to prevent the loss of heat from the filament to the bulb that takes place by convection when gas is present. But the vacuum has the disadvantage that the filament vaporizes at a lower temperature than it does with the bulb filled with a gas, the effect being very similar to the variation in the boiling point of water with surface pressure.

The vaporization of the filament not only reduces the sectional area of the filament, thereby increasing its resistance and reducing the temperature and the candlepower of the lamp, but it also allows tungsten to condense on the internal surface of the bulb, blackening the latter and reducing the candlepower still further. Consequently the highest temperature at which it is practicable to operate the filament is limited to about 2000°C with a vacuum of about 0·0001 mm of mercury. In the vacuum lamp the filament is usually of the hairpin type, being arranged in a zig-zag manner around a central support. The introduction of an inert gas, e.g.

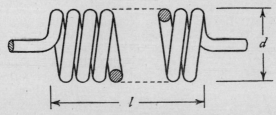

FIG. 276.—Spiralized filament.

nitrogen or argon, enables the filament temperature to be raised to about 2500°C before blackening takes place at an excessive rate. If no other change were made except to introduce a gas, it would be found that the heat lost by convection would be so great that the power required to maintain the filament at 2500°C would have increased more in proportion than the light given out by the lamp. Consequently the efficiency of the gas-filled lamp would be lower than that of the vacuum lamp. This difficulty is overcome by winding the filament as a very close helix, as shown in Fig. 276. Langmuir* discovered that a thin layer of the gas adheres to the filament and that the convection current of gas merely glides over this

* *Transactions of American Institute of Electrical Engineers,* October 1913.

fixed layer. It follows that if the clearance between adjacent turns of the filament is less than the thickness of two of these layers, the latter prevent any gas passing between the turns. Hence the surface with which the gas can come into contact is practically the same as that of a rod of diameter d and length l (Fig. 276); and since this area is far less than the surface area of the filament, the loss of heat by convection is very considerably reduced.

In gas-filled lamps up to 100-W size, the coiled filament is wound into a coarser helix, thereby reducing still further the effective filament surface exposed to the gas. The coiled-coil lamp has an efficiency of about 10 to 20 per cent higher than that of the corresponding lamp with the filament wound as a single helix.

183. Arc Lamps.

An arc lamp consists of two carbon rods, A and C, connected in series with a stabilizing resistance R, as in Fig. 277. The arc is struck by

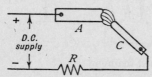

FIG. 277.   An arc lamp.

bringing the electrodes into contact with each other and then drawing them apart. When the electrodes are about to be separated, the area of contact is very small and the resistance of the contact is therefore high. Consequently the heat generated is sufficient to raise the tips of the electrodes to a state of incandescence, thereby enabling the negative electrode C to emit electrons immediately the electrodes are separated (see Art. 163). These electrons are attracted towards anode A and attain sufficiently high velocity to ionize the carbon vapour occupying the gap between the electrodes. The positive ions formed by this ionization travel towards the cathode C and, by their bombardment of the latter, maintain the tip sufficiently hot* to continue emitting electrons.

* The necessity for an incandescent cathode is emphasized because it is possible to have an arc between a cool anode and an incandescent cathode, but not between a cool cathode and an incandescent anode.

The temperature of the crater formed on the positive carbon is about 3500°C, with the result that about 85 per cent of the light emitted by an arc lamp is obtained from the crater. Also the positive carbon tends to be consumed much more rapidly than the negative carbon; consequently the cross-section of the former is made about twice that of the latter, so that the electrodes may be consumed at approximately the same rate.

The p.d. across the arc is usually about 45 to 60 V and the supply voltage is about 70–100 V. Arc lamps are mainly used in cinema projectors and searchlights, where a concentrated source of light is essential.

184. Electric Discharge Lamps. It was pointed out in Art. 163 that ionization in a gas tube is accompanied by a glow, and this phenomenon is utilized in the modern electric discharge lamp, of which there are two main types, namely:

(a) those in which the radiation is produced directly by the discharge, as in the high-pressure mercury-vapour lamp and in the low-pressure sodium-vapour lamp,

(b) those in which the radiation from the discharge excites a fluorescent material, as in the fluorescent mercury-vapour lamp.

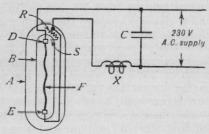

FIG. 278.—High-pressure mercury-vapour lamp.

185. High-pressure Mercury-vapour Lamp. Fig. 278 shows one arrangement of this type of lamp. For simplicity, some of the constructional features, such as the lamp cap, have been omitted. The lamp consists of an outer bulb A and an inner bulb B, the space between the two being partially evacuated. The inner bulb contains a small quantity of mercury and argon. It has three electrodes, namely the main electrodes D and E and a starting electrode S. The latter is connected through a high resistance R of about 50,000 Ω to the main electrode situated at the other end of the tube. The main electrodes consist of electron-emitting cathodes held in tungsten-wire helices.

When the lamp is switched on, the ionization for the first few seconds occurs in the argon between D and S and then in the argon between D and E. As the lamp warms up, the mercury is vaporized so that the pressure inside the lamp increases and the p.d. across electrodes D and E grows from about 20 V up to about 120–140 V, the operation taking about 6 minutes. During this time the colour changes from the red of argon to the greenish-blue of mercury. The final vapour pressure inside the bulb is about 1 atmosphere. If the arc is examined through a dark glass, it appears as a thick flexible cord F, about 5 mm diameter, between the electrodes, as shown in Fig. 278. The function of the choking coil X is to limit the current to a safe value; but since the presence of X produces a lagging power factor, a capacitor C is connected to neutralize this effect. The outer bulb A prevents loss of heat by convection from the inner bulb and assists in keeping the temperature of the latter as uniform as possible at about 500°C.

If a mercury lamp were operated at a low vapour-pressure, a large fraction of the output would be radiated at a wavelength of 2537 Å, which is in the ultra-violet range and is far below the visible range. When the vapour pressure is increased to about 1 atmosphere, much of the ultra-violet energy emitted by the arc is absorbed by the surrounding mercury vapour and is re-radiated at wavelengths that are in the visual range. This effect is evident from a comparison of the two diagrams of Fig. 279, where the vertical lines indicate the wavelengths in the visible band at which radiations are emitted from low-pressure and high-pressure lamps, and the heights of the lines represent the relative values of the powers radiated per watt supplied to the lamp. The main dis-

advantages of the high-pressure mercury-vapour lamp
are: (i) owing to the absence of red lines the light is
greenish-blue and therefore produces colour distortion,
(ii) if the lamp is switched off, it cannot be restarted
immediately.   The vapour pressure is too high to allow
the supply voltage to start ionization, and the lamp must
cool sufficiently for the vapour pressure to fall to the

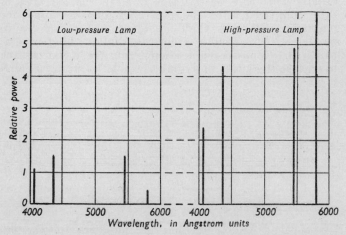

FIG. 279.—Radiation in the visible range from a mercury-
vapour lamp.

value at which ionization between electrodes D and S
can take place.

The average efficiency of a 400-W high-pressure
mercury-vapour lamp is about 36 lumens/W and its
luminance is about 120 candelas/cm².

186. Low-pressure Sodium-vapour Lamp.   One type of
sodium-vapour lamp consists of a U-tube A (Fig. 280)
containing sodium and a small amount of neon.   The
oxide-coated tungsten electrodes are connected to a
step-up auto-transformer T, designed to have a relatively
large leakage reactance.   When this transformer is on
open circuit, its output voltage is about 450 V, and this is

sufficient to initiate a discharge through the neon. This discharge has a reddish colour but changes to yellow as the temperature rises and the sodium is vaporized and ionized.

The efficiency of the lamp decreases rapidly as the current density is increased above a certain value. Consequently, the lamp has to be operated at a low current density and this necessitates a large surface area of tube compared with the power dissipated. Also, for maximum efficiency, the temperature of the tube has to be about 220°C; and in order to maintain this temperature with low power per unit length of tube, it is necessary to enclose the latter in a double-walled vacuum jacket B

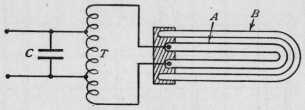

Fig. 280.—A sodium-vapour lamp.

—somewhat similar to that of the domestic vacuum flask. This jacket is in most cases detachable and may be used with a replacement tube.

Hot sodium vapour is very active chemically and therefore the tube has to be made of ply glass, the inner layer being a special sodium-resisting glass and the outer ordinary soda glass. Since the sodium solidifies when the tube cools, it is necessary to ensure that the sodium is deposited reasonably uniformly along the whole of the tube and not concentrated at one end. Consequently, the lamp must be used horizontally.

The average efficiency of the sodium-vapour lamp is about 50 to 65 lumens/W and its luminance is about 8 candelas/cm^2.

187. Fluorescent Mercury-vapour Lamp. One type of fluorescent lamp consists of a long glass tube T (Fig. 281), internally coated with a fluorescent powder. The tube contains a small amount of argon together with a little mercury. At each end of the tube is an electrode E consisting of a spiral of tungsten wire coated with a mixture of barium and strontium oxides. Each electrode is fitted with a nickel strip extension which acts as an anode for withstanding bombardment by the electrons during alternate half-cycles, while the adjacent hot filament acts as a cathode during the other half-cycles. The lamp may be started with the aid of a thermal* switch contained in a hydrogen-filled glass bulb G. One of the strips forming the switch is bimetallic and so arranged that the strips are in contact when the lamp is not in

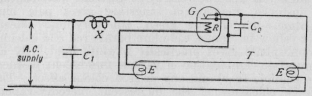

FIG. 281.—A fluorescent mercury-vapour lamp.

operation. Consequently when the lamp is switched on to the a.c. supply, the two electrodes EE are connected together through the thermal switch and a relatively large current flows through these electrodes, raising them to incandescence. This current passes through the tungsten heating-element R, causing the bimetallic strip to bend sufficiently to break the circuit between EE. This sudden reduction of current induces in

---

* An alternative arrangement is the "glow" switch, consisting of two bimetallic strips enclosed in a glass bulb containing helium at a low pressure. The contacts are normally open, but the application of the supply voltage starts a glow discharge between the strips and the heat generated is sufficient to bend the strips until they make contact, thereby closing the circuit between filaments EE. After a few seconds the bimetallic strips will have cooled sufficiently to break contact, and the sudden reduction of current induces an e.m.f. in X large enough to start the discharge between the main electrodes EE. The p.d. between EE is then not sufficient to restart the glow in the switch.

choking coil X an e.m.f. of the order of 750–1000 V, and this surge is sufficient to ionize the argon in the main tube. The heat generated in the tube vaporizes the mercury, the final vapour pressure being about 0·01 mm of mercury and the p.d. across the tube about 100–120 V. The function of C_2 is to suppress radio-interference and its capacitance is about 0·02 μF. Capacitor C_1 is introduced to improve the power factor.

It has already been mentioned that most of the energy radiated from a low-pressure mercury-vapour lamp is in the ultra-violet range of the spectrum. The fluorescent powder absorbs this ultra-violet energy and converts it into visible radiation. Different fluorescent powders re-radiate the absorbed energy at different wavelengths: for instance, magnesium tungstate gives pale blue radiation, zinc silicate green, zinc-beryllium silicate gives yellow to orange, cadmium borate red and calcium halophosphate gives practically a white light. By an appropriate combination of various fluorescent powders it is possible to obtain any desired colour effect. The average efficiency of the fluorescent mercury-vapour lamp (warm-white type) is about 50 lumens/W, and its luminance is about 0·9 candela/cm^2.

Mercury-vapour fluorescent tubes with cold cathodes have also been developed. The electrodes are generally plain nickel or iron cylinders, and it is usual to connect three tubes (each about 9 ft. long) in series across the secondary of a transformer having a relatively large leakage reactance. The secondary terminal voltage is about 3600 V on open circuit and about 1900 V under working conditions; and each tube is rated at 70 W. Since no pre-heating is required, the tubes strike immediately the supply is switched on. Their life is practically unaffected by the number of times the lamps are switched on and off, and they can be dimmed down to almost zero light output.

188. Comparison of the Efficiency of Different Lamps.
The following table gives the approximate values of the luminous efficiency in lumens per watt for different types of lamps. For a given type of lamp, the number of

lumens per watt increases with the size of the lamp; for example, the efficiency of a sodium-vapour lamp increases from about 50 lumens/W for a 45-W lamp to about 65 lumens/W for the 140-W size.

Type of lamp	Lumens/watt (approximately)
Carbon	3
Tungsten, gas-filled (100 W) . . .	12
Mercury, high-pressure (400 W) . .	36
Mercury, low-pressure, fluorescent (80 W) .	50
Sodium, low pressure (140 W) . . .	65

189. Units of Light and Illumination. (a) The standard originally used in photometry was a wax candle, but owing to its unreliability it was replaced by a lamp burning vaporized pentane. The luminous intensity of this lamp was equal to about ten of the original candles. Even this standard was difficult to reproduce accurately, and in 1909 the incandescent filament lamp was adopted as the standard. The candlepower of a number of such lamps was measured by comparison with the pentane lamp and these lamps were then used as standards for determining the candlepower of other lamps. It is very desirable that the primary standard should be capable of being accurately reproduced from a specification; and in 1948 it was decided to base the unit of candlepower upon the luminance (or objective brightness) of a small aperture due to light emitted from a radiator maintained at the temperature of solidification of platinum, namely 1773°C. The construction of this primary standard, as it has been widely used, is shown in Fig. 282. The radiator consists of a tube of fused thoria (thorium oxide), about 45 mm long, with an internal diameter of about 2·5 mm, the bottom of the tube being packed with powdered fused thoria. The tube is supported vertically in pure platinum contained in a fused thoria crucible. The latter has a lid with a small hole in the centre, about 1·5 mm in diameter, and is almost embedded in powdered fused thoria in a larger refractory container having a funnel-shaped opening. The reason for the use of pure fused thoria is that this material is unaffected at the temperature of melting platinum and does not contaminate the latter. The presence of any impurity in the platinum would alter the melting-point temperature and therefore affect the luminance of the aperture.

The platinum is first melted by eddy currents induced in it by a high-frequency current in a coil surrounding the outer container and is then allowed to cool very slowly. While the platinum is changing from the liquid to the solid state, the temperature remains constant

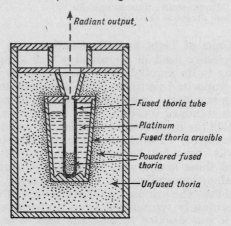

FIG. 282.—Primary standard of light.

sufficently long for measurements to be made of the luminous intensity of the light beam passing through the aperture of known diameter. The luminance of this new primary standard was found to be 58·9 international candles/cm², the international candle being the unit of luminous intensity previously used. In 1948 the International Conference of Weights and Measures decided to adopt 60 units/cm² as the luminance of the platinum primary standard and to refer to the new unit of luminous intensity as the *candela**, so as to avoid confusion with

* Pronounced "candeela," with the accent on the second syllable.

the international candle. *The candela is therefore defined as the unit of luminous intensity of such magnitude that the luminance of a radiator maintained at the temperature of solidification of platinum is 60 candelas/cm².*

The *candlepower* of a lamp is defined as the light-radiating capacity of a source in a given direction in terms of the luminous intensity expressed in candelas.

(b) A *point source* of light is a source which, for photometric purposes, can with sufficient accuracy be considered as concentrated at a point.

(c) A *uniform point source* is a point source emitting light uniformly in all directions.

(d) If a uniform point source of 1 candela is placed at the centre of a perfectly transparent sphere of, say, 1 ft radius (Fig. 283), then the solid angle subtended at the centre by 1 ft² of area on the surface of the sphere is termed a *unit solid angle* or *steradian*; and the quantity of light emitted through a unit solid angle and therefore passing through 1 ft² of the surface area of the sphere is termed a *lumen.*

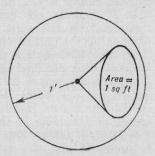

FIG. 283. — Relationship between the candela and the lumen.

(e) The *luminous flux* from a light source is the radiant power evaluated according to its ability to produce visual sensation on the basis of the relative luminous efficiency (Art. 181). The unit of luminous flux is the *lumen*, namely the light flux emitted in unit solid angle by a uniform point source having a luminous intensity of 1 candela. Thus for a uniform point source of 1 candela at the centre of the transparent sphere of 1 ft radius (Fig. 283), the luminous flux passing outwards through each square foot of the surface is 1 lumen. Since the surface area of the sphere is 4π ft², it follows that the total luminous flux from a uniform point source of 1 candela is 4π lumens. Hence, for a point source having a luminous intensity of I candelas

$$\left.\begin{array}{l}\text{total luminous flux emitted}\\ \text{in solid angle } d\omega\end{array}\right\} = dF = I \;.\; d\omega \text{ lumens}$$

or $\hspace{4cm} I = dF/d\omega \text{ candelas,}$

i.e. the luminous intensity of a point source can be defined as the luminous flux per unit solid angle. In the case of an actual lamp, it is usually necessary to estimate the optical centre of the lamp and to regard the light as being emitted from that point.

(f) The *mean spherical candlepower* (m.s.c.p.) of a luminous source is the average value of the candlepower in all directions. Hence if a luminous source has a m.s.c.p. of I candelas, the total luminous flux emitted by that source is $4\pi I$ lumens. It is not correct to say that I candelas are equal to $4\pi I$ lumens, since the "candela" is the unit of "intensity," whereas the "lumen" is the unit of "flux."

(g) The *illumination* at a point of a surface is the luminous flux per unit area of the surface. The unit of illumination adopted in this country is the *lumen per square foot* (the term *foot-candle* is deprecated by the British Standards Institution). With a uniform point source of 1 candela at the centre of a hollow sphere of 1 ft internal radius, the illumination on the surface* is 1 lumen/ft² and the rays of light reach the surface normally, i.e. at right angles.

If the internal radius of the sphere is increased from 1 ft to r ft, the surface area is increased from 4π to $4\pi r^2$ ft². With a point source of 1 candela at the centre,

$$\left.\begin{array}{l}\text{no. of lumens/ft}^2 \text{ on a sphere}\\ \text{of radius } r \text{ feet}\end{array}\right\} = \frac{4\pi}{4\pi r^2} = \frac{1}{r^2}$$

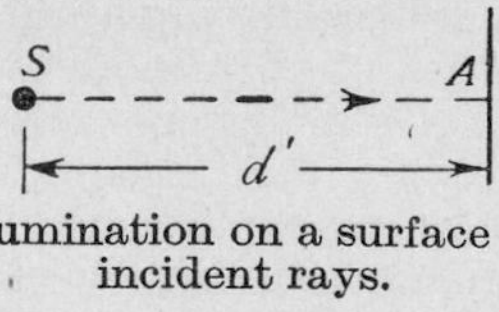

FIG. 284.—Illumination on a surface normal to the incident rays.

* It is assumed that no light is reflected by the internal surface. This condition can be fulfilled by using a blackened surface.

Hence the illumination of a surface is inversely proportional to the square of its distance from the source. It follows that if the candlepower of a source S in direction SA (Fig. 284) is I candelas and if the distance between S and A is d feet, then for a surface at right angles to the incident ray SA,

$$\text{illumination at } A = \frac{I}{d^2} \text{ lumens/ft}^2.$$

An alternative unit of illumination is the *lux*, namely 1 lumen/m^2.

(h) *The cosine law of illumination.*   Suppose that the surface to be illuminated is so placed that the angle between the incident ray and the normal (or perpendicular) to the surface is θ (Fig. 285).   The luminous flux

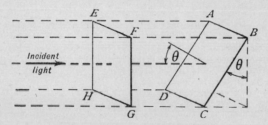

Fig. 285—Cosine law of illumination.

falling on $ABCD$ is exactly the same as that which would fall on a surface $EFGH$, normal to the rays.

But $\dfrac{\text{area of surface } EFGH}{\text{area of surface } ABCD} = \cos \theta$

∴ $\dfrac{\text{illumination on } ABCD}{\text{illumination on } EFGH} = \dfrac{\text{area of } EFGH}{\text{area of } ABCD} = \cos \theta$

so that $\left. \text{illumination on} \atop ABCD \right\} = \dfrac{I}{d^2} \cdot \cos \theta$.   .   (246)

where d is the distance in feet of the surface from a source having a luminous intensity of I candelas in the direction of the surface.

(i) The *mean horizontal candlepower* is the average value of the candlepower of a luminous source in all directions in a plane through the centre of the source and perpendicular to its axis.

(j) The *reduction factor* of a luminous source is the ratio of the mean spherical candlepower to the mean horizontal candlepower.

(k) The *mean hemispherical candlepower* is the average value of the candlepower in all directions within the hemisphere, either above or below the horizontal plane through the centre of the source.

(l) The *luminance** of a source in a given direction is the luminous intensity in that direction per unit of projected area. It is usual to express the luminance either in candelas/cm^2 or candelas/in.^{2} of projected area. Approximate values of the luminance of different sources are given in the following table:

Source	Luminance (in candelas/cm^2)
Zenith sun	160,000
Crater of carbon arc (25 A) . . .	20,000
Tungsten, gas-filled, clear (100 W) . .	650
Tungsten, gas-filled, pearl (100 W) . .	8
Mercury, high pressure, clear (400 W) .	120
Mercury, low-pressure, fluorescent (80 W) .	0·9
Sodium, low-pressure, clear (140 W) .	8
Clear blue sky	0·4

It is extremely important in practice to avoid considerable contrast of brightness in the line of vision of the eye, since this causes glare and an intense eyestrain.

---

* The term "brightness" by itself is ambiguous since it is necessary to distinguish between "objective" and "subjective" brightness. The brightness of a source, as judged by the eye, depends upon a number of factors such as the brightness of the surrounding surface; for instance, a light source appears brighter if the surroundings are dark. Such interpretation of brightness is referred to as *subjective brightness* or *luminosity*. If the brightness of a source is measured photometrically in terms of the candelas per unit of projected area, the value is a definite quantity for a given source and is independent of such factors as the surrounding surfaces. Hence, this interpretation of brightness is referred to as *objective brightness* or *luminance*. Luminosity and luminance are not proportional to each other; for instance, a surface having twice the luminance of another surface may not *look* twice as bright.

From the above table it will be seen that the luminance of a pearl lamp is only about $\frac{1}{80}$th of that of the corresponding lamp with a clear bulb; consequently there is far less risk of discomfort or glare with the former than with the latter. The very low luminance of the fluorescent lamp constitutes one of its main advantages.

190. Illumination on a Surface. Suppose A in Fig. 286 to represent a luminous source suspended h feet above the ground; then:

$$\text{illumination at } B = \frac{\text{candlepower in direction } AB}{h^2}.$$

$$\text{and illumination at } C = \frac{\text{candlepower in direction } AC \times \cos \theta}{AC^2}$$

$$= \frac{(\text{candlepower in direction } AC) \times h}{(h^2 + d^2)^{3/2}}.$$

If the candlepower of the lamp is uniform in the lower hemisphere, then:

illumination at C

$= $ illumination at $B \times \cos^3 \theta$

$$= \frac{\text{illumination at } B}{[1 + (d/h)^2]^{3/2}}$$

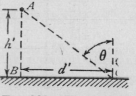

FIG. 286.—Illumination on a surface.

The above relationship is represented graphically in Fig. 287, from which it will be seen that the illumination on the ground falls off very rapidly with increase of distance from the point directly underneath the lamp This effect can be reduced by using a glass fitting or a reflector to distribute most of the light at an angle of about 60° to 75° to the vertical.

By using a number of lamps, suitably spaced, it is possible to obtain fairly even illumination over the working surface. With such an arrangement, the following method may be used to calculate the illumination. Suppose the area of the surface to be illuminated to be A ft² and the average illumination on that surface to be E lumens/ft². The useful luminous flux is therefore

EA lumens. But the lamps must emit a larger number of lumens since some of the light from the lamps is absorbed by the ceiling, the walls and the lamp reflectors (if any). The ratio of the useful number of lumens to the total lumens emitted by the lamps is termed the *coefficient of utilization* or *utilization factor*.

Hence,
$$\left.\begin{array}{l}\text{total lumens}\\\text{from lamps}\end{array}\right\} = \frac{EA}{\text{coefficient of utilization}}.$$

The value of this coefficient depends upon the colour of the walls and ceilings, the room proportions, the height

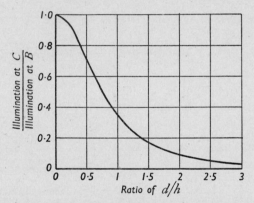

Fig. 287.—Illumination due to a source of uniform c.p.

of the lamp above the working plane and particularly upon the type of lamp fitting. Thus, with open reflectors, the coefficient of utilization lies between 0·3 and 0·6, whereas with pendant fittings giving indirect lighting the light has to be reflected from the ceiling and walls and the coefficient of utilization lies between 0·1 and 0·4.

Finally, it is necessary to allow for the depreciation in the value of the useful luminous flux due partly to the accumulation of dust on the lamp bulb and fitting and partly to the fall in the light output of the lamp during its life.   This effect is taken into account by applying a *depreciation factor* or a *maintenance factor*, where

depreciation factor

$$= \frac{\text{illumination with lamps new and fittings clean}}{\text{illumination under normal conditions}}$$

$=1\cdot2$ to $1\cdot4$, depending upon circumstances

and   maintenance factor $= \dfrac{1}{\text{depreciation factor}}$.

Hence,

$$\left.\begin{array}{c}\text{total lumens from}\\ \text{lamps when new}\end{array}\right\} = \frac{EA \times \text{depreciation factor}}{\text{coefficient of utilization}} \quad (247)$$

$$= \frac{EA}{\left(\begin{array}{c}\text{coefficient of}\\ \text{utilization}\end{array}\right) \times \left(\begin{array}{c}\text{maintenance}\\ \text{factor}\end{array}\right)}.$$

The most suitable number of lamps depends upon the type of lamp fitting used and the height of the lamps above the working plane.   The position of the lamps and their height is to a considerable extent governed by the constructional characteristics of the room to be illuminated.   In general, the spacing between the lamps should not exceed $1\cdot5$ times their height above the working plane.

191. Measurement of Candlepower.   The candlepower of a lamp L (Fig. 288) is determined by comparison with

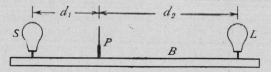

FIG. 288.—Measurement of candlepower.

that of a standard lamp S, the candlepower of which is known.   The lamps are supported on an optical bench B with a photometer-head P so mounted that its position can be varied until its two sides are equally bright.   If

14

the distances of S and L from P are d_1 and d_2 when a balance is obtained,

$$\frac{\text{candlepower of } S}{d_1^2} = \frac{\text{candlepower of } L}{d_2^2}$$

$$\therefore \quad \text{candlepower of } L = \text{candlepower of } S \times \left(\frac{d_2}{d_1}\right)^2.$$

For reasonably accurate comparisons, the Lummer-Brodhun photometer-head is usually employed. This is shown in its simplest form in Fig. 289. A matt-white

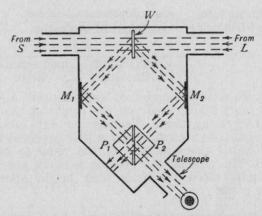

Fig. 289.—The Lummer-Brodhun photometer-head.

screen W has its surfaces illuminated by the two lamps S and L. These surfaces are such as to diffuse the light and some of this light is reflected by mirrors M_1 and M_2 on to a compound prism $P_1 P_2$. The latter consists of two right-angled prisms, but P_1 has the outer portion of its principal surface ground away so that only the flat part at the centre makes optical contact with P_2; and of the light reflected from M_1, only the portion passing through this contact area is seen through the telescope. As to the beam of light reflected by M_2, its central core passes through the contact surface between P_1 and P_2, but the remainder of this beam is totally reflected by P_2.

Consequently the eye sees two zones of light as indicated in the bottom right-hand corner of Fig. 289. The position of the photometer-head is adjusted until these zones appear equally bright.

192. Polar Curves of Light Distribution.   It is often of importance to know the candlepower of a lamp in different directions and particularly the effect of a shade or reflector upon the distribution of candlepower. This effect is most conveniently represented by polar co-ordinates. Thus, curve *A* in Fig. 290 represents the

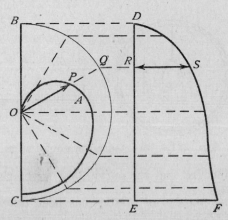

FIG. 290.—A polar curve of light distribution and the corresponding Rousseau diagram.

relationship between the candlepower and the angle made with the vertical axis for a pearl-type lamp used without a shade.

193. Measurement of the Luminous Flux and the M.S.C.P. of a Lamp.   The number of lumens emitted by a lamp and its m.s.c.p. can be determined from the polar curve of light distribution, but not by merely taking the mean value of the polar co-ordinates. The construction usually employed is that known as the *Rousseau diagram* and is shown in Fig. 290. Suppose curve A to represent the polar curve of light distribution for the lamp under consideration. With centre O, a semi-circle of any convenient radius OB is drawn and a number of radii are inserted. From the ends of these radii, horizontal lines are drawn to cut a vertical line DE. These lines are extended to the right of DE to represent to scale the candlepowers in the direction of the respective radii; thus, for radius OQ, RS is made equal to the candlepower OP in direction OQ. The points on the horizontal lines are then joined by a smooth curve DSF. It can be shown* that the average width between the

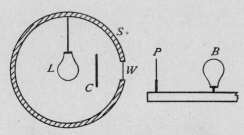

Fig. 291.—An integrating photometer.

vertical line DE and the curve DSF gives the m.s.c.p. of the lamp.

Once the m.s.c.p. of a lamp has been determined as described above, that lamp can then be used as a standard for measuring the m.s.c.p. and the lumen output of other lamps by means of an *integrating photometer*. In its most accurate form the integrating photometer consists of a hollow sphere S (Fig. 291), with matt-white surface on the inside, so that the light from lamp L is thoroughly diffused and the internal surface of the sphere thereby uniformly illuminated. A milk-glass window W is shielded by a screen C from the direct rays of the lamp. Consequently the illumination of W is entirely due to diffused light, and this is proportional to the total luminous flux of the lamp.

* See *Electrical Measurements and Measuring Instruments*, by E. W. Golding.

The relative luminance of the window with different lamps in the sphere can be determined by means of a photometer-head P and a comparison lamp B. Thus, if d_1 is the distance between B and P with a standard lamp of known m.s.c.p. in the sphere, and if d_2 is the distance when the standard lamp is replaced by the lamp the m.s.c.p. of which is required, then assuming the distance between P and W to remain unaltered, we have:

$$\frac{\text{m.s.c.p of new lamp}}{\text{m.s.c.p. of standard lamp}}$$
$$=\frac{\text{luminance of } W \text{ with new lamp}}{\text{luminance of } W \text{ with standard lamp}}=\left(\frac{d_1}{d_2}\right)^2.$$

The number of lumens emitted by the new lamp is 4π times its m.s.c.p.

194. Measurement of Illumination. The type of illumination photometer most commonly employed is

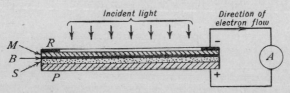

FIG. 292.—Photo-electric illumination photometer.

that which utilizes the barrier-layer photo-electric cell. The latter consists of an iron plate P (Fig. 292), coated with a thin layer S of selenium. This selenium layer is covered with a very thin transparent film M of metal such as gold; and a collecting ring R of metal is sprayed around the edge of the film. Between the selenium S and the film M, there appears to be a "barrier-layer" B (see Art. 166). When light falls on the cell, it passes through the transparent film M and causes electrons to be released from the metallic selenium. These electrons travel across the barrier-layer to the metal film M, from which they are collected by ring R. A microammeter A is connected between R and P; and it is found that with a suitable resistance of the external circuit between R and P, the current through A is practically proportional to the illumination. Hence the microammeter can be calibrated to read the illumination directly in lumens/ft^2.

The sensitivity of the barrier-layer photo-electric cell to light of different wavelengths is not exactly the same as that of the eye, the cell being relatively more sensitive at each end of the visible spectrum. Consequently, if the meter has been calibrated with light from an incandescent tungsten lamp, a correction factor has to be applied when it is used to measure the illumination due to light of a different colour. The necessary correction factors are usually supplied with each illumination photometer.

Summary of Important Relationships in Chapter XIV

1 Ångstrom unit $=10^{-10}$ m $=10^{-4}$ micron.

$$\left.\begin{array}{l}\text{No. of lumens emitted} \\ \text{by a lamp}\end{array}\right\}=4\pi \times\text{m.s.c.p. of lamp.}$$

For a surface having an angle of incidence θ, at distance d feet from a source having luminous intensity of I candelas,

$$\text{illumination}=\frac{I}{d^2} . \cos \theta \text{ lumens/ft}^2 \qquad (246)$$

To produce an average illumination of E lumens/ft^2 on a surface of A ft^2,

$$\left.\begin{array}{l}\text{total lumens from} \\ \text{lamps when new}\end{array}\right\}=\frac{EA \times\text{depreciation factor}}{\text{coefficient of utilization}} \qquad (247)$$

$$\left.\begin{array}{l}\text{where coefficient of} \\ \text{utilization}\end{array}\right\}=\frac{\text{no. of lumens on working plane}}{\text{no. of lumens emitted by lamps}}$$

and depreciation factor

$$=\frac{\text{illumination with new lamps and clean fittings}}{\text{illumination under normal conditions}}$$

$$=\frac{1}{\text{maintenance factor}}.$$

EXAMPLES XIV

1. A metal-filament gas-filled lamp takes 0·42 A from a 230-V supply and emits 1120 lumens.   Calculate (a) the number of lumens per watt, (b) the mean spherical candlepower of the lamp and (c) the m.s.c.p. per watt.

2. Six lamps are used to illuminate a certain room.   If the efficiency of each lamp is 11 lumens/W and the lamps have to emit a total of 10,000 lumens, calculate (a) the m.s.c.p./lamp and (b) the cost of the energy consumed in 4 hours if the charge for electrical energy is 1·3d. per kWh.

3. The effective area of the filament of a certain pearl-type lamp, when viewed from below, was about 3 in.[2], and the luminous intensity in the downward direction was 153 candelas.   Calculate the luminance of the lamp when viewed from that direction.

4. The length of the fluorescent coating of a certain fluorescent lamp is 57·5 in. and the diameter is 1·5 in.   If the candlepower in a radial direction is 340 candelas, what is the luminance of the lamp?

5. Derive the relationship between the mean spherical candlepower of a lamp and the number of lumens emitted.

A lamp having a mean spherical candlepower of 80 has 70 per cent of the light reflected uniformly on to a circular screen 10 ft in diameter. Find the illumination on the screen.   (App. El., L.U.)

6. Describe, with a sketch, the construction of a gas-filled tungsten-filament lamp.   Give reasons why this type of lamp has replaced the carbon-filament lamp for general lighting purposes.

In a test on a photometric bench, a filament lamp was placed at a distance of 50 cm from the photometer head, the corresponding distance of a standard 60-c.p. lamp being 35 cm.   Find the candle-power of the test lamp.   (U.L.C.I.)

7. Explain the terms: "candlepower," "cosine law" and "illumination."

In a photometric bench test, balance is obtained when a standard lamp of 25 c.p. in the horizontal direction is 40 in. and the lamp being tested is 50 in. from the photometer screen.   What is the candlepower of the test lamp?

If the light from the test lamp is reduced by 15 per cent, what will be the respective distances of the lamps from the photometer screen? In this case, the lamps are fixed 100 in. apart, and the photometer screen moves between them.   (U.E.I.)

8. A projector lamp has an output of 1000 lumens and is fitted with a reflector which directs 75 per cent of the light along a beam which has a divergence of 16°.   Calculate the average illumination on a surface placed 60 ft away from and normal to the source of light and also on the same surface when rotated through 60° (tan 8° = 0·1405).

(C. & G., El. Eng. Pract., Int.)

9. Describe a method of measuring the candlepower of a metal-filament lamp in different directions.

A lamp giving 200 c.p. in all directions below the horizontal is suspended 6 ft above the centre of a square table of 3 ft side.   Calculate the maximum and the minimum illumination on the surface of the table.

(U.L.C.I.)

10. Four lamps are suspended 24 ft above the ground at the corners of a square of 10 ft side.   Each lamp gives 250 candle-power uniformly

below the horizontal plane. Calculate the illumination (a) on the ground directly under each lamp, (b) at the centre of the square, and state in what units it is measured.   (U.E.I.)

11. Define the terms: candlepower, lumen, mean spherical candlepower, foot-candle.

Two lamps, each of the same rating and equipped with an industrial-type reflector giving a distribution curve as shown below, are suspended 12 ft apart and 6 ft above a horizontal working plane. Calculate the illumination on this plane (a) at the point A, vertically below one of the lamps, (b) at the point B, 4 ft from A along the line joining A with the point vertically below the other lamp. The polar curve for a lamp and reflector is as follows:

Angle (in degrees measured from horizontal axis)	.	.	.	15	30	45	60	75	90
Candlepower	.	.	.	50	125	240	190	155	140

(App. El., L.U.)

12. Explain the terms "lumen," "luminous intensity," "illumination," and "coefficient of utilization."

Explain how the luminous intensity of a light source may be measured.

A lighting unit which may be considered as a point source gives a total output of 4000 lumens. Determine the direct illumination on a horizontal surface at a point 6 ft below the unit and 4 ft from its vertical axis.   (N.C.T.E.C.)

13. What is meant by the "illumination" on a surface and in what units is it usually expressed?

A lamp giving a uniform luminous intensity of 200 c.p. is suspended 5 ft above a horizontal plane. Calculate the illumination (a) at a point on the plane directly beneath the lamp and (b) at a point on the plane 10 ft away from point (a).   (N.C.T.E.C.)

14. Derive the relationship between the number of lumens emitted by a lamp and the mean spherical candlepower of that lamp.

A 200-c.p. lamp emits light uniformly in all directions and is suspended 15 ft above the centre of a working plane which is 20 ft square. Calculate the illumination immediately below the lamp and also at each corner of the square. If the lamp is fitted with a reflector which distributes 60 per cent of the light emitted uniformly over a circular area 15 ft in diameter, calculate the illumination over this area.

(U.E.I.)

15. The polar curve of a lamp with its reflector is as follows:

Angle with vertical (degrees)	.	.	0	15	30	45	60
Candle-power	.	.	.	300	355	375	250	75

One of these lamps is suspended 10 ft above a horizontal plane. Calculate the illumination on this plane (a) immediately beneath the lamp, (b) 7 ft 6 in from the point immediately beneath the lamp.

(U.L.C.I.)

16. A room measuring 36 ft by 48 ft is to be provided with an illumination of 20 lumens/ft^2 over the horizontal plane using fluorescent tubes each 6 ft long. Each tube gives an output of 3200 lumens, 60 per cent of which is effective over the working plane. If a depreciation factor of 1·3 is to be allowed for, find the number of tubes required and sketch a plan view of a suitable arrangement for them.

(U.L.C.I.)

17. Describe the construction and explain the operation of a direct-reading photometer for measuring the mean spherical candlepower of a 100-W gas-filled lamp.

A room 30 ft by 60 ft is to be illuminated by eight lamps and the average illumination is to be 5 lumens/ft². If the utilization factor is 0·48 and the depreciation factor is 1·2, calculate the mean spherical candlepower per lamp.   (App. El., L.U.)

18. Describe one type of illumination meter suitable for measuring the illumination in a factory.

A factory space of 100 ft by 40 ft is to be illuminated with an average illumination of 8 lumens/ft² by 200-W lamps. If the coefficient of utilization is 0·4 and the depreciation factor is 1·43, calculate the number of lamps required. The lumen output of a 200-W lamp is 2730 lumens.   (E.M.E.U.)

19. Describe an experiment to determine the constants α and β in the relationship c.p. $= \alpha V^\beta$ for a metal-filament lamp.

If for a given lamp the value of β is 4, find the percentage change in the candlepower of the lamp for a change of 2 per cent in the voltage across the lamp.

20. What is the effect of incorrect voltage on the life and efficiency of electric lamps?

Two 110-V lamps, one of 60 W and the other of 75 W, are connected in series on a 220-V supply. Calculate the current taken by and the p.d. across each lamp, neglecting any variation in resistance. Assuming the candlepower to be proportional to the fourth power of the current, calculate the percentage value for each lamp compared with normal operation on a 110-V circuit.   (U.E.I.)

21. A certain lamp gave the following distribution of candlepower in a vertical plane, the angle being measured from the axis through the centre of the lamp cap:

Angle, in

degrees	0	15	30	45	60	90	120	150	165	180
Candlepower	0	84	154	200	224	254	266	276	283	288

Find (a) the mean spherical candlepower and (b) the luminous flux of the lamp.

14*

CHAPTER XV

SYMBOLIC NOTATION

195. The _j_ Operator. In Chapter V, problems on a.c.
circuits were solved with the aid of vector diagrams. So
long as the circuits are fairly simple, this method is satisfactory; but with a more involved circuit, such as that
of Fig. 309, the calculation can be simplified by using
symbolic notation. This system is based upon the idea
that a vector can be resolved into two components at
right angles to each other. For instance, in Fig. 293 (a),

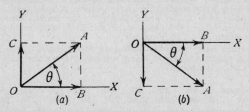

FIG. 293.—Resolution of vectors.

vector OA can be resolved into components OB along the
X axis and OC along the Y axis, where $OB = OA \cos \theta$
and $OC = OA \sin \theta$. It would obviously be incorrect
to state that $OA = OB + OC$, since OA is actually
$\sqrt{(OB^2 + OC^2)}$; but by introducing a symbol j to denote
that OC is the vertical component, we can represent the
vector thus:

$$\mathbf{OA}^* = OB + jOC = OA(\cos \theta + j \sin \theta).$$

The vector OA may alternatively be expressed thus:

$$\mathbf{OA} = OA \angle \theta.$$

* The B.S.I. Specification on Symbols recommends that
heavy-faced (or clarendon) type should be used for vector
notation in printing, but that in manuscript this may be
indicated by a horizontal bar above the symbols.

426

If *OA* is occupying the position shown in Fig. 293 (b), the vertical component is negative, so that

$$\mathbf{OA} = OB - jOC = OA \angle -\theta = OA \diagdown \theta.$$

Fig. 294 represents four vectors occupying different quadrants. These vectors may be represented symbolically thus:

$$\mathbf{A_1} = a_1 + jb_1 = A_1 \angle \theta_1 \qquad . \quad . \quad (248)$$

where $A_1 = \sqrt{(a_1^2 + b_1^2)}$ and $\tan \theta_1 = \dfrac{b_1}{a_1}$.

Similarly $\qquad \mathbf{A_2} = -a_2 + jb_2 = A_2 \angle \theta_2$

$$\mathbf{A_3} = -a_3 - jb_3 = A_3 \diagdown \theta_3$$

and $\qquad \mathbf{A_4} = a_4 - jb_4 = A_4 \diagdown \theta_4.$

The symbol j, when applied to a vector alters its direction by $90°$ in an anti-clockwise direction and is

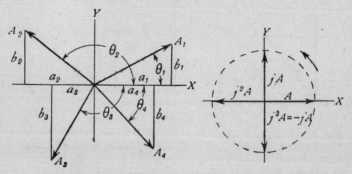

FIG. 294.—Resolution of vectors.

FIG. 295.—Significance of the j operator.

consequently referred to as an *operator*. For example, if we start with a vector A in phase with the X axis, then jA represents a vector of the same length upwards along the Y axis. If we apply the operator j to jA, we turn the vector anti-clockwise through another $90°$, thus giving jjA or j^2A in Fig. 295. The symbol j^2 signifies that we have applied the operator j twice in succession, thereby rotating the vector through $180°$. This reversal of the vector is equivalent to multiplying by -1; i.e. $j^2 A = -A$, so that j^2 may be regarded as being numerically equal to -1.

It is not necessary to trouble about the arithmetical significance of the imaginary quantity $\sqrt{-1}$ when j appears in such expressions as $\mathbf{A} = 3 + j4$. All that we have to realize is that the vector is the resultant of three units measured along the X axis, and four units along the Y axis, as indicated in Fig. 296. It is very misleading to regard 3 as the real component and $j4$ as the imaginary component of A in the above expression; and it is to avoid this erroneous conception that the quantity

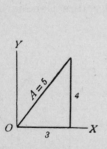

FIG. 296.—Representation of $\mathbf{A} = 3 + j4$.

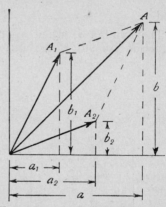

FIG. 297.—Addition of vectors.

along the X axis is termed the x or *in-phase* component (i.e. the component in phase with the axis of reference) and that along the Y axis is termed the y or *quadrature-phase* component or merely the *quadrature* component.

196. Addition and Subtraction of Vectors Symbolically. Suppose A_1 and A_2 in Fig. 297 to be two vectors to be added. From this diagram, it is evident that:

$$\mathbf{A}_1 = a_1 + jb_1 \quad \text{and} \quad \mathbf{A}_2 = a_2 + jb_2.$$

It was shown in Art. 83 that the resultant of A_1 and

A_2 is given by A, the diagonal of the parallelogram drawn on A_1 and A_2. If a and b be the x and y components respectively of A, then $\mathbf{A}=a+jb$.

But it is evident from Fig. 297 that:

$$a=a_1+a_2 \quad \text{and} \quad b=b_1+b_2$$

$$\therefore \quad \mathbf{A}=a_1+a_2+j(b_1+b_2)$$
$$=(a_1+jb_1)+(a_2+jb_2)$$
$$=\mathbf{A}_1+\mathbf{A}_2.$$

Fig. 298 shows the construction for subtracting A_2

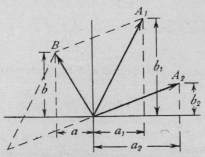

FIG. 298.—Subtraction of vectors.

vectorially from A_1. If B is the vectorial difference of these quantities and if a_1 is assumed less than a_2, then the x component of B is negative,

$$\therefore \quad \mathbf{B}=-a+jb=a_1-a_2+j(b_1-b_2)$$
$$=(a_1+jb_1)-(a_2+jb_2)=\mathbf{A}_1-\mathbf{A}_2.$$

197. Symbolic Expression for an Impedance. Let us first consider a simple circuit consisting of a resistance R in *series* with an inductive reactance X_L. The vector diagram is given in Fig. 299, where I is drawn along the X axis and is therefore the reference vector, i.e. $\mathbf{I}=I+j0$ It is evident that:

$$\mathbf{V}=\mathbf{I}R+j\mathbf{I}X_L=\mathbf{I}(R+jX_L)=\mathbf{I}\mathbf{Z}=\mathbf{I}Z\angle\phi$$
where $\mathbf{Z}=R+jX_L=Z\angle\phi$ and $\tan\phi=X_L/R$ (249)

430 FUNDAMENTALS OF ELECTRICAL ENGINEERING

Fig. 300 gives the vector diagram for a circuit having a resistance R in series with a capacitive reactance X_C. From this diagram:

$$\mathbf{V}=\mathbf{I}R-j\mathbf{I}X_C=\mathbf{I}(R-jX_C)=\mathbf{I}\mathbf{Z}=\mathbf{I}Z\diagdown\phi$$

where $\mathbf{Z}=R-jX_C=Z\diagdown\phi$ and $\tan\phi=-X_C/R$ (250)

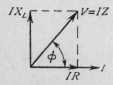

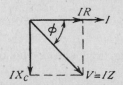

FIG. 299.—Vector diagram for R and L in series.

FIG. 300.—Vector diagram for R and C in series.

Hence for the general case of a circuit having R, X_L and X_C in series,

$$\mathbf{Z}=R+j(X_L-X_C)   \text{and}   \tan\phi=(X_L-X_C)/R$$

Example 58. *State, in symbolic notation, the impedances of each of the following circuits at a frequency of 50 c/s:*

(a) *A resistance of 20 Ω in series with an inductance of 0·1 H.*

(b) *A resistance of 50 Ω in series with a capacitance of 40 μF.*

(c) *Circuits (a) and (b) in series.*

If the terminal voltage is 230 V, find the value of the current in each case and the phase of each current relative to the applied voltage.

(a) For 50 c/s, $\omega=2\pi\times50=314$ radians/second

$\therefore$ $\mathbf{Z}=20+j314\times0\cdot1=20+j31\cdot4$ Ω

Hence $Z=\sqrt{[(20)^2+(31\cdot4)^2]}=37\cdot2$ Ω

and $I=\dfrac{230}{37\cdot2}=6\cdot18$ A.

If ϕ be the phase difference between the applied voltage and the current,

$$\tan\phi=31\cdot4/20=1\cdot57,$$

$\therefore$ $\phi=57°$ 30', current lagging.

The impedance can also be expressed:

$$\mathbf{Z} = 37 \cdot 2 \angle 57° \ 30'^* \ \Omega.$$

If the applied voltage be taken as the reference quantity, then

$$\mathbf{V} = 230 \angle 0°,$$

$$\therefore \qquad \mathbf{I} = \frac{230 \angle 0°}{37 \cdot 2 \angle 57° 30'} = 6 \cdot 18 \diagdown 57° \ 30' \ \mathrm{A}.$$

(b) $\qquad \mathbf{Z} = 50 - j\dfrac{10^6}{314 \times 40} = 50 - j79 \cdot 6 \ \Omega$

$$\therefore \qquad Z = \sqrt{[(50)^2 + (79 \cdot 6)^2]} = 94 \ \Omega,$$

and $\qquad I = \dfrac{230}{94} = 2 \cdot 447 \ \mathrm{A}.$

Tan $\phi = -79 \cdot 6 / 50 = -1 \cdot 592,$

$$\therefore \qquad \phi = 57° \ 52', \quad \text{current leading.}$$

The impedance can also be expressed thus:

$$\mathbf{Z} = 94 \angle -57° \ 52' = 94 \diagdown 57° \ 52' \ \Omega.$$

$$\therefore \qquad \mathbf{I} = \frac{230 \angle 0°}{94 \diagdown 57° 52'} = 2 \cdot 447 \angle 57° \ 52' \ \mathrm{A}.$$

(c) $\qquad \mathbf{Z} = 20 + j31 \cdot 4 + 50 - j79 \cdot 6$

$$= 70 - j48 \cdot 2 \ \Omega.$$

$$\therefore \qquad Z = \sqrt{[(70)^2 + (48 \cdot 2)^2]} = 85 \ \Omega,$$

and $\qquad I = \dfrac{230}{85} = 2 \cdot 706 \ \mathrm{A}.$

Tan $\phi = -48 \cdot 2 / 70 = -0 \cdot 689,$

$$\therefore \qquad \phi = 34° \ 34', \quad \text{current leading.}$$

The impedance can also be expressed:

$$\mathbf{Z} = 85 \diagdown 34° \ 34' \ \Omega$$

so that $\qquad \mathbf{I} = \dfrac{230 \angle 0°}{85 \diagdown 34° 34'} = 2 \cdot 706 \angle 34° \ 34' \ \mathrm{A}.$

---

* This form is more convenient than that involving the j term when it is required to find the product or the quotient of two complex numbers; thus, $A \angle \alpha \times B \angle \beta = AB \angle (\alpha + \beta)$ and $A \angle \alpha / B \angle \beta = A / B \angle (\alpha - \beta).$

Example 59. *Calculate the resistance and the inductance (or capacitance) in series for each of the following impedances:* (a) $10+j15$, (b) $-j80$, (c) $50\angle 30°$ and (d) $120\diagdown 60°$ Ω. *Assume the frequency to be 50 c/s.*

(a) For $\mathbf{Z}=10+j15$ Ω, resistance $=10$ Ω,

and inductive reactance $=15$ Ω,

$\therefore$ inductance $=15/314=0\cdot 0478$ H.

(b) For $\mathbf{Z}=-j80$ Ω, resistance $=0$,

and capacitive reactance $=80$ Ω,

$\therefore$ capacitance $=\dfrac{1}{314\times 80}$ F $=39\cdot 8$ μF.

(c) Fig. 301 (a) is an impedance triangle representing

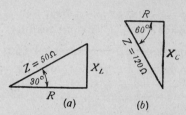

FIG. 301.—Impedance triangles for Example 59 (c) and (d).

$50\angle 30°$ Ω. From this diagram, it follows that the reactance is inductive and that $R=Z\cos\phi$ and $X_L=Z\sin\phi$,

$\therefore$ $\mathbf{Z}=R+jX_L=Z$ $(\cos\phi+j\sin\phi)$

$=50$ $(\cos 30°+j\sin 30°)=43\cdot 3+j25$ Ω.

Hence, resistance $=43\cdot 3$ Ω

and inductive reactance $=25$ Ω,

so that inductance $=25/314=0\cdot 0796$ H.

(d) Fig. 301 (b) is an impedance triangle representing $120\diagdown 60°$ Ω. It will be seen that the reactance is capacitive, so that

$\mathbf{Z}=R-jX_C=Z(\cos\phi-j\sin\phi)$

$=120(\cos 60°-j\sin 60°)=60-j103\cdot 9$ Ω.

Hence,   resistance $=60$ Ω

and   capacitive reactance $=103 \cdot 9$ Ω

$$\therefore \qquad \text{capacitance} = \frac{10^6}{314 \times 103 \cdot 9} = 30 \cdot 7 \ \mu\text{F}.$$

198. Admittance, Conductance and Susceptance. In Art. 24 of *Principles of Electricity*, it was shown that for resistances R_1, R_2, etc., in parallel, the equivalent resistance R is given by:

$$\frac{1}{R} = \frac{1}{R_1} + \frac{1}{R_2} + \cdots$$

In d.c. work the reciprocal of the resistance is known as *conductance*. It is represented by symbol G and the unit of conductance is the *mho*. Hence, if conductances G_1, G_2, etc., are connected in parallel, the total conductance G is given by:

$$G = G_1 + G_2 + \cdots$$

In a.c. work the conductance is the reciprocal of the resistance *only when the circuit possesses no reactance*. This matter is dealt with more fully in Art. 199.

If impedances Z_1, Z_2, etc., are connected in parallel across a supply voltage V, then:

$$I_1 = \frac{V}{Z_1}, \ I_2 = \frac{V}{Z_2}, \ \text{etc.}$$

If Z be the equivalent impedance of Z_1, Z_2, etc., in parallel and if I be the resultant current, then, using symbolic notation,

$$\mathbf{I} = \mathbf{I_1} + \mathbf{I_2} + \cdots$$

$$\therefore \qquad \frac{\mathbf{V}}{\mathbf{Z}} = \frac{\mathbf{V}}{\mathbf{Z_1}} + \frac{\mathbf{V}}{\mathbf{Z_2}} + \cdots$$

so that $\qquad \dfrac{1}{\mathbf{Z}} = \dfrac{1}{\mathbf{Z_1}} + \dfrac{1}{\mathbf{Z_2}} + \cdots \qquad . \quad . \quad . \quad (251)$

The reciprocal of the impedance is termed *admittance* and is represented by the symbol Y, the unit being again the *mho*. Hence, we may write expression (251) thus:

$$\mathbf{Y} = \mathbf{Y_1} + \mathbf{Y_2} + \cdots \qquad . \quad . \quad . \quad (252)$$

It has already been shown that an impedance can be resolved into an in-phase resistance component R and a quadrature reactance component X, as in Fig. 302 (a). Similarly, an admittance may be resolved into an in-phase component termed *conductance* and a quadrature component termed *susceptance*, represented by symbols G and B respectively as in Fig. 302 (b),

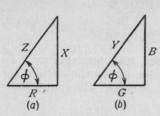

FIG. 302.—Impedance and admittance triangles.

i.e. $$\mathbf{Y} = G + jB \quad \text{and} \quad \tan \phi = B/G.$$

The significance of these terms will be more obvious when we consider their application to actual circuits.

199. Admittance of a Circuit having Resistance and Inductive Reactance in Series. The vector diagram for this circuit has already been given in Fig. 299. From the latter it will be seen that the resultant voltage can be represented symbolically thus:

$$\mathbf{V} = \mathbf{I}R + j\mathbf{I}X_L$$

$$\therefore \qquad \mathbf{Z} = \frac{\mathbf{V}}{\mathbf{I}} = R + jX_L$$

If Y be the admittance of the circuit, then:

$$\mathbf{Y} = \frac{1}{\mathbf{Z}} = \frac{1}{R + jX_L} = \frac{R - jX_L}{R^2 + X_L^2} \, ^*$$

$$= \frac{R}{R^2 + X_L^2} - \frac{jX_L}{R^2 + X_L^2} = G - jB_L \quad . \quad (253)$$

where $$G = \text{conductance} = \frac{R}{R^2 + X_L^2} = \frac{R}{Z^2} \quad . \quad (254)$$

---

* This method of transferring the j term from the denominator to the numerator is known as "rationalizing"; thus,

$$\frac{1}{a + jb} = \frac{a - jb}{(a + jb)(a - jb)} = \frac{a - jb}{a^2 + b^2} \quad . \quad . \quad (256)$$

and $\qquad B_L=$inductive susceptance

$$=\frac{X_L}{R^2+X_L^2}=\frac{X_L}{Z^2} \quad . \quad . \quad . \quad . \quad (255)$$

From (254) it is evident that if the circuit has no reactance, i.e. if $X_L=0$, then the conductance is $1/R$, namely the reciprocal of the resistance. Similarly, from (255) it follows that if the circuit has no resistance, i.e. if $R=0$, the susceptance is $1/X_L$, namely the reciprocal of the reactance. In general, we may define the *conductance* of a *series* circuit as the ratio of the resistance to the square of the impedance and the *susceptance* as the ratio of the reactance to the square of the impedance.

200. Admittance of a Circuit having Resistance and Capacitive Reactance in Series. Fig. 300 gives the vector diagram for this circuit. From this diagram it follows that:

$$\mathbf{V}=\mathbf{I}R-j\mathbf{I}X_C$$

$\therefore \qquad \mathbf{Z}=\dfrac{\mathbf{V}}{\mathbf{I}}=R-jX_C$

and $\qquad \mathbf{Y}=\dfrac{1}{R-jX_C}=\dfrac{R+jX_C}{R^2+X_C^2}$

$$=\frac{R}{R^2+X_C^2}+\frac{jX_C}{R^2+X_C^2}=G+jB_C \quad . \quad (257)$$

where $\qquad B_C=$capacitive susceptance

$$=\frac{X_C}{R^2+X_C^2} \quad . \quad . \quad . \quad . \quad . \quad (258)$$

It will be seen that in the symbolic expression for an *inductive* circuit, the *impedance* has a *positive* sign in front of the quadrature component, whereas the quadrature component of the *admittance* is preceded by a negative sign. On the other hand, for a *capacitive* circuit, the quadrature component of the *impedance* has a *negative* sign and that of the *admittance* has a *positive* sign. Thus if the impedance of a circuit is represented by $(2-j3)$ Ω, we know immediately that the circuit is capacitive; but if the admittance is $(2-j3)$ mhos, the circuit must be inductive.

201. Admittance of a Circuit having Resistance and Reactance in Parallel. (a) *Inductive reactance.* From

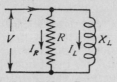

FIG. 303.—*R* and *L* in parallel.

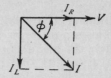

FIG. 304.—Vector diagram for Fig. 303.

the circuit and vector diagrams of Fig. 303 and 304 respectively, it follows that:

$$\mathbf{I} = I_R - jI_L = \frac{\mathbf{V}}{R} - \frac{j\mathbf{V}}{X_L}$$

$$\therefore \qquad \mathbf{Y} = \frac{\mathbf{I}}{\mathbf{V}} = \frac{1}{R} - \frac{j}{X_L} = G - jB_L \quad . \quad . \quad (259)$$

(b) *Capacitive circuit.* From Fig. 305 and 306, it follows that:

$$\mathbf{I} = I_R + jI_C = \frac{\mathbf{V}}{R} + \frac{j\mathbf{V}}{X_C}$$

$$\therefore \qquad \mathbf{Y} = \frac{\mathbf{I}}{\mathbf{V}} = \frac{1}{R} + \frac{j}{X_C} = G + jB_C \quad . \quad . \quad (260)$$

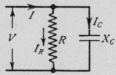

FIG. 305.—*R* and *C* in parallel.

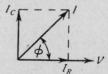

FIG. 306.—Vector diagram for Fig. 305.

From (259) and (260), it will be seen that if the admittance of a circuit is expressed as $(0 \cdot 2 - j0 \cdot 1)$ mho, such a circuit can be represented as a resistance of 5 Ω in *parallel* with an inductive reactance of 10 Ω; whereas if the impedance of a circuit is $(5 + j10)$ Ω, such a circuit can be represented as a resistance of 5 Ω in *series* with an inductive reactance of 10 Ω.

Example 60. *Find the symbolic expressions for the admittance of circuits having the following impedances:* (a) $(4+j6)$, (b) $20\diagdown 30°$ Ω.

(a) $\mathbf{Z}=4+j6$ Ω,

$\therefore$ $\mathbf{Y}=\dfrac{1}{4+j6}=\dfrac{4-j6}{16+36}=0\cdot0769-j0\cdot1154$ mho.

(b) $\mathbf{Z}=20\diagdown 30°=20(\cos 30°-j\sin 30°)$

$=20(0\cdot866-j0\cdot5)=17\cdot32-j10$ Ω,

$\therefore$ $\mathbf{Y}=\dfrac{1}{17\cdot32-j10}=\dfrac{17\cdot32+j10}{400}$

$=0\cdot0433+j0\cdot025$ mho.

Alternatively, $\mathbf{Y}=\dfrac{1}{20\diagdown 30°}=0\cdot05\angle 30°$

$=0\cdot0433+j0\cdot025$ mho.

Example 61. *The admittance of a circuit is* $(0\cdot05-j0\cdot08)$ *mho. Find the values of the resistance and the inductive reactance of the circuit if they are* (a) *in parallel,* (b) *in series.*

(a) The conductance of the circuit is $0\cdot05$ mho and its inductive susceptance is $0\cdot08$ mho. From (259) it follows that if the circuit consists of a resistance in parallel with an inductive reactance, then:

$$\text{resistance}=\frac{1}{\text{conductance}}=\frac{1}{0\cdot05}=20 \ \Omega,$$

and inductive reactance

$$=\frac{1}{\text{inductive susceptance}}=\frac{1}{0\cdot08}=12\cdot5 \ \Omega.$$

(b) Since $\mathbf{Y}=0\cdot05-j0\cdot08$ mho,

$\therefore$ $\mathbf{Z}=\dfrac{1}{0\cdot05-j0\cdot08}=\dfrac{0\cdot05+j0\cdot08}{0\cdot0089}=5\cdot62+j8\cdot99 \ \Omega.$

Hence if the circuit consists of a resistance in series with an inductance, the resistance is $5\cdot62$ Ω and the inductive reactance is $8 \cdot 99 \, \Omega$. The two circuit diagrams are shown in Fig. 307 (a) and (b), and their vector diagrams are given in Fig. 308 (a) and (b) respectively. The two circuits are equivalent in that they take the same current I for a given supply voltage V, and the phase

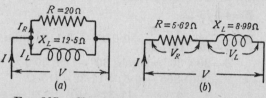

FIG. 307.—Circuit diagrams for Example 61.

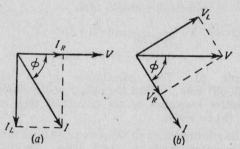

FIG. 308.—Vector diagrams for Example 61.

difference ϕ between the supply voltage and the current is the same in the two cases.

Example 62. *A circuit is arranged as indicated in Fig. 309, the values being as shown. Calculate the value of the current in each branch and its phase relative to the supply voltage. Draw the complete vector diagram.*

$$\mathbf{Z}_A = 20 + j0 \; \Omega,$$

$$\therefore \quad \mathbf{Y}_A = \frac{1}{20} = 0 \cdot 05 \text{ mho.}$$

$$\mathbf{Z}_B = 5 + j314 \times 0 \cdot 1 = 5 + j31 \cdot 4 \; \Omega,$$

$$\therefore \quad \mathbf{Y}_B = \frac{1}{5 + j31 \cdot 4} = \frac{5 - j31 \cdot 4}{1010} = 0 \cdot 00495 - j0 \cdot 0311 \text{ mho.}$$

If Y_{AB} be the combined admittance of circuits A and B,

$$\mathbf{Y}_{AB} = 0 \cdot 05 + 0 \cdot 00495 - j0 \cdot 0311$$
$$= 0 \cdot 05495 - j0 \cdot 0311 \text{ mho.}$$

If Z_{AB} be the equivalent impedance of circuits A and B,

$$\mathbf{Z}_{AB} = \frac{1}{0 \cdot 05495 - j0 \cdot 0311} = \frac{0 \cdot 05495 + j0 \cdot 0311}{0 \cdot 003987}$$
$$= 13 \cdot 78 + j7 \cdot 8 \ \Omega.$$

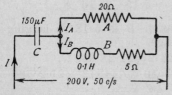

FIG. 309.—Circuit diagram for Example 62.

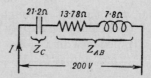

FIG. 310.—Equivalent circuit of Fig. 309.

Hence the circuit of Fig. 309 can be replaced by that shown in Fig. 310.

$$\mathbf{Z}_C = -j\frac{10^6}{314 \times 150} = -j21 \cdot 2 \ \Omega,$$

∴ total impedance $= \mathbf{Z}$

$$= 13 \cdot 78 + j7 \cdot 8 - j21 \cdot 2 = 13 \cdot 78 - j13 \cdot 4$$
$$= \sqrt{[(13 \cdot 78)^2 + (13 \cdot 4)^2]} \angle \tan^{-1} -13 \cdot 4/13 \cdot 78$$
$$= 19 \cdot 22 \diagdown 44° \ 12' \ \Omega.$$

If the supply voltage $= \mathbf{V} = 200 \angle 0°$ volts,

∴ supply current $= \mathbf{I} = \dfrac{200 \angle 0°}{19 \cdot 22 \diagdown 44° \ 12'} = 10 \cdot 4 \angle 44° \ 12' \ \text{A,}$

i.e. the supply current is $10 \cdot 4$ A leading $44° \ 12'$ in front of the *supply* voltage.

The p.d. across circuit $AB = \mathbf{V}_{AB} = \mathbf{I}\mathbf{Z}_{AB}$.

But $\mathbf{Z}_{AB} = 13 \cdot 78 + j7 \cdot 8$

$$= \sqrt{[(13 \cdot 78)^2 + (7 \cdot 8)^2]} \angle \tan^{-1} 7 \cdot 8/13 \cdot 78$$
$$= 15 \cdot 85 \angle 29° \ 30' \ \Omega,$$

$$\therefore \quad \mathbf{V}_{AB} = 10 \cdot 4 \angle 44° \ 12' \times 15 \cdot 85 \angle 29° \ 30'$$
$$= 164 \cdot 8 \angle 73° \ 42' \ \text{V}.$$

Since $\mathbf{Z}_A = 20 + j0 = 20 \angle 0° \ \Omega,$

$$\therefore \quad \mathbf{I}_A = \frac{164 \cdot 8 \angle 73° \ 42'}{20 \angle 0°} = 8 \cdot 24 \angle 73° \ 42' \ \text{A},$$

i.e. the current through branch A is $8 \cdot 24$ A leading $73° \ 42'$ in front of the *supply* voltage.

Similarly $\mathbf{Z}_B = 5 + j31 \cdot 4 = 31 \cdot 8 \angle 80° \ 58' \ \Omega,$

$$\therefore \quad \mathbf{I}_B = \frac{164 \cdot 8 \angle 73° \ 42'}{31 \cdot 8 \angle 80° \ 58'} = 5 \cdot 18 \diagdown 7° \ 16' \ \text{A},$$

i.e. the current through branch B is $5 \cdot 18$ A lagging $7° \ 16'$ behind the *supply* voltage.

Impedance of $C = \mathbf{Z}_C = -j21 \cdot 2 = 21 \cdot 2 \diagdown 90° \ \Omega,$

$\therefore$ p.d. across $C = \mathbf{V}_C = \mathbf{I}\mathbf{Z}_C = 10 \cdot 4 \angle 44° \ 12' \times 21 \cdot 2 \diagdown 90°$
$$= 220 \diagdown 45° \ 48' \ \text{V}.$$

The various voltages and currents of this example are shown vectorially in Fig. 311.

202. Calculation of Power, using Symbolic Notation.

Suppose the alternating voltage across and the current in a circuit to be represented respectively by:

$$\mathbf{V} = V \angle \alpha = V(\cos \alpha + j \sin \alpha) = a + jb \quad (261)$$
and
$$\mathbf{I} = I \angle \beta = I(\cos \beta + j \sin \beta) = c + jd \ . \quad (262)$$

Since the phase difference between the voltage and current is $(\alpha - \beta)$,

$$\begin{aligned} \text{power} &= VI \cos (\alpha - \beta) \\ &= VI (\cos \alpha \, . \, \cos \beta + \sin \alpha \, . \, \sin \beta) \\ &= ac + bd \ . \quad\quad\quad\quad\quad\quad (263) \end{aligned}$$

i.e. the power is given by the sum of the products of the in-phase components and of the quadrature-phase components.

$$\left. \begin{aligned} \text{Reactive volt-} \\ \text{amperes} \end{aligned} \right\} = VI \sin (\alpha - \beta)$$
$$= VI (\sin \alpha \, . \, \cos \beta - \cos \alpha \, . \, \sin \beta)$$
$$= bc - ad \ . \quad\quad\quad\quad\quad (264)$$
$$= (\text{quadrature-phase voltage} \times \text{in-phase current})$$
$$- (\text{in-phase voltage} \times \text{quadrature-phase current})$$

If we had proceeded by multiplying (261) by (262), the result would have been:

$$(ac - bd) + j(bc + ad).$$

The terms within the brackets represent neither the power nor the reactive volt-amperes. The correct

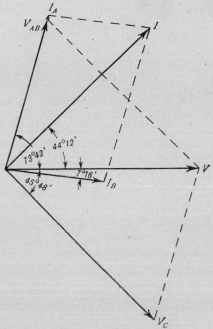

Fig. 311.—Vector diagram for Example 62.

expressions for these quantities are derived by multiplying the voltage by the *conjugate* of the current, the conjugate of a complex number being a quantity that differs only in the sign of the quadrature component; thus the conjugate of the current represented by (262) is $c - jd$. Hence:

$$(a + jb)(c - jd) = (ac + bd) + j(bc - ad)$$
$$= \text{power in watts} + j(\text{reactive volt-amperes}).$$

Example 63. *The p.d. across and the current in a circuit are represented by* $(100+j200)$ *volts and* $(10+j5)$ *amperes respectively. Calculate the power and the reactive volt-amperes.*

From (263),

$$\text{power} = (100 \times 10) + (200 \times 5)$$
$$= 2000 \text{ W.}$$

From (264), reactive volt-amperes $\Big\} = (200 \times 10) - (100 \times 5)$

$$= 1500 \text{ VAr.}$$

Alternatively, $100 + j200 = 223 \cdot 6 \angle 63° \, 26'$ V

and $\qquad\qquad 10 + j5 = 11 \cdot 18 \angle 26° \, 34'$ A,

∴ phase difference between voltage and current $\Big\} = 63° \, 26' - 26° \, 34' = 36° \, 52'$

Hence, $\qquad\qquad \text{power} = 223 \cdot 6 \times 11 \cdot 18 \cos 36° \, 52'$

$$= 2000 \text{ W}$$

and reactive volt-amperes $= 223 \cdot 6 \times 11 \cdot 18 \sin 36° \, 52'$

$$= 1500 \text{ VAr.}$$

Summary of Important Formulae in Chapter XV

$$\mathbf{A} = a + jb = A(\cos \theta + j \sin \theta) = A \angle \theta$$

where $A = \sqrt{(a^2 + b^2)}$ and $\theta = \tan^{-1} b/a$

$$A \angle \alpha \times B \angle \beta = AB \angle (\alpha + \beta)$$

$$\frac{A \angle \alpha}{B \angle \beta} = \frac{A}{B} \angle (\alpha - \beta) = \frac{A}{B} \diagdown (\beta - \alpha)$$

$$\frac{1}{a + jb} = \frac{a - jb}{a^2 + b^2} \quad \cdots \quad \cdots \quad (256)$$

For a circuit having R and L in *series*,

$$\mathbf{Z} = R + jX_L = Z \angle \phi \quad \cdots \quad \cdots \quad (249)$$

Admittance $= \mathbf{Y} = \dfrac{1}{\mathbf{Z}} = \dfrac{R}{Z^2} - \dfrac{jX_L}{Z^2} = G - jB_L = Y \diagdown \phi$ (253)

For a circuit having R and C in *series*,

$$\mathbf{Z} = R - jX_C = Z \diagdown \phi \quad \cdots \quad \cdots \quad (250)$$

and $\qquad \mathbf{Y} = \dfrac{R}{Z^2} + \dfrac{jX_C}{Z^2} = G + jB_C = Y \angle \phi \quad \cdots \quad (257)$

Conductance $=G=\dfrac{R}{Z^2}$ and is $1/R$ only when $X=0$.

Susceptance $=B=\dfrac{X}{Z^2}$ and is $1/X$ only when $R=0$.

For impedances $\mathbf{Z}_1=R_1+jX_1$ and $\mathbf{Z}_2=R_2+jX_2$ in *series*,

total impedance $=\mathbf{Z}=\mathbf{Z}_1+\mathbf{Z}_2=(R_1+R_2)+j(X_1+X_2)$
$\qquad\qquad\qquad =Z\angle\phi$

where $Z=\sqrt{[(R_1+R_2)^2+(X_1+X_2)^2]}$
and $\quad\phi=\tan^{-1}(X_1+X_2)/(R_1+R_2)$.

For a circuit having R and L in *parallel*,

$$\mathbf{Y}=\frac{1}{R}-\frac{j}{X_L}=G-jB_L=Y\searrow\phi \qquad . \qquad (259)$$

For a circuit having R and C in *parallel*,

$$\mathbf{Y}=\frac{1}{R}+\frac{j}{X_C}=G+jB_C=Y\angle\phi \qquad . \qquad (260)$$

For admittances $\mathbf{Y}_1=G_1+jB_1$ and $\mathbf{Y}_2=G_2+jB_2$ in *parallel*,

total admittance $=\mathbf{Y}=\mathbf{Y}_1+\mathbf{Y}_2=(G_1+G_2)+j(B_1+B_2)$
$\qquad\qquad\qquad =Y\angle\phi$

where $Y=\sqrt{[(G_1+G_2)^2+(B_1+B_2)^2]}$
and $\quad\phi=\tan^{-1}(B_1+B_2)/(G_1+G_2)$.

$$\text{Power}=ac+bd \qquad . \qquad . \qquad (263)$$

and $\qquad$ reactive volt-$\big\}=bc-ad \qquad . \qquad . \qquad . \qquad (264)$
$\qquad\qquad$ amperes

where $\qquad\qquad\qquad \mathbf{V}=a+jb$
and $\qquad\qquad\qquad \mathbf{I}=c+jd$.

EXAMPLES XV

1. Explain the method of representing a vector quantity by the j notation.

The current in a circuit is given by $4{\cdot}5+j12$ A when the applied voltage is $100+j150$ V. Determine (a) the complex expression for the impedance, stating whether it is inductive or capacitive, (b) the power, (c) the phase angle between voltage and current.

(C. & G., El. Eng. Pract., Final, Part I)

2. Explain how alternating quantities may be represented by complex numbers.

If the potential difference across a circuit is represented by $40 + j25$ V, and the circuit consists of a resistance of 20 Ω in series with an inductance of 0·06 H and the frequency is 79·5 c/s, find the complex number representing the current in amperes. (App El., L.U.)

3. The impedances of two parallel circuits can be represented by $(20 + j15)$ and $(10 - j60)$ Ω respectively. If the supply frequency is 50 c/s, find the resistance and the inductance or capacitance of each circuit. Also, derive a symbolic expression for the admittance of the combined circuits, and thence find the phase angle between the applied voltage and the resultant current. State whether this current is leading or lagging relatively to the voltage. (App. El., L.U.)

4. A variable condenser is connected in series with a circuit consisting of a non-inductive resistance of 50 Ω in parallel with a coil across a 200-V, 50-c/s supply. The coil has an inductance of 0·2 H and a negligible resistance. Calculate (a) the capacitance of the condenser when the power factor of the whole circuit is unity and (b) the corresponding p.d. across the condenser. Draw a vector diagram (not to scale) representing the voltages and the currents.
(App. El., L.U.)

5. The active and lagging reactive components of the current taken by an a.c. circuit from a 250-V supply are 50 A and 25 A respectively. Calculate the conductance, susceptance, admittance and power factor of the circuit.

What resistance and reactance would an inductive coil have if it took the same current from the same mains at the same power factor?
(U.L.C.I.)

6. A resistance of 150 Ω and a capacitance are connected in parallel across a 240-V, 50-c/s supply. If the total current taken from the supply is 1·9 A, find, graphically or otherwise, the current taken by the condenser and the phase angle of the total current. What is the value of the capacitance?

Calculate the resistance and capacitance of the series circuit which would take 1·9 A at the same phase angle from the 240-V supply.
(U.L.C.I.)

7. Define impedance, admittance, conductance and susceptance.

Two equal non-inductive resistances and two identical choke-coils of negligible resistance, when connected in series form an impedance of 200 Ω, power factor 0·8. Calculate the admittance, conductance and susceptance when all four components are connected in parallel.
(N.C.T.E.C.)

8. Explain what you understand by power factor.

A circuit connected to a 115-V, 50-c/s supply takes 0·8 A at power factor of 0·3 lagging. Calculate the resistance and inductance of the circuit assuming (a) the circuit consists of a resistance and inductance in series, (b) the circuit consists of a resistance and inductance in parallel. (E.M.E.U.)

9. Find the values of conductance and susceptance which, when connected in parallel, will be equivalent to a circuit consisting of a resistance of 20 Ω in series with an inductive reactance of 10 Ω.

10. An alternating e.m.f. of 100 V is induced in a coil of impedance $10 + j25$ Ω. To the terminals of this coil there is joined a circuit consisting of two parallel impedances, one of $30 - j20$ and the other of $50 + j0$ Ω. Calculate the current in the coil in magnitude and phase with respect to the induced voltage. (U.L.C.I., Adv. El. Tech.)

11. Three impedances, $6+j5$ Ω, $8-j6$ Ω and $8+j10$ Ω, are connected in parallel. Calculate the current in each branch when the current in the main circuit is 20 A.   (C. & G., El. Eng. Pract., Final, Part I)

12. A capacitor of 220 μF is shunted across an inductance of 0·14 H. If a resistance of 41·5 Ω is placed in series with the combination, find the current taken from a 200-V, 25-c/s supply.

What would be the effect of increasing the capacitance of the capacitor? For what capacitance would the current taken from the supply be a minimum? What would then be the value of the current?
(U.E.I.)

13. A circuit consists of a resistance of 30 Ω in series with a coil having an inductance of 0·1 H and a resistance of 10 Ω. A capacitance of 60 μF is connected in parallel with the *coil*. The circuit is connected across a 200-V, 50-c/s supply. Calculate the value of the current in each branch and its phase relative to the supply voltage.

14. An impedance of $2+j6$ Ω is connected in series with two impedances of $10+j4$ Ω and $12-j8$ Ω, which are in parallel. Calculate the magnitude and power factor of the main current when the combined circuit is supplied at 200 V.   (U.L.C.I., Adv. El. Tech.)

15. The arms of an a.c. bridge (Maxwell) are arranged thus:

AB: a non-reactive resistance of 300 Ω.
BC: a variable resistance R in series with a variable inductance L.
CD: a coil, the resistance and reactance of which are required.
DA: a non-reactive resistance of 100 Ω.

An alternating voltage is applied across AC. Deduce the conditions for zero p.d. across BD, and calculate the resistance and the inductance of the coil if balance is obtained with $R=64$ Ω and $L=0·28$ H.

Note. The solution makes use of the fact that if
$$a+jb=c+jd$$
then $a=c$ and $b=d$.

16. The arms of an a.c. bridge (de Sauty) are arranged thus:
AB: a non-reactive resistance of 1000 Ω.
BC: a variable no-loss capacitance C.
CD: a capacitor X, the capacitance of which is required.
DA: a non-reactive resistance of 100 Ω.
If an alternating voltage is applied across AC, deduce the condition for zero p.d. across BD. If the value of capacitance C be 0·068 μF when the bridge is balanced, calculate the capacitance of X.

17. The arms of an a.c. bridge (Owen) have the following impedances:
AB: a coil in series with a variable resistance P.
BC: a no-loss capacitor of capacitance 0·5 μF in series with a variable resistance Q.
CD: a no-loss capacitor of capacitance 0·3 μF.
DA: a resistance of 500 Ω.
If an alternating voltage be applied across AC, deduce the conditions for zero p.d. across BD. If the values of P and Q to give a balance be 126 and 534 Ω respectively, calculate the resistance and the inductance of the coil.

18. The p.d. across and the current in a given circuit are represented by $(200+j30)$ V and $(5-j2)$ A respectively. Calculate the power and the reactive voltamperes. State whether the reactive voltamperes are leading or lagging.

19. Had the current in Q.18 been represented by $(2+j5)$ A, what would have been the power and the reactive voltamperes? Again state whether the reactive voltamperes are leading or lagging.

APPENDIX

SUPPLEMENTARY QUESTIONS ON D.C. MACHINES

The following questions refer to branches of the subject covered in *Principles of Electricity* which are also closely related to the subject-matter of Chap. IV of this volume.

1. Discuss the essential point of difference between lap and wave windings. Why are equalizer rings necessary on large lap-wound machines? An eight-pole generator has 120 slots with 8 conductors per slot, employing single-turn coils. Sketch *one* of the coils, showing the accommodation in the slots and the connections to the commutator. Tabulate the connections to 10 equalizer rings.

(U.L.C.I.)

2. Explain why equalizing rings are fitted to lap-wound armatures. A 100-V, 50-kW, 750-r.p.m. generator has 4 poles and is lap-wound with 4 conductors per slot in 80 slots. The coils consist of a single turn and the resistance of the armature circuit is $0.01\ \Omega$. There are 9 brushes per arm, each $\frac{7}{8}$ in by $\frac{5}{8}$ in.
Obtain: (a) The number of commutator segments. (b) The number of brush arms. (c) The current density in the brushes. (d) The flux per pole when on load. (e) The number of connections to each equalizing ring.

(U.L.C.I.)

3. Draw a parallel or lap-winding for a four-pole machine with 12 slots and 12 commutator segments. Trace the various parallel circuits on your diagram and show 2 equalizer rings suitably connected to the winding, also the position and polarity of the brushes.

(U.E.I.)

4. What are the essential differences between lap and wave windings? Explain the use of (a) dummy coil, (b) equalizer connections, stating for which type of armature winding they can be used. State for what type of winding each of the following armatures could be used and whether the winding must be four- or six-pole if no dummy coils are to be used: (a) 33 slots, 165 commutator segments, (b) 64 slots, 256 commutator segments, (c) 65 slots, 260 commutator segments.

(N.C.T.E.C.)

5. Develop the law for the commutator pitch of a simple wave-winding.
A four-pole wave-wound armature has 151 commutator segments. How many armature coils are traversed in tracing through the winding between segments 1 and 5? The winding has a positive creep.
Prove that for a simple wave-winding, $a = 1$, and for a simple lap-winding $a = p$, where $a =$ number of pairs of paths in parallel through winding and $p =$ number of pole pairs. (Assoc. Mem., I.E.E.)

6. A four-pole wave-wound armature has 39 slots, with 18 conductors per slot and 117 segments. If the useful flux per pole is 0.02 weber, find the speed in r.p.m. at which the armature must be rotated to generate 440 V. Sketch *one* of the coils, indicating clearly the number of turns and how it is accommodated in the slots.

7. Distinguish between lap-connected and wave-connected armature windings and deduce the e.m.f. equation for a d.c. machine.

Calculate the flux in a four-pole dynamo with 722 armature conductors generating 500 V when running at 1000 r.p.m., when the armature is (a) lap-connected and (b) wave-connected.

(C. & G., El. Eng. Pract., Int.)

8. Explain the causes which may lead to a d.c. generator failing to excite and indicate how you would determine the reason in any particular case.

The following figures give the open-circuit characteristic of a d.c. shunt generator at 300 r.p.m.:

Field amperes	0	2	3	4	5	6	7
Armature volts	7·5	93	135	165	186	202	215

Plot the open-circuit characteristic for a speed of 375 r.p.m. and determine the voltage to which the machine will excite if the field-circuit resistance is 40 Ω. What additional resistance would have to be inserted in the field circuit to reduce the voltage to 200 V at 375 r.p.m.? (App. El., L.U.)

9. The open-circuit characteristic of a shunt generator running at 1500 r.p.m. is given by the following table:

Field current (amperes)	.	0	0·1	0·2	0·3	0·4	0·5	0·6	0·7	0·75
Open-circuit voltage (volts)	.	0	87	154	207	238	260	278	290	295

The resistance of the field coils is 400 Ω. Determine the no-load voltage to which the machine will build up as a shunt generator. Calculate the value of the resistance which must be connected in series with the shunt field to reduce the no-load voltage to 200 V.

If the armature resistance is 0·8 Ω, find the terminal voltage (a) without the added field resistance, (b) with the added field resistance, for an armature current of 15 A. (E.M.E.U.)

10. Explain fully the reasons for the variation in the terminal voltage of a d.c. shunt generator with increasing load.

A 250-V, 50-kW d.c. generator has 1000 turns on each pole of its shunt field winding. On no load a current of 3·5 A in the shunt field produces a terminal voltage of 250 V but on full load the exciting current needs to be 5 A for the same terminal voltage at the same speed. Calculate the series field turns required for level compounding.

(U.E.I.)

11. Deduce the speed equation for a d.c. motor. A shunt-wound motor runs at 600 r.p.m. from a 230-V supply when taking a line current of 50 A. Its armature and field resistances are 0·4 and 104·5 Ω respectively. Neglecting the effects of armature reaction and allowing 2 V brush drop, calculate: (a) the no-load speed if the no-load line current is 5 A; (b) the resistance to be placed in the armature circuit in order to reduce the speed to 500 r.p.m. when taking a line current of 50 A; (c) the percentage reduction in the flux per pole in order that the speed may be 750 r.p.m. when taking an armature current of 30 A with no added resistance in the armature circuit.

(N.C.T.E.C.)

12. Derive an expression for the total torque developed by a d.c. motor. Using this expression, draw graphs showing the relationship between the torque and the armature current for (a) a shunt motor and (b) a series motor, assuming the supply voltage to remain constant.

A 460-V series motor runs at 500 r.p.m. taking a current of 40 A. Calculate the speed and the percentage change of torque if the load is reduced so that the motor is taking 30 A. Total resistance of the armature and field circuits is 0·8 Ω. Assume the flux to be proportional to the field current. (App. El., L.U.)

13. A 200-V, d.c., 12-h.p. series motor has an armature resistance of 0·4 Ω and a field resistance of 0·2 Ω. The open-circuit characteristic when run as a separately excited generator at 600 r.p.m. is:

| Current (amperes) | 10 | 20 | 30 | 40 | 50 | 60 |
| E.M.F. (volts) | 72 | 129 | 163 | 183 | 196 | 202 |

The drop of volts at the brushes on load may be taken as 2 V and the friction, windage and iron losses as 600 W. Plot the curve of speed in r.p.m. to a base of torque in lb.ft. and determine the speed at which full load is developed. (App. El., L.U.)

14. State the type of drive for which a series motor is suitable and state how it should be coupled to the load.

A 230-V series motor runs at 1200 r.p.m. at a quarter full-load torque, taking a current of 16 A. Calculate its speed at half- and full-load torque. The resistance of the armature, brushes and field coils is 0·25 Ω. Assume the flux per pole to be proportional to the current. Plot a torque-speed graph, between full and quarter load. (U.E.I.)

15. The following figures refer to the magnetization curve of a 240-V d.c. series motor:

| Exciting current (amperes) | 10 | 20 | 30 | 40 | 50 |
| E.M.F. (volts) at 1000 r.p.m. | 90 | 184 | 244 | 274 | 285 |

The armature resistance is 0·35 Ω and the field circuit resistance 0·15 Ω. Plot the speed/current curve when working from 240-V d.c. mains. (Joint Section A)

16. Obtain an expression for the torque developed by a d.c. motor. Use the expression to determine the general shape of the current/torque characteristic for a d.c. series motor.

A d.c. series motor is connected to a 220-V supply and runs at 500 r.p.m., taking a current of 50 A. Calculate the value of a resistance which, when inserted in series with the motor, will reduce the speed to 300 r.p.m., the load torque being then one-half of its previous value. Resistance of motor = 0·1 Ω. Assume the flux to be proportional to the field current. (Assoc. Mem., I.E.E.)

17. Sketch a typical speed-current curve for a d.c. series motor working at a constant voltage, and explain its shape.

A d.c. series motor runs at 1000 r.p.m. when taking 20 A at 200 V. The resistance of the armature winding is 0·5 Ω and that of the field winding 0·2 Ω. Find the speed for a total current of 20 A, 200 V, when a 0·2-Ω resistor is joined in parallel with the field winding. The flux for a field current of 10 A is 70 per cent of that for 20 A.

(App. El., L.U.)

18. Deduce from first principles the e.m.f. equation of a d.c. generator.

A 250-V, d.c. shunt motor has an armature-circuit resistance of 0·5 Ω and a field-circuit resistance of 125 Ω. It drives a load at 1000 r.p.m. and takes 30 A. The field-circuit resistance is then slowly increased to 150 Ω. If the flux and field current can be assumed to be proportional and if the load torque remains constant, calculate the final speed and armature current. Why is a sudden change of field-circuit resistance undesirable? (Joint Section A)

19. Explain how a resistance in series with the armature of a d.c. shunt motor affects the speed of the machine and state the advantages and disadvantages of this method of speed control.

A series motor runs at 500 r.p.m. on a certain load.   Calculate the resistance of a divertor required to raise the speed to 650 r.p.m. with the same load current, given that the series field resistance is 0·05 Ω and the field is unsaturated.   Assume the ohmic drop in the field and armature to be negligible.   (U.L.C.I.)

20. Calculate, from first principles, the diameter of copper wire required for the winding of a field coil to give 15,000 ampere-turns at an applied p.d. of 200 V.   At the working temperature of the field coil the specific resistance of the copper may be taken as 0·88 microhm-inch and the length of the mean turn is 24 in.

Assuming that the current density is 2 A/mm^2, find the number of turns.   (U.L.C.I.)

COMPARISON OF RATIONALIZED M.K.S. AND UNRATIONALIZED C.G.S. UNITS

Term	M.K.S. units (Rationalized system)	Equivalent in C.G.S. units (Unrationalized system)	
		Electromagnetic	Electrostatic
Length . .	1 metre	100 cm	100 cm
Mass . .	1 kilogram	1000 g	1000 g
Time . .	1 second	1 sec	1 sec
Force . .	1 newton	10^5 dynes	10^5 dynes
Work . .	1 joule	10^7 ergs	10^7 ergs
Power . .	1 watt	10^7 ergs/sec	10^7 ergs/sec
Current .	1 ampere	0·1 unit	3×10^9 units
Charge . .	1 coulomb	0·1 unit	3×10^9 units
E.m.f. and p.d.	1 volt	10^8 units	1/300 unit
Resistance .	1 ohm	10^9 units	$1·11 \times 10^{-12}$ unit
Inductance .	1 henry	10^9 units	$1·11 \times 10^{-12}$ unit
Capacitance .	1 farad	10^{-9} unit	9×10^{11} units
Magnetomotive force . .	1 ampere-turn	$0·4\pi$ gilberts	—
Magnetizing force . .	1 ampere-turn per metre	$4\pi \times 10^{-3}$ oersted	—
Magnetic flux	1 weber	10^8 maxwells	—
Magnetic flux density .	1 weber/metre^2	10^4 gauss	—
Permeability of free space .	$4\pi \times 10^{-7}$ unit	1 unit	—
Electric force .	1 volt/metre	—	$\frac{1}{3} \times 10^{-4}$ unit/cm
Electric flux .	1 coulomb	—	$12\pi \times 10^9$ units
Electric flux density .	1 coulomb/metre^2	—	$12\pi \times 10^5$ units /cm^2
Permittivity of free space .	$8·85 \times 10^{-12}$ unit	—	1 unit

MATHEMATICAL CONSTANTS

$\pi = 3·1416;$ $1/\pi = 0·3183$

$e = 2·718;$ $\log e = 0·4343$

$\log x = 0·4343 \ln x;$ $\ln x = 2·303 \log x$

PHYSICAL CONSTANTS IN RATIONALIZED M.K.S. UNITS

Permeability of free space	$4\pi \times 10^{-7}$
Permittivity of free space	$8\cdot85 \times 10^{-12}$
Electron-volt	$1\cdot602 \times 10^{-19}$J
Electron charge	$1\cdot602 \times 10^{-19}$C
Electron mass	$9\cdot107 \times 10^{-31}$kg
Velocity of electromagnetic waves in free space	$2\cdot998 \times 10^{8}$ m/sec
Micron	10^{-6}m
Ångstrom unit	10^{-10}m

CONVERSION FACTORS

To convert	Multiply by	Reciprocal
Radian to degrees	$57\cdot30$	$0\cdot01745$
Inches to metres	$0\cdot0254$	$39\cdot37$
Yards to metres	$0\cdot9144$	$1\cdot094$
Miles/hour to metres/sec	$0\cdot447$	$2\cdot237$
Pounds to kilograms	$0\cdot4536$	$2\cdot205$
Pounds (force) to newtons	$4\cdot45$	$0\cdot225$
Kilograms (force) to newtons	$9\cdot81$	$0\cdot1019$
Newton-metres to lb.ft.	$0\cdot738$	$1\cdot355$
Newton-metres to g.cm.	$1\cdot019 \times 10^{4}$	$9\cdot81 \times 10^{-5}$
Horsepower to ft.lb./min	$33,000$	$3\cdot031 \times 10^{-5}$
Horsepower to ft.lb./sec	550	$0\cdot001818$
Horsepower to kilowatts	$0\cdot746$	$1\cdot341$
Therms to B.T.U.	$100,000$	10^{-5}
B.T.U. to kilogram-calories	$0\cdot252$	$3\cdot97$
B.T.U. to kWh	$2\cdot934 \times 10^{-4}$	3409
Ft.lb. to B.T.U.	$0\cdot001285$	778
Ft.lb. to joules	$1\cdot356$	$0\cdot7374$
Kilogram-calories to joules	4187	$2\cdot388 \times 10^{-4}$
Joules to kWh	$0\cdot2778 \times 10^{-6}$	$3,600,000$

	0	1	2	3	4	5	6	7	8	9	1	2	3	4	5	6	7	8	9
10	0000	0043	0086	0128	0170	0212	0253	0294	0334	0374	4	9	13	17	21	26	30	34	38
											4	8	12	16	20	24	28	32	37
11	0414	0453	0492	0531	0569	0607	0645	0682	0719	0755	4	8	12	15	19	23	27	31	35
											4	7	11	15	19	22	26	30	33
12	0792	0828	0864	0899	0934	0969	1004	1038	1072	1106	3	7	11	14	18	21	25	28	32
											3	7	10	14	17	20	24	27	31
13	1139	1173	1206	1239	1271	1303	1335	1367	1399	1430	3	7	10	13	16	20	23	26	30
											3	7	10	12	16	19	22	25	29
14	1461	1492	1523	1553	1584	1614	1644	1673	1703	1732	3	6	9	12	15	18	21	24	28
											3	6	9	12	15	17	20	23	26
15	1761	1790	1818	1847	1875	1903	1931	1959	1987	2014	3	6	9	11	14	17	20	23	26
											3	5	8	11	14	16	19	22	25
16	2041	2068	2095	2122	2148	2175	2201	2227	2253	2279	3	5	8	11	14	16	19	22	24
											3	5	8	10	13	15	18	21	23
17	2304	2330	2355	2380	2405	2430	2455	2480	2504	2529	3	5	8	10	13	15	18	20	23
											2	5	7	10	12	15	17	19	22
18	2553	2577	2601	2625	2648	2672	2695	2718	2742	2765	2	5	7	9	12	14	16	19	21
											2	5	7	9	11	14	16	18	21
19	2788	2810	2833	2856	2878	2900	2923	2945	2967	2989	2	4	7	9	11	13	16	18	20
											2	4	6	8	11	13	15	17	19
20	3010	3032	3054	3075	3096	3118	3139	3160	3181	3201	2	4	6	8	11	13	15	17	19
21	3222	3243	3263	3284	3304	3324	3345	3365	3385	3404	2	4	6	8	10	12	14	16	18
22	3424	3444	3464	3483	3502	3522	3541	3560	3579	3598	2	4	6	8	10	12	14	15	17
23	3617	3636	3655	3674	3692	3711	3729	3747	3766	3784	2	4	6	7	9	11	13	15	17
24	3802	3820	3838	3856	3874	3892	3909	3927	3945	3962	2	4	5	7	9	11	12	14	16
25	3979	3997	4014	4031	4048	4065	4082	4099	4116	4133	2	3	5	7	9	10	12	14	15
26	4150	4166	4183	4200	4216	4232	4249	4265	4281	4298	2	3	5	7	8	10	11	13	15
27	4314	4330	4346	4362	4378	4393	4409	4425	4440	4456	2	3	5	6	8	9	11	13	14
28	4472	4487	4502	4518	4533	4548	4564	4579	4594	4609	2	3	5	6	8	9	11	12	14
29	4624	4639	4654	4669	4683	4698	4713	4728	4742	4757	1	3	4	6	7	9	10	12	13
30	4771	4786	4800	4814	4829	4843	4857	4871	4886	4900	1	3	4	6	7	9	10	11	13
31	4914	4928	4942	4955	4969	4983	4997	5011	5024	5038	1	3	4	6	7	8	10	11	12
32	5051	5065	5079	5092	5105	5119	5132	5145	5159	5172	1	3	4	5	7	8	9	11	12
33	5185	5198	5211	5224	5237	5250	5263	5276	5289	5302	1	3	4	5	6	8	9	10	12
34	5315	5328	5340	5353	5366	5378	5391	5403	5416	5428	1	3	4	5	6	8	9	10	11
35	5441	5453	5465	5478	5490	5502	5514	5527	5539	5551	1	2	4	5	6	7	9	10	11
36	5563	5575	5587	5599	5611	5623	5635	5647	5658	5670	1	2	4	5	6	7	8	10	11
37	5682	5694	5705	5717	5729	5740	5752	5763	5775	5786	1	2	3	5	6	7	8	9	10
38	5798	5809	5821	5832	5843	5855	5866	5877	5888	5899	1	2	3	5	6	7	8	9	10
39	5911	5922	5933	5944	5955	5966	5977	5988	5999	6010	1	2	3	4	5	7	8	9	10
40	6021	6031	6042	6053	6064	6075	6085	6096	6107	6117	1	2	3	4	5	6	8	9	10
41	6128	6138	6149	6160	6170	6180	6191	6201	6212	6222	1	2	3	4	5	6	7	8	9
42	6232	6243	6253	6263	6274	6284	6294	6304	6314	6325	1	2	3	4	5	6	7	8	9
43	6335	6345	6355	6365	6375	6385	6395	6405	6415	6425	1	2	3	4	5	6	7	8	9
44	6435	6444	6454	6464	6474	6484	6493	6503	6513	6522	1	2	3	4	5	6	7	8	9
45	6532	6542	6551	6561	6571	6580	6590	6599	6609	6618	1	2	3	4	5	6	7	8	9
46	6628	6637	6646	6656	6665	6675	6684	6693	6702	6712	1	2	3	4	5	6	7	7	8
47	6721	6730	6739	6749	6758	6767	6776	6785	6794	6803	1	2	3	4	5	5	6	7	8
48	6812	6821	6830	6839	6848	6857	6866	6875	6884	6893	1	2	3	4	4	5	6	7	8
49	6902	6911	6920	6928	6937	6946	6955	6964	6972	6981	1	2	3	4	4	5	6	7	8
50	6990	6998	7007	7016	7024	7033	7042	7050	7059	7067	1	2	3	3	4	5	6	7	8

	0	1	2	3	4	5	6	7	8	9	1	2	3	4	5	6	7	8	9
51	7076	7084	7093	7101	7110	7118	7126	7135	7143	7152	1	2	3	3	4	5	6	7	8
52	7160	7168	7177	7185	7193	7202	7210	7218	7226	7235	1	2	2	3	4	5	6	7	7
53	7243	7251	7259	7267	7275	7284	7292	7300	7308	7316	1	2	2	3	4	5	6	6	7
54	7324	7332	7340	7348	7356	7364	7372	7380	7388	7396	1	2	2	3	4	5	6	6	7
55	7404	7412	7419	7427	7435	7443	7451	7459	7466	7474	1	2	2	3	4	5	5	6	7
56	7482	7490	7497	7505	7513	7520	7528	7536	7543	7551	1	2	2	3	4	5	5	6	7
57	7559	7566	7574	7582	7589	7597	7604	7612	7619	7627	1	2	2	3	4	5	5	6	7
58	7634	7642	7649	7657	7664	7672	7679	7686	7694	7701	1	1	2	3	4	5	5	6	7
59	7709	7716	7723	7731	7738	7745	7752	7760	7767	7774	1	1	2	3	4	4	5	6	7
60	7782	7789	7796	7803	7810	7818	7825	7832	7839	7846	1	1	2	3	4	4	5	6	6
61	7853	7860	7868	7875	7882	7889	7896	7903	7910	7917	1	1	2	3	4	4	5	6	6
62	7924	7931	7938	7945	7952	7959	7966	7973	7980	7987	1	1	2	3	3	4	5	6	6
63	7993	8000	8007	8014	8021	8028	8035	8041	8048	8055	1	1	2	3	3	4	5	5	6
64	8062	8069	8075	8082	8089	8096	8102	8109	8116	8122	1	1	2	3	3	4	5	5	6
65	8129	8136	8142	8149	8156	8162	8169	8176	8182	8189	1	1	2	3	3	4	5	5	6
66	8195	8202	8209	8215	8222	8228	8235	8241	8248	8254	1	1	2	3	3	4	5	5	6
67	8261	8267	8274	8280	8287	8293	8299	8306	8312	8319	1	1	2	3	3	4	5	5	6
68	8325	8331	8338	8344	8351	8357	8363	8370	8376	8382	1	1	2	3	3	4	4	5	6
69	8388	8395	8401	8407	8414	8420	8426	8432	8439	8445	1	1	2	2	3	4	4	5	6
70	8451	8457	8463	8470	8476	8482	8488	8494	8500	8506	1	1	2	2	3	4	4	5	6
71	8513	8519	8525	8531	8537	8543	8549	8555	8561	8567	1	1	2	2	3	4	4	5	5
72	8573	8579	8585	8591	8597	8603	8609	8615	8621	8627	1	1	2	2	3	4	4	5	5
73	8633	8639	8645	8651	8657	8663	8669	8675	8681	8686	1	1	2	2	3	4	4	5	5
74	8692	8698	8704	8710	8716	8722	8727	8733	8739	8745	1	1	2	2	3	4	4	5	5
75	8751	8756	8762	8768	8774	8779	8785	8791	8797	8802	1	1	2	2	3	3	4	5	5
76	8808	8814	8820	8825	8831	8837	8842	8848	8854	8859	1	1	2	2	3	3	4	5	5
77	8865	8871	8876	8882	8887	8893	8899	8904	8910	8915	1	1	2	2	3	3	4	4	5
78	8921	8927	8932	8938	8943	8949	8954	8960	8965	8971	1	1	2	2	3	3	4	4	5
79	8976	8982	8987	8993	8998	9004	9009	9015	9020	9025	1	1	2	2	3	3	4	4	5
80	9031	9036	9042	9047	9053	9058	9063	9069	9074	9079	1	1	2	2	3	3	4	4	5
81	9085	9090	9096	9101	9106	9112	9117	9122	9128	9133	1	1	2	2	3	3	4	4	5
82	9138	9143	9149	9154	9159	9165	9170	9175	9180	9186	1	1	2	2	3	3	4	4	5
83	9191	9196	9201	9206	9212	9217	9222	9227	9232	9238	1	1	2	2	3	3	4	4	5
84	9243	9248	9253	9258	9263	9269	9274	9279	9284	9289	1	1	2	2	3	3	4	4	5
85	9294	9299	9304	9309	9315	9320	9325	9330	9335	9340	1	1	2	2	3	3	4	4	5
86	9345	9350	9355	9360	9365	9370	9375	9380	9385	9390	1	1	2	2	3	3	4	4	5
87	9395	9400	9405	9410	9415	9420	9425	9430	9435	9440	0	1	1	2	2	3	3	4	4
88	9445	9450	9455	9460	9465	9469	9474	9479	9484	9489	0	1	1	2	2	3	3	4	4
89	9494	9499	9504	9509	9513	9518	9523	9528	9533	9538	0	1	1	2	2	3	3	4	4
90	9542	9547	9552	9557	9562	9566	9571	9576	9581	9586	0	1	1	2	2	3	3	4	4
91	9590	9595	9600	9605	9609	9614	9619	9624	9628	9633	0	1	1	2	2	3	3	4	4
92	9638	9643	9647	9652	9657	9661	9666	9671	9675	9680	0	1	1	2	2	3	3	4	4
93	9685	9689	9694	9699	9703	9708	9713	9717	9722	9727	0	1	1	2	2	3	3	4	4
94	9731	9736	9741	9745	9750	9754	9759	9763	9768	9773	0	1	1	2	2	3	3	4	4
95	9777	9782	9786	9791	9795	9800	9805	9809	9814	9818	0	1	1	2	2	3	3	4	4
96	9823	9827	9832	9836	9841	9845	9850	9854	9859	9863	0	1	1	2	2	3	3	4	4
97	9868	9872	9877	9881	9886	9890	9894	9899	9903	9908	0	1	1	2	2	3	3	4	4
98	9912	9917	9921	9926	9930	9934	9939	9943	9948	9952	0	1	1	2	2	3	3	4	4
99	9956	9961	9965	9969	9974	9978	9983	9987	9991	9996	0	1	1	2	2	3	3	3	4

	0	1	2	3	4	5	6	7	8	9	1	2	3	4	5	6	7	8	9
·00	1000	1002	1005	1007	1009	1012	1014	1016	1019	1021	0	0	1	1	1	1	2	2	2
·01	1023	1026	1028	1030	1033	1035	1038	1040	1042	1045	0	0	1	1	1	1	2	2	2
·02	1047	1050	1052	1054	1057	1059	1062	1064	1067	1069	0	0	1	1	1	1	2	2	2
·03	1072	1074	1076	1079	1081	1084	1086	1089	1091	1094	0	0	1	1	1	1	2	2	2
·04	1096	1099	1102	1104	1107	1109	1112	1114	1117	1119	0	1	1	1	1	2	2	2	2
·05	1122	1125	1127	1130	1132	1135	1138	1140	1143	1146	0	1	1	1	1	2	2	2	2
·06	1148	1151	1153	1156	1159	1161	1164	1167	1169	1172	0	1	1	1	1	2	2	2	2
·07	1175	1178	1180	1183	1186	1189	1191	1194	1197	1199	0	1	1	1	1	2	2	2	2
·08	1202	1205	1208	1211	1213	1216	1219	1222	1225	1227	0	1	1	1	1	2	2	2	2
·09	1230	1233	1236	1239	1242	1245	1247	1250	1253	1256	0	1	1	1	1	2	2	2	3
·10	1259	1262	1265	1268	1271	1274	1276	1279	1282	1285	0	1	1	1	1	2	2	2	3
·11	1288	1291	1294	1297	1300	1303	1306	1309	1312	1315	0	1	1	1	2	2	2	2	3
·12	1318	1321	1324	1327	1330	1334	1337	1340	1343	1346	0	1	1	1	2	2	2	2	3
·13	1349	1352	1355	1358	1361	1365	1368	1371	1374	1377	0	1	1	1	2	2	2	3	3
·14	1380	1384	1387	1390	1393	1396	1400	1403	1406	1409	0	1	1	1	2	2	2	3	3
·15	1413	1416	1419	1422	1426	1429	1432	1435	1439	1442	0	1	1	1	2	2	2	3	3
·16	1445	1449	1452	1455	1459	1462	1466	1469	1472	1476	0	1	1	1	2	2	3	3	3
·17	1479	1483	1486	1489	1493	1496	1500	1503	1507	1510	0	1	1	1	2	2	2	3	3
·18	1514	1517	1521	1524	1528	1531	1535	1538	1542	1545	0	1	1	1	2	2	2	3	3
·19	1549	1552	1556	1560	1563	1567	1570	1574	1578	1581	0	1	1	1	2	2	3	3	3
·20	1585	1589	1592	1596	1600	1603	1607	1611	1614	1618	0	1	1	1	2	2	3	3	3
·21	1622	1626	1629	1633	1637	1641	1644	1648	1652	1656	0	1	1	2	2	2	3	3	3
·22	1660	1663	1667	1671	1675	1679	1683	1687	1690	1694	0	1	1	2	2	2	3	3	3
·23	1698	1702	1706	1710	1714	1718	1722	1726	1730	1734	0	1	1	2	2	2	3	3	4
·24	1738	1742	1746	1750	1754	1758	1762	1766	1770	1774	0	1	1	2	2	2	3	3	4
·25	1778	1782	1786	1791	1795	1799	1803	1807	1811	1816	0	1	1	2	2	2	3	3	4
·26	1820	1824	1828	1832	1837	1841	1845	1849	1854	1858	0	1	1	2	2	3	3	3	4
·27	1862	1866	1871	1875	1879	1884	1888	1892	1897	1901	0	1	1	2	2	3	3	4	4
·28	1905	1910	1914	1919	1923	1928	1932	1936	1941	1945	0	1	1	2	2	3	3	4	4
·29	1950	1954	1959	1963	1968	1972	1977	1982	1986	1991	0	1	1	2	2	3	3	4	4
·30	1995	2000	2004	2009	2014	2018	2023	2028	2032	2037	0	1	1	2	2	3	3	4	4
·31	2042	2046	2051	2056	2061	2065	2070	2075	2080	2084	0	1	1	2	2	3	3	4	4
·32	2089	2094	2099	2104	2109	2113	2118	2123	2128	2133	0	1	1	2	2	3	3	4	4
·33	2138	2143	2148	2153	2158	2163	2168	2173	2178	2183	0	1	1	2	2	3	3	4	4
·34	2188	2193	2198	2203	2208	2213	2218	2223	2228	2234	1	1	2	2	3	3	4	4	5
·35	2239	2244	2249	2254	2259	2265	2270	2275	2280	2286	1	1	2	2	3	3	4	4	5
·36	2291	2296	2301	2307	2312	2317	2323	2328	2333	2339	1	1	2	2	3	3	4	4	5
·37	2344	2350	2355	2360	2366	2371	2377	2382	2388	2393	1	1	2	2	3	3	4	4	5
·38	2399	2404	2410	2415	2421	2427	2432	2438	2443	2449	1	1	2	2	3	3	4	5	5
·39	2455	2460	2466	2472	2477	2483	2489	2495	2500	2506	1	1	2	2	3	3	4	5	5
·40	2512	2518	2523	2529	2535	2541	2547	2553	2559	2564	1	1	2	2	3	4	4	5	5
·41	2570	2576	2582	2588	2594	2600	2606	2612	2618	2624	1	1	2	2	3	4	4	5	5
·42	2630	2636	2642	2649	2655	2661	2667	2673	2679	2685	1	1	2	2	3	4	4	5	5
·43	2692	2698	2704	2710	2716	2723	2729	2735	2742	2748	1	1	2	3	3	4	4	5	6
·44	2754	2761	2767	2773	2780	2786	2793	2799	2805	2812	1	1	2	3	3	4	4	5	6
·45	2818	2825	2831	2838	2844	2851	2858	2864	2871	2877	1	1	2	3	3	4	5	5	6
·46	2884	2891	2897	2904	2911	2917	2924	2931	2938	2944	1	1	2	3	3	4	5	5	6
·47	2951	2958	2965	2972	2979	2985	2992	2999	3006	3013	1	1	2	3	3	4	5	5	6
·48	3020	3027	3034	3041	3048	3055	3062	3069	3076	3083	1	1	2	3	4	4	5	6	6
·49	3090	3097	3105	3112	3119	3126	3133	3141	3148	3155	1	1	2	3	4	4	5	6	6

	0	1	2	3	4	5	6	7	8	9	1	2	3	4	5	6	7	8	9
·50	3162	3170	3177	3184	3192	3199	3206	3214	3221	3228	1	1	2	3	4	4	5	6	7
·51	3236	3243	3251	3258	3266	3273	3281	3289	3296	3304	1	2	2	3	4	5	5	6	7
·52	3311	3319	3327	3334	3342	3350	3357	3365	3373	3381	1	2	2	3	4	5	5	6	7
·53	3388	3396	3404	3412	3420	3428	3436	3443	3451	3459	1	2	2	3	4	5	6	6	7
·54	3467	3475	3483	3491	3499	3508	3516	3524	3532	3540	1	2	2	3	4	5	6	6	7
·55	3548	3556	3565	3573	3581	3589	3597	3606	3614	3622	1	2	2	3	4	5	6	7	7
·56	3631	3639	3648	3656	3664	3673	3681	3690	3698	3707	1	2	3	3	4	5	6	7	8
·57	3715	3724	3733	3741	3750	3758	3767	3776	3784	3793	1	2	3	3	4	5	6	7	8
·58	3802	3811	3819	3828	3837	3846	3855	3864	3873	3882	1	2	3	4	4	5	6	7	8
·59	3890	3899	3908	3917	3926	3936	3945	3954	3963	3972	1	2	3	4	5	5	6	7	8
·60	3981	3990	3999	4009	4018	4027	4036	4046	4055	4064	1	2	3	4	5	6	6	7	9
·61	4074	4083	4093	4102	4111	4121	4130	4140	4150	4159	1	2	3	4	5	6	7	8	9
·62	4169	4178	4188	4198	4207	4217	4227	4236	4246	4256	1	2	3	4	5	6	7	8	9
·63	4266	4276	4285	4295	4305	4315	4325	4335	4345	4355	1	2	3	4	5	6	7	8	9
·64	4365	4375	4385	4395	4406	4416	4426	4436	4446	4457	1	2	3	4	5	6	7	8	9
·65	4467	4477	4487	4498	4508	4519	4529	4539	4550	4560	1	2	3	4	5	6	7	8	9
·66	4571	4581	4592	4603	4613	4624	4634	4645	4656	4667	1	2	3	4	5	6	7	9	10
·67	4677	4688	4699	4710	4721	4732	4742	4753	4764	4775	1	2	3	4	5	7	8	9	10
·68	4786	4797	4808	4819	4831	4842	4853	4864	4875	4887	1	2	3	4	6	7	8	9	10
·69	4898	4909	4920	4932	4943	4955	4966	4977	4989	5000	1	2	3	5	6	7	8	9	10
·70	5012	5023	5035	5047	5058	5070	5082	5093	5105	5117	1	2	4	5	6	7	8	9	11
·71	5129	5140	5152	5164	5176	5188	5200	5212	5224	5236	1	2	4	5	6	7	8	10	11
·72	5248	5260	5272	5284	5297	5309	5321	5333	5346	5358	1	2	4	5	6	7	9	10	11
·73	5370	5383	5395	5408	5420	5433	5445	5458	5470	5483	1	3	4	5	6	8	9	10	11
·74	5495	5508	5521	5534	5546	5559	5572	5585	5598	5610	1	3	4	5	6	8	9	10	12
·75	5623	5636	5649	5662	5675	5689	5702	5715	5728	5741	1	3	4	5	7	8	9	10	12
·76	5754	5768	5781	5794	5808	5821	5834	5848	5861	5875	1	3	4	5	7	8	9	11	12
·77	5888	5902	5916	5929	5943	5957	5970	5984	5998	6012	1	3	4	5	7	8	10	11	12
·78	6026	6039	6053	6067	6081	6095	6109	6124	6138	6152	1	3	4	6	7	8	10	11	13
·79	6166	6180	6194	6209	6223	6237	6252	6266	6281	6295	1	3	4	6	7	9	10	11	13
·80	6310	6324	6339	6353	6368	6383	6397	6412	6427	6442	1	3	4	6	7	9	10	12	13
·81	6457	6471	6486	6501	6516	6531	6546	6561	6577	6592	2	3	5	6	8	9	11	12	14
·82	6607	6622	6637	6653	6668	6683	6699	6714	6730	6745	2	3	5	6	8	9	11	12	14
·83	6761	6776	6792	6808	6823	6839	6855	6871	6887	6902	2	3	5	6	8	9	11	13	14
·84	6918	6934	6950	6966	6982	6998	7015	7031	7047	7063	2	3	5	6	8	10	11	13	15
·85	7079	7096	7112	7129	7145	7161	7178	7194	7211	7228	2	3	5	7	8	10	12	13	15
·86	7244	7261	7278	7295	7311	7328	7345	7362	7379	7396	2	3	5	7	8	10	12	13	15
·87	7413	7430	7447	7464	7482	7499	7516	7534	7551	7568	2	3	5	7	9	10	12	14	16
·88	7586	7603	7621	7638	7656	7674	7691	7709	7727	7745	2	4	5	7	9	11	12	14	16
·89	7762	7780	7798	7816	7834	7852	7870	7889	7907	7925	2	4	5	7	9	11	13	14	16
·90	7943	7962	7980	7998	8017	8035	8054	8072	8091	8110	2	4	6	7	9	11	13	15	17
·91	8128	8147	8166	8185	8204	8222	8241	8260	8279	8299	2	4	6	8	9	11	13	15	17
·92	8318	8337	8356	8375	8395	8414	8433	8453	8472	8492	2	4	6	8	10	12	14	15	17
·93	8511	8531	8551	8570	8590	8610	8630	8650	8670	8690	2	4	6	8	10	12	14	16	18
·94	8710	8730	8750	8770	8790	8810	8831	8851	8872	8892	2	4	6	8	10	12	14	16	18
·95	8913	8933	8954	8974	8995	9016	9036	9057	9078	9099	2	4	6	8	10	12	15	17	19
·96	9120	9141	9162	9183	9204	9226	9247	9268	9290	9311	2	4	6	8	11	13	15	17	19
·97	9333	9354	9376	9397	9419	9441	9462	9484	9506	9528	2	4	7	9	11	13	15	17	20
·98	9550	9572	9594	9616	9638	9661	9683	9705	9727	9750	2	4	7	9	11	13	16	18	20
·99	9772	9795	9817	9840	9863	9886	9908	9931	9954	9977	2	5	7	9	11	14	16	18	20

Angle.		Chord	Sine	Tangent	Co-tangent	Cosine			
Degrees.	Radians								
0°	0	0	0	0	∞	1	1·414	1·5708	90°
1	·0175	·017	·0175	·0175	57·2900	·9998	1·402	1·5533	89
2	·0349	·035	·0348	·0349	28·6363	·9994	1·389	1·5359	88
3	·0524	·052	·0523	·0524	19·0811	·9986	1·377	1·5184	87
4	·0698	·070	·0698	·0699	14·3007	·9976	1·364	1·5010	86
5	·0873	·087	·0872	·0875	11·4301	·9962	1·351	1·4835	85
6	·1047	·105	·1045	·1051	9·5144	·9945	1·338	1·4661	84
7	·1222	·122	·1219	·1228	8·1443	·9925	1·325	1·4486	83
8	·1396	·140	·1392	·1405	7·1154	·9903	1·312	1·4312	82
9	·1571	·157	·1564	·1584	6·3138	·9877	1·299	1·4137	81
10	·1745	·174	·1736	·1763	5·6713	·9848	1·286	1·3963	80
11	·1920	·192	·1908	·1944	5·1446	·9816	1·272	1·3788	79
12	·2094	·209	·2079	·2126	4·7046	·9781	1·259	1·3614	78
13	·2269	·226	·2250	·2309	4·3315	·9744	1·245	1·3439	77
14	·2443	·244	·2419	·2493	4·0108	·9703	1·231	1·3265	76
15	·2618	·261	·2588	·2679	3·7321	·9659	1·218	1·3090	75
16	·2793	·278	·2756	·2867	3·4874	·9613	1·204	1·2915	74
17	·2967	·296	·2924	·3057	3·2709	·9563	1·190	1·2741	73
18	·3142	·313	·3090	·3249	3·0777	·9511	1·176	1·2566	72
19	·3316	·330	·3256	·3443	2·9042	·9455	1·161	1·2392	71
20	·3491	·347	·3420	·3640	2·7475	·9397	1·147	1·2217	70
21	·3665	·364	·3584	·3839	2·6051	·9336	1·133	1·2043	69
22	·3840	·382	·3746	·4040	2·4751	·9272	1·118	1·1868	68
23	·4014	·399	·3907	·4245	2·3559	·9205	1·104	1·1694	67
24	·4189	·416	·4067	·4452	2·2460	·9135	1·089	1·1519	66
25	·4363	·433	·4226	·4663	2·1445	·9063	1·075	1·1345	65
26	·4538	·450	·4384	·4877	2·0503	·8988	1·060	1·1170	64
27	·4712	·467	·4540	·5095	1·9626	·8910	1·045	1·0996	63
28	·4887	·484	·4695	·5317	1·8807	·8829	1·030	1·0821	62
29	·5061	·501	·4848	·5543	1·8040	·8746	1·015	1·0647	61
30	·5236	·518	·5000	·5774	1·7321	·8660	1·000	1·0472	60
31	·5411	·534	·5150	·6009	1·6643	·8572	·985	1·0297	59
32	·5585	·551	·5299	·6249	1·6003	·8480	·970	1·0123	58
33	·5760	·568	·5446	·6494	1·5399	·8387	·954	·9948	57
34	·5934	·585	·5592	·6745	1·4826	·8290	·939	·9774	56
35	·6109	·601	·5736	·7002	1·4281	·8192	·923	·9599	55
36	·6283	·618	·5878	·7265	1·3764	·8090	·908	·9425	54
37	·6458	·625	·6018	·7536	1·3270	·7986	·892	·9250	53
38	·6632	·651	·6157	·7813	1·2799	·7880	·877	·9076	52
39	·6807	·668	·6293	·8098	1·2349	·7771	·861	·8901	51
40	·6981	·684	·6428	·8391	1·1918	·7660	·845	·8727	50
41	·7156	·700	·6561	·8693	1·1504	·7547	·829	·8552	49
42	·7330	·717	·6691	·9004	1·1106	·7431	·813	·8378	48
43	·7505	·733	·6820	·9325	1·0724	·7314	·797	·8203	47
44	·7679	·749	·6947	·9657	1·0355	·7193	·781	·8029	46
45°	·7854	·765	·7071	1·0000	1·0000	·7071	·765	·7854	45°
			Cosine	Co-tangent	Tangent	Sine	Chord	Radians	Degrees
								Angle.	

ANSWERS TO EXAMPLES

1. 0·4 m/sec².   2. 276·5 N.
3. 13,350 N; 1·79 × 10⁸ J, 49·7 kWh; 298·2 kW; 21·2 kWh.
4. 16,370 newton-metres; 12,080 lb.ft.
5. 117 lb.ft; 158·5 newton-metres.
6. 73·7 A, 11s 0d.   7. 54·5 Ω, 0·162d.
8. 1·98 g.   9. 241 min.   10. 4·035 V, 780 J.
11. 26·57 V, 13·8 W.   12. 40 Ω, 302·5 W.
13. 70°C.   14. A, 20·6 yd; B, 200 yd.
15. 100·5°C.   16. 42°C.   17. 41·2 min.
18. 40 min, 33·4°C; 22·4 min.
19. 4·8 hours, 22·7 min.   20. 0·32 A.
21. AB, 0·645 A; BC, 0·678 A; AD, 1·025 A; DC, 0·992 A; DB, 0·033 A.
22. 108·9 V; 0·1785 A, discharge; 5·27 A, discharge.
23. B 2 volts above A.   24. 2·84 Ω, 1·45 Ω.
25. 20·6 mA from B to E.   26. 0·047 A.
27. 0·192 A.   28. AB, 183·3 Ω; BC, 550 Ω; CA, 275 Ω.
29. A, 4·615 Ω; B, 12·31 Ω; C, 18·46 Ω.
30. 240·1 V, 227·9 V; 1,317 W.
31. 66·25 A at A, 46·25 A, 6·25 A, 18·75 A, 48·75 A at B; 232·3 V, 100 yd from A.
32. AB, 20·67 A; BC, 5·67 A; DC, 4·33 A; ED, 9·33 A; AE, 24·33 A; B, 198·33 V; C, 198·1 V; D, 198·45 V; E, 199·02 V.
33. 0·0833 m³, 12·75 kW; 0·0521 m³, 7·96 kW.
34. 240·33 V, 66·7 A; 255 V; 1,078 W.
35. 230·2 V, 231·4 V.
36. B, 242 V; C, 243 V; 234·4 V midway between D and E.
37. 0·1008 in.²; 0·111 in.².   38. 231·8 V at 60-A load.
39. 244·9 V, positive to neutral; 247·9 V, negative to neutral.
40. 20 A, −20 A, 50 A, −10 A, 30 A; in second and fourth sections, current flows from supply end; 197·1 V.
41. 237·5 V.   42. 0·1736 Ω, 80 kW.
43. 214·51 V, positive to neutral; 206·11 V, negative to neutral.

1. 60 N.   2. 24·35 A.
3. 19·1 × 10⁻⁶ newton-metre.
4. 0·109 Wb/m², 0·00075 Ω.
5. 0·375 Wb/m², 0·1406 N, 14·33 g.
6. −33·3 V, 0, 100 V.
7. 476 AT; 1·19 × 10⁶ AT/Wb; 1120.

8. 3·25 A; 1293   9. 46·2 mA.   10. 1520 AT.
11. 3090 AT, 1·0 ton.   12. 1220 AT.   13. 5·65A.
14. 13·16 A, 29·85 N.   15. 580.
16. 1·2 Wb/m², 8·17 A.   17. 44·6 N.
18. 1·28 Wb/m²; 1,415.   19. 1200; 0·24 cm²; 60,000 AT.
20. 129 W.   21. 6·15 W.   22. 1·11 J.
23. 0·578 mV.   24. 0·37 Wb/m²; 26,200 AT/m.
25. 9·95 cm × 4·21 cm².   26. 17·5.   27. 220 mm².
28. 0·00764 J.   29. 995 AT/m, 0·00125 Wb/m².
30. 125 N/m, 25·7 lb/yd.
31. A, 4780 AT/m, 0·006 Wb/m²; B, 6370 AT/m, 0·008 Wb/m²;
    C, 2390 AT/m, 0·003 Wb/m²; A, 0; B, 3185 AT/m,
    0·004 Wb/m²; C, 2390 AT/m, 0·003 Wb/m².
32. 13·28 A.   33. 447 µWb/m².   34. 13·38 A.
35. 120 µH, 9·6 mV.   36. 4100.   37. 3·12 mH.
38. 1·474 µH.   39. 0·277 µH, 800 µWb/m².
40. 0·275 sec.   41. 50 A/sec, 0·5A.
42. 277 millisec.
43. 2·68 A, 1·797 A, 1·204 A, 0·808 A, 0·541 A.
44. 125 µJ.   45. 9·375 J.   46. 0·24 H, 0·06 H.
47. 11·52 µH, 6·912 mV. 48. 1000 V; 1·73 A.
49. 740 µH.   50. 12·8 × 10⁻¹⁰ C, 10·65 µH.
51. 1·612 mH, 0·417.

EXAMPLES III. Page 120

1. 1327 pF; 0·531 µC; 8·85 µC/m², 200 kV/m.
2. (a) 300ε; (b) 600ε, where ε=absolute permittivity.
3. 2.   4. 8·57 kV/cm in airgap.   5. 1475 cm²/plate.
6. 15 µF in series.   7. 2·77 µF, 18·46 µC.
8. 310 pF, 0·208 kV/mm in glass, 1·456 kV/mm in air.
9. 0·00212 µF, 50 V.
10. 569 pF; 128·6 V, 385·8 V, 85·6 V; 64·3 V/mm, 128·6 V/mm,
    85·6 V/mm.
11. 50 W, 0·5 A.   12. 120 V, 0·06 J, 0·036 J.
13. 72 V, 48 V; 0·01037 J, 0·00691 J; 2·4 µF.
14. 397 pF, 8·82 × 10⁻¹².   15. 6·4 mA, 461 J, 28·8 × 10²⁰ eV.
16. 2·496 × 10¹⁶ electrons/sec, 6·75 × 10²⁰ eV, 108 J.
17. 0·0024 C, 0·48 J, 1·498 × 10¹⁶ electrons, 2 min.
18. 1·875 × 10⁻⁴ N.   19. 1·83 mm.
20. 0·995 µC/m², 28·1 kV/m, 1·87 kV.
21. 18 kV/m, 0·159 µC/m², 270 V.
22. 25 pF, 9.35 V/mm.   23. 0·4 N, repulsion.
24. 2 N, attraction.   25. 0·00167 µC/m.
26. 60 kV/m, 0·531 µC/m², 341 V.
27. 18·5 kV/m, 0·164 µC/m²; 24·7 kV/m, 0·218 µC/m²;
    9·25 kV/m, 0·082 µC/m².
28. 1·28 × 10⁻¹⁴ N; 400 eV, 6·4 × 10⁻¹⁷ J; 0·843 × 10⁻⁹ sec.
29. 0·0143 µF.   30. 7·6 pF/m.
31. 129·6 pF/m; 278 kV/m, 6·88 µC/m², 83·2 kV/m, 2·06 µC/m².
32. 47·7pF, cylinder of radius 3·87 mm.

33. 11·65 mm, 11·75 A.
34. 0·647 μF, 4·06 A, 6·34 and 3·58 kV/mm (r.m.s.), 8 kV/mm (r.m.s.).
35. 213 MΩ.   36. 5·66 ×10⁸ MΩcm.
38. 50 mA, 500 mA, 1·25 J.   39. 100 V, 0·1056 millisec.
40. 18·4 μA 0·004 J.   41. 0·903 μF.
42. 100 μA, 36·8 μA, 1000 V/sec, 0·0005 J.
43. 1342 sec.   44. 2·31 μF.   45. 100 MΩ.
46. 0·00251 J/m³.   47. 20·8 N/m², 20·8 J/m³.
48. 0·01593 μF, 3000 kV/m, 159·3 μC/m², 7300 g.

Examples IV.   Page 166

2. 200; 3400.   3. 255; 2740.
4. (a) 4440, 555; (b) 0·4625 A.   5. 8.
6. 3150.   7. 2475.   8. 2·32 millisec.
9. 19·8 V (neglecting thickness of mica).
10. 530 V; 795 and 530 kW.   11. 169 A, 131 A, 223·1 V.
12. 30·24 kW from each of 4 machines, 133 kW, 504 V.
13. 437·5 A; 362·5 A, 226·9 V.
14. −7·4 per cent, 0·0016 Ω.
15. 1·5, 1·125, 0·845, 0·633, 0·475, 0·355, 0·267, 0·2 Ω.
16. 4·5 Ω; 50·5 A, 46 V.   17. 4·667 Ω, 2·667 Ω, 251 r.p.m.
18. 2·48, 1·811, 1·322, 0·966, 0·705, 0·515, 0·376, 0·275 Ω.
19. 10·56 h.p., 0·762 p.u.   20. 0·87 p.u.
21. Shunt loss, 800 W; armature copper loss, 1600 W; brush contact loss, 80 W; iron and friction loss, 892 W; 0·758 p.u.; 8·94 h.p.
22. 871 W, 16·9 A.   23. 523 W.
24. 12 h.p., 0·83 p.u.   25. 60·6 h.p., 0·904 p.u.
26. 2760 W, 23·1 h.p., 0·862 p.u., 64·25 A.
27. 9·25 h.p., 0·857 p.u., 0·871 p.u., 9·24 kW.
28. 0·914 p.u., 0·896 p.u.
29. 22·6 h.p., 0·842 p.u., 5·65 per cent.
30. 4·76 h.p., 0·845 p.u.   31. 0·901 p.u., 50·5 kW.
32. 72·6 h.p., 0·905 p.u., 146·5 A.
33. 2·37 A, 776 r.p.m., 10 A.   34. 0·914 p.u.
35. Generator, 0·879 p.u.; motor, 0·877 p.u.
36. 0·359 Ω.   37. 3·57 kW.

Examples V.   Page 209

1. 30 A, r.m.s.; 20 A, average.
2. 223·5 V, 276 V, 1·235.   3. 0·245 A, 1·225.
4. 0·816, none.   5. 40·8 A, 1·088.   6. 1 A.
7. 5·1 A, 2·55 A, 3·82 A.
8. 6·76 A, 9·87 V, 19·75 A, 33·3 c/s, 82·8 c/s, 49·7 A.
9. 7·96 c/s, 4·33 A, 5·4 A, 4·44 A.
10. $v = 339·4 \sin 314t$, $i = 14·14 \sin (314t − 0·524)$;   12·25 A, 7·07 A, −12·25 A.
11. 72 sin (ωt + 0·443).

12. 208 sin($\omega t - 0.202$), 11° 34′ leading, 18° 26′ lagging, 76 sin($\omega t + 0.528$).
13. 42·3 V, 17° 42′ lagging; 16·1 V, 53° 3′ leading.
14. 66·6 c/s, 32 Ω, 0·3825 H, 1·414 A, 64 W.
15. 314 radians/sec, 15°, 59·5 A (max), 35°, 1725 W.
16. 31·85 μWb.   17. 546 W, 0·331.
18. 61.1 Ω, 0·229 H, 34° 20′. 19. 78·6 W, 0·0376 H, 0·716.
20. 0·129 H, 0·0818 H, 0·706 or 1·72 A.
21. 1·25 kW, 0·11 H, 0·5, 12 5 Ω.
22. 0·0933 H, 20·4 Ω.   23. 1·55 A, 60 W, 0·1684.
24. 0·0132 H, 8·33 Ω, 97·5 V, 143·5 V.
25. 31·1 Ω, 0·4125 H, 199 μWb.
26. 796 c/s, 0·0707 A, 0·1 sin ($5000t - 0.927$) A, 500 A/sec, 4 V.
27. 8 Ω, 0·0255 H, 53° 7′, 96 W.
28. 18·55 Ω, 0·059 H, 186 V.
29. 1·103 Wb-turns, 0·974 Wb-turns.
30. 0·72 per cent, 36 per cent.
31. Current waveform rectangular, 1·5 A; power waveform triangular, 225 W, peak.
32. 9·95 A, 290·4 J (max).
33. 1·083 A; 172·5 V, 57·5 V; 0·595 J, 0·1985 J.
34. 20 Ω, 212 μF.
35. 15·63 A, 50° 12′; 23 Ω, 166 μF; 9·42 Ω, 282 μF.
36. 11·67 Ω, 144 μF; 14·55 A, 0·884 leading.
37. 25·8 μF, 0·478 leading, 145·5 V.
38. 10·3 A, 1060 W, 0·447 lagging, 103 V, 515 V, 309 V.
39. 21·95 A, 13·3 A.   40. 7·07 A, 0·707 leading, 70·7 c/s.
41. 14·85 A, 2385 W, 0·67 leading, 443 V, 591 V.
42. 1·595 A, 149·5 V, 100·5 V.
43. 14·14 A, 8·94 A, 18·98 A, 0·948 lagging.
44. 49 Ω, 0·565 H.   45. 3·75 A, 0·264 lagging.
46. 44·5 Ω, 27°; 39·7 Ω, 20·2 Ω (capacitive).
47. 5·3V, 0·0265 H, 40·4 V.
48. 15·4 A, 17·16 A, 20 A, 34·75 A, 0° 48′ leading.
49. 3·57 A, 2·16 A; 1·67 A, 0·616 lagging; 84·8 Ω, 0·345 H.
50. 32·8 μF, 0·546 A, 1·35 A, 1·235 A.
51. 33·8 μF, 230 V, 1083 V, 1083 V, 2·645 kW, 4·71.
52. 37·2 μF.   53. 57·2 c/s, 167 Ω. 54. 185·5 V, 0·198 H.
55. 106·7 W, 0·1433 H.   56. 1·592 A, 11·4 Ω.
57. 21·2 μF, 0·952 A.
58. 5·8 kW, 7·03 kVA, 0·825 lagging.
59. 102 kW, 103·8 kVA, 0·9825 lagging.
60. 104 μF, 5·22 kVAr.   61. 324 μF, 33·3 A, 50 A.
62. 21·4 kVA, 0·746 lagging, 180 μF, £7 18s.

Examples VI.   Page 239

1. 346 V; 346 V, 200 V, 200 V.
2. 9·24 A, 5130 W, 0·8 lagging, 14·3 μF, 7·78 A.
3. 30·95 A, 19·2 kW, 21·45 kVA.
4. 115 Ω, 0·274 H, 1·667 A, 958 W; 1·445 A, 1·445 A, 0.

5 4·26 Ω, 0·0665 H, 18·75 A, 18·75 A, 32·45 A.
6. 3·26 A, 479 W, 117 Ω.
7. 462 V, 267 V, 16·7 kVAr, 5·87 Ω, 8·92 Ω, 75 A, 33 kW.
8. 9·4 A, 5·43 A, 4·42 kW, 7·15 kVA.
9. 115 A, 0·932 lagging.
10. 43·3 A, 26 A, 17·3 A, 22·9 A.   11. 17·3 A, 31·2 kW.
12. 1·525 A; 2·64 A, 2·64 A, 4·57 A; 1·32 A, 1·32 A, 0; 210 V.
13. 4 A, 6·67 A, 3·08 A; 6·84 A in R, 10·33 A in Y, 5·79 A in B.
14. 21·6 A in R, 49·6 A in Y, 43·5 A in B.   15. 59·2 A, 231 V.
16. 17·35 kW, 21·7 kVA, 13 kVAr, 18·1 A.
17. 33·6 A.   18. 0·655, 0·359.
19. −585 W, 2184 W.   20. 3450 W, −248 W.
21. 100·5 A, 0·966 lagging, 11·43 kVAr.
22. Line amperes ×line volts ×sin φ =8570 VAr.
23. 269 kVA, 0·998 leading.   24. 35·7 kV.
25. 85·7 mm², 55·9 kW, 3360 V.   26. 1/1·155, 17·7 A.

Examples VII.   Page 282

1. 1·287 Wb/m², 924.   2. 115 V, 6·67 A, 87 A, 0·01875 Wb.
3. 14, 22, 3500, 805 (primary).   4. 57·2 A, 0·717 lagging.
5. 10, 87 (assuming 10 per cent for core insulation).
6. 13·9 A.   7. 476 V, 29·1 A, 16·8 A, 672 A.
8. Primary and secondary phase currents, 120 A; 69·3 A in
   resistors; 208 A from supply; 120 A to load; 144 kW;
   48 kW.
9. 317·5 V, 952·5 V.   10. 5·18 mWb, 345 W, 4·77 A (r.m.s.).
11. 300, 0·144 cm, 88°.   12. 2·3 A, 0·164.
13. 176·6 V.   14. 4 per cent.   15. 394 V, 377·6 V.
16. 1063 V.   17. 377·6 V.   18. 199·5 V, 3·1 per cent.
19. 0·972 p.u., 9·75 V.
20. 2·13 per cent, 225·1 V; 4·22 per cent, 220·3 V; −0·81 per
    cent, 231·86 V; 0·960 p.u., 0·9585 p.u.; 56·25 kVA.
21. 636 V, 54 kW.   22. 0·9744 p.u., 0·9809 p.u.
23. 0·905 p.u.
24. 0·9597 p.u., 8·65 kVA, 0·9601 p.u. at unity p.f.
25. 1·777 kW, 2·09 kW, 0·9792 p.u.
26. 0·9751 p.u., 0·9418 p.u.
27. 0·9853 p.u. at 335 kW, 0·9778 p.u.
28. A, 93·8, 96·24, 96·97 per cent; B, 96·42, 97·34, 96·97 per
    cent; A, 40 kVA; B, 23·1 kVA.
29. A, 0·9553 p.u.; B, 0·9682 p.u.; £3 3s.   30. 0·9225 p.u.
31. 83·3 W (hysteresis loss, 51·3 W; eddy-current loss, 32 W).
32. 44 W, 10 W.
33. Hysteresis loss, 250 W; eddy-current loss, 50 W.
35. 0·80 p.u.   36. 1·16 A, 132 W, 0·01 Wb.

Examples VIII.   Page 300

4. 120 V.   5. 0·742 Wb/m², 0·085 Wb.
6. 0·504 Wb/m², 1·225.   7. 38·6 V.   8. 38·64 V.
9. 411 V.   10. 8 poles, 0·0323 Wb.   11. 8.
12. 3·54 kV.   13. 818 V.   14. 600 V, 852 V/phase.

EXAMPLES IX. Page 308

1. 500 r.p.m. 2. 4 poles. 3. 150 c/s.

EXAMPLES X. Page 323

1. 4·4 per cent , 14·0 per cent, −7·3 per cent.
2. 2,412 V; 436 A. 3. 1,585 V. 4. 12·5 per cent increase.
5. 39·8 A, 3·29 kV, 130·7 kW, 7·92 kW.
6. 115 A, 1·845 kV, 634 kW, 14·7 kW.
7. 74·4 A, 1·92 kV, 36·9 kW, 6·15 kW.

EXAMPLES XI. Page 330

1. 2195 V; 2020 V; 2360 V. 2. 229 V, 193·5 V, 265 V.
3. 206 V, 14° 2'; 9·85 A, 0·914 lagging.
4. 1200 kW; 0·3875 leading.
5. 318 kVA, 0·828 leading, 52·5 A, 60·7 A.
6. 74·8 A, 0·995 lagging. 7. £10·7/kVA.

EXAMPLES XII. Page 347

1. 3 c/s, 600 r.p.m. (nearly). 2. 3 per cent, 1·5 c/s.
3. 4·6 per cent, 954 r.p.m. 4. 1·585 c/s, 3·17 per cent.
5. 3 per cent, 1·5 c/s.
6. 48·8 A, 200 V; 6·8 V, 3·4 per cent, 724 r.p.m.; 0·42 Ω;
   659 r.p.m.; 16 per cent.
7. 0·07 Ω, 37·5 per cent. 8. 960 r.p.m., 943 W.
9. 1471 r.p.m.; 1434 r.p.m. 10. 8·94 A.
11. 5·1 A, 20 per cent, 18·4 A. 12. 10,650 W; 426 W.
13. 10·67 A, 0·376; 21·95 A, 0·303.
14. 27·5 per cent, 41 per cent.

EXAMPLES XIII. Page 393

1. 5500 Ω; 31·3 mA. 2. 38·2 Ah. 3. 6·5 mA.
4. 6·5, 4. 5. 2·6 mA/V; 7800 Ω; 20·3.
6. 4000 Ω; 15; 3·75 mA/V 7. 12,500 Ω; 1·667 mA/V; 20·83.
8. 11,400 Ω; 4·9; 4·3 mA/V.
9. 5200 Ω; 3·5 mA/V (approx); 18·2.
10. 40·6; 2·9 mA/V; 14,000 Ω; 23·9. 12. 25·2, 18·5.
13. 18·75 V. 14. 4·69 V. 15. 16·9.
16. 11·13, 23·6. 17. 2·37 V. 18. 33·7 V, 52·1 V.

EXAMPLES XIV. Page 423

1. 11·6 lm/W, 89·2 cd, 0·923 cd/W. 2. 132·6 cd, 4·73d.
3. 7·9 cd/cm². 4. 0·61 cd/cm². 5. 8·96 lm/ft².
6. 122·5 cd.
7. 39·1 cd; standard lamp, 46·5 in., test lamp, 53·5 in.
8. 3·36 lm/ft², 1·68 lm/ft². 9. 5·55 lm/ft², 4·65 lm/ft².

10. 1·395 lm/ft^2, 1·533 lm/ft^2.
11. 4·18 lm/ft^2 at A; about 4·2 lm/ft^2 at B.
12. 8·85 lm/ft^2, 5·1 lm/ft^2.   13. 8 lm/ft^2, 0·715 lm/ft^2.
14. 0·89 lm/ft^2, 0·342 lm/ft^2; 8·53 lm/ft^2.
15. 3 lm/ft^2, 1·74 lm/ft^2 (approx).   16. 24.
17. 224 cd.   18. 42.   19. 8·2 per cent.
20. 0·606 A, 122·2 V, 97·8 V, 152·4 per cent, 62·5 per cent.
21. 236 cd; 2960 lm.

EXAMPLES XV.   Page 443

1. $(13·7 - j3·2)\Omega$, capacitive; 2250 W; 13° 9′.
2. $(1·192 - j0·538)$ A.
3. 20 Ω, 0·0478 H; 10 Ω, 53 μF; $(0·0347 - j0·00778)$ mho, 12° 38′ lagging.
4. 130·7 μF, 159·2 V.
5. 0·2 mho, 0·1 mho, 0·224 mho, 0·894 lagging; 4 Ω, 2 Ω.
6. 1·025 A, 32° 39′, 13·6 μF; 106·3 Ω, 46·7 μF.
7. 0·04167 mho, 0·025 mho, 0·0333 mho.
8. 43·1 Ω, 0·436 H; 479 Ω, 0·48 H.   9. 0·04 mho, 0·02 mho.
10. 2·83 A, lagging 30°.   11. 10·58 A, 8·26 A, 6·45 A.
12. 2 A, 290 μF, 0.
13. 2·08 A, lagging 34° 13′, from supply; 4·64 A, lagging 59°, through coil; 2·88 A, leading 103° 16′, through capacitor.
14. 18·75 A, 0·839 lagging   15. 21·33 Ω, 93·3 mH.
16. 0·68 μF.   17. 174 Ω, 80·1 mH.
18. 940 W; 550 VAr, lagging. 19. 1060 W, 250 VAr, leading.

SUPPLEMENTARY QUESTIONS.   Page 446

1. To ring 1: 1, 241, 481, 721; to ring 2: 25, 265, 505, 745; etc.
2. 160, 4, 50·8 A/in.^{2}, 0·02625 Wb, 2.
4. 4-pole wave with commutator pitch of 82 or 83, or 6-pole lap; 4-pole lap or 6-pole wave with commutator pitch of 85; 6-pole wave with commutator pitch of 87.
5. 8 (commutator pitch of 76).
6. 940 r.p.m., 3 turns/segment.
7. 0·0415 Wb, 0·02075 Wb.   8. 262 V, 12·4 Ω.
9. 294 V, 300 Ω, 277 V, about 155 V.   10. 7·5.
11. 652 r.p.m., 0·73 Ω, 17·3 per cent.
12. 680 r.p.m., 43·75 per cent.
13. 1600 r.p.m. at 8·45 lb.ft. (gross), 864 r.p.m. at 30·3 lb.ft, etc., 485 r.p.m., 58·7 A at full load.
14. 115 newton-metres (84·8 lb.ft.), 590 r.p.m.; 57·5 newton-metres, 843 r.p.m.; 28·75 newton-metres, 1200 r.p.m.
15. 2610 r.p.m. 10 A; 1250 r.p.m., 20 A; etc.
16. 3·54 Ω.   17. 1444 r.p.m.   18. 1186 r.p.m.; 33·6 A.
19. 0·1665 Ω.   20. 0·0449 inch; 7330.

INDEX

A.C. bridges, 445
Acceptor, 195
Active component, 204
— network, 15
Admittance, 433
All-day efficiency, 286
Alternator, armature reaction, 309
—, construction, 288
—, e.m.f. equation, 296
—, o.c. and s.c. tests, 317
—, parallel operation, 320
—, voltage regulation, 313
—, windings, 291
Ampere, 3
Ampère's Theorem, 68
Ampere-turns, 36
—, d.c. armature, 135
Amplification factor, 372
—, voltage, 376
Ångstrom unit, 397
Anode, 351
— slope resistance, 372
Arc lamp, 402
Armature reaction, alternator, 309
— —, d.c. machine, 128
Armature winding, a.c. machine, 291
— —, d.c. machine, 126
Attraction between charged surfaces, 116
— — electric charges, 106
— — magnetized surfaces, 66
Auto-transformer, 276
Auto-starter, 345
Average value, 172

Balancer, rotary, 29
Ballistic galvanometer, 48
Barrier layer, 365
— — photo-electric cell, 421

B/H characteristics, 41
— measurement, 48
Brake test, 156
Breadth factor, 298
Bridge circuit, rectifiers, 369
Brightness, 414
Brush lead, 134

Cadmium cell, 5
Candela, 410
Candlepower, 411
Capacitance in a.c. circuit, 186
— in d.c. circuit, 110
— of concentric cylinders, 108
— — — spheres, 104
— of parallel-plate capacitor, 95
— of parallel wires, 107
Capacitive reactance, 187
Capacitor, 92, 100
Carbon arc lamp, 402
— brushes, 143, 154
— filament lamp, 400
Cathode, 351
Cathode-ray oscillograph, 389
Charging current of capacitor, 110
Circuit, electric, 1 et seq.
—, magnetic, 37
Coefficient of coupling, 81
— of mutual inductance, 80
— of resistance, temperature, 7
— of self-inductance, 71
— of utilization, 416
Coercive force, 52
Coercivity, 53
Commutating poles, 144
Commutation, 139
Commutator losses, 154
Compensating winding, 137
Condenser, 92

Conductance, 6, 434
Conductivity, 7
Conjugate, 441
Control ratio, 387
Cooling of transformers, 276
— time constant, 11
Copper-oxide rectifier, 365
Core-type transformer, 259
Coulomb, 3
Coulomb's Law, 104
Coupling, coefficient of, 81
— of triodes, 379
Crest factor, 174
Cross ampere-turns, 135
Current transformer, 278
Cylindrical rotor, 289

Delta connection, 219
Delta-star transformation, 18
Demagnetizing ampere-turns, 135
Density, current, 7
—, electric flux, 93
—, magnetic flux, 36
Depreciation factor, 417
Dielectric constant, 95
— strength, 117
Diode, 350
Discharge current of capacitor, 110
Distorting ampere-turns, 135
Distribution factor, 298
— systems, 24
Double-diode, 358
Dynamic characteristic, 353, 377
— impedance, 198
Dyne, 450

Eddy-current loss, 154, 286
Effective resistance of coil, 188
— value, 174
Efficiency, condition for maximum, 156, 270
—, d.c. machines, 155
—, lamps, 408
—, mercury-arc rectifier, 363
—, transformer, 268

Electric charge, 92
— circuit, 1 et seq.
— field strength, 93
— flux, 93
— force, 93
Electrical reference standards, 5
Electrochemical equivalent, 3
Electromagnetism, 36 et seq.
Electromotive force, 4
Electron, 92, 350
Electron-volt, 92
Electrostatics, 92 et seq.
Energy, units of, 2
— in electric field, 115
— in magnetic field, 79
Equalizing bus-bar, 149
— rings, 126
Equipotential surface, 97, 103, 105
Equivalent circuit of transformer, 259
— — of triode, 378
— impedance of transformer, 263
Erg, 450

Farad, 92
Fluorescent lamp, 406
Flux density, electric, 93
— —, magnetic, 36
Flux-linkage, 51
Fluxmeter, 51
Foot-candle, 412
Force between charged surfaces, 116
— — electric charges, 104
— — magnetized surfaces, 66
— — parallel wires, 70
— on conductor, 36
— on isolated charge, 101
Form factor, 174
Frequency, 172

Galvanometer, ballistic, 48
Gaseous-discharge lamps, 403
Gas-filled filament lamp, 401
— rectifier, 358
— triode, 385

Gauss, 450
Gilbert, 450
Grading of starting resistance, 150
Grid of triode, 370, 385
Growth of current in inductor, 76
— of p.d. across capacitor, 110

Heating time constant, 10
Helmholtz equation, 78
— Theorem, 16
Henry, 71
High-pressure lamp, 403
Hopkinson test, 160
Hysteresis loop, 52
— loss, 56, 286

Ideal transformer, 260
Illumination, calculation of, 415
— photometer, 421
Impedance, 189
Incandescent electric lamp, 398
Inductance, mutual, 80
— of concentric cylinders, 75
— of parallel wires, 74
Inductance, self-, 71
Induction motor, 332 et seq.
Inductive reactance, 185
Inherent ampere-turns of magnet, 62
In-phase component, 428
Instrument transformers, 281
Insulation resistance, concentric cable, 123
Integrating photometer, 420
Intensity, luminous, 411
Interpoles, 144
Ionization, 359
Iron loss, d.c. machine, 154
— —, transformer, 269, 286

j notation, 426 et seq.
Joule, 1

Kilowatt, 2
Kilowatt-hour, 2
Kirchhoff's laws, electric circuit, 14
— —, magnetic circuit, 37

Lamps, carbon arc, 402
—, filament, 398
— gaseous-discharge, 403
Lap winding, 126
Laplace's Theorem, 68
Lead of brushes, 134
Leakage coefficient, 45
Lenz's Law, 36, 76, 245
Light units, 409
Linkage, flux-, 51
Locus diagrams, 199
Losses, d.c. machines, 154
—, transformers, 268
Lumen, 411
Luminance, 414
Luminous flux, 411
— intensity, 411
Lummer - Brodhun photometer, 418

Magnet, minimum volume of, 61
Magnetic circuit, 37
— energy, 79
— field around conductor, 39, 67
— — of long solenoid, 59
— — strength, 37
— leakage, 44
— pull, 66
— testing, 48
Magnetizing force, 37
Magnetomotive force, 36
Maintenance factor, 417
Maxwell, 450
Mean horizontal candlepower, 413
— spherical candlepower, 412
Mercury-arc rectifier, 360
Mercury-vapour lamps, 403
Mesh connection, 219
Metal rectifiers, 365
Mho, 6

Microfarad, 92
Micron, 397
Minimum volume of magnet, 61
M.K.S. units, 1
Motor, induction, 332 *et seq.*
—, grading of starter of d.c., 150
—, synchronous, 325 *et seq.*
Mutual conductance, 372
— inductance, 80

Network theorems, 12
Neutral point, 222
Neutral wire, 28, 222
Newton, 1

Oersted, 450
Ohm, 3
Ohm's Law, 4
Open-circuit test, alternator, 317
— —, transformer, 272
Operator *j*, 426
Oscillograph, cathode-ray, 389

Parallel operation, alternators, 320
— —, d.c. generators, 146
Passive network, 12
Peak factor, 174
Permanent magnet, minimum volume of, 61
Permeability, absolute, 41
— of free space, 39
—, relative, 40
Permittivity, absolute, 95
— of free space, 94
—, relative, 95
Per-unit value, 163
Photometers, 417, 420, 421
Picofarad, 92
Platinum standard of luminance, 410
Polar curve, light distribution, 419
Potential difference, 3
— gradient, 93, 109

Power factor, 203
— —, improvement, 205, 330
— measurement, single-phase, 206
— —, three-phase, 232
Primary standard of light, 410

Q-factor, 193, 197
Quadrature component, 428
Quantity of electricity, 3

Rationalization, magnetic field, 36
—, electric field, 93
Reactance, capacitive, 187
—, inductive, 185
—, leakage, 255
— voltage in d.c. machine, 141
Reactive component, 204
— volt-amperes, 440
Rectifier, copper-oxide, 365
—, diode, 350
—, gas-filled, 358
—, mercury-arc, 360
—, selenium, 368
Reduction factor, 414
Regenerative test, d.c. machines, 160
Rejector, 198
Relative luminous efficiency, 398
Reluctance, 41
Remanence, 53
Remanent flux density, 52
Resistance of armature circuit, 158
— — — winding, 128
—, temperature coefficient of, 7
Resistance-capacitance coupling, 379
Resistivity, 6
Resistors in parallel, 6
— in series, 6
Resonance, parallel, 196
—, series, 193
Reversal of rotation of magnetic flux, 307

Root-mean-square value, 174
Rotating magnetic flux, 302
Rousseau diagram, 419

Salient poles, 289
Saturation current, 351
Selenium rectifier, 368
Self-inductance, 71
Separation of hysteresis and eddy losses, 286
Shell-type transformer, 259
Short-circuit test, alternator, 317
— —, transformer, 272
Sine wave, 175
Slip, 333
Slip-ring rotor, 342
Slope resistance, anode, 372
Sodium lamp, 405
Solenoid, magnetic field of long, 59
Space-charge limited current, 352
Spectral power distribution, 399
Spectrum, 397
Squirrel-cage rotor, 332
Standard cell, 5
Standards, electrical reference, 5
Star connection, 221
— point, 222
Star-delta starter, 345
— transformation, 20
Starter, grading of, 150
—, induction motor, 342
Static characteristics, 353, 367, 371
Steinmetz, 58
Steradian, 411
Stray load loss, 155
Striking voltage, 386
Superposition Theorem, 12
Susceptance, 434
Swinburne test, 157
Symbolic notation, 426 et seq.
Synchronizing of alternators, 318
Synchronous impedance, 317
— motor, 325 et seq.

Synchronous speed, 305
— watts, 338
Synchroscope, 320

Temperature coefficient of resistance, 7
— rise, 9
Temperature-limited current, 352
Testing of d.c. machines, 156
— of transformers, 271
Thermionic emission, 350
Thévenin's Theorem, 15
Three-phase circuits, 217 et seq.
— transformer, 275
Three-wire d.c. system, 27
Thyratron, 385
Time base for C.R.O., 391
— constant, 10, 78, 112
Torque, 2, 138
—, alternator, 311
—, induction motor, 339
—, synchronous motor, 326
Transformer, action of, 244
—, auto-, 276
—, cooling, 276
—, core-type, 259
—, coupling of triodes, 382
—, current, 278
—, efficiency, 268
—, e.m.f. equation, 246
—, equivalent circuit, 259
—, leakage reactance, 254
—, o.c. and s.c. tests, 271
—, shell-type, 259
—, three-phase, 275
—, voltage regulation, 263, 273
Triode, gas-filled, 385
—, vacuum, 370
Tuned-anode coupling, 381
Tungsten-filament lamps, 400
Turbo-alternator, 290
Two-wattmeter method, 232

Uniformly distributed load on distributor, 25

Units, conversion table,
  C.G.S. and M.K.S., 450
—, electrical, 2
—, electromagnetic, 36
—, electrostatic, 92
—, photometric, 409
Utilization factor, 416

Valve, thermionic, 351
Vectors, 179
Velocity of electromagnetic
  waves, 397
Volt, 3
Voltage amplification, 379
— regulation, alternator, 313

Voltage regulation, transformer, 263, 273
Volt-amperes, 203

Watt, 2
Wattless component, 204
Wave winding, 128
Weber, 36
Weston cell, 5
Windage loss, 155
Windings, a.c. machines, 291
—, d.c. machines, 126

Yoke, 244, 275, 290